D1298734

WHITE SETTLERS IN THE TROPICS

AMERICAN GEOGRAPHICAL SOCIETY

SPECIAL PUBLICATION NO. 23

Edited by J. K. WRIGHT

WHITE SETTLERS IN THE TROPICS

BY

A. GRENFELL PRICE

Master of St. Mark's College
University of Adelaide

with additional notes by

ROBERT G. STONE

Blue Hill Meteorological Observatory
Harvard University

AMERICAN GEOGRAPHICAL SOCIETY

BROADWAY AT 156TH STREET

NEW YORK, N. Y.

1939

COPYRIGHT, 1939

BY

AMERICAN GEOGRAPHICAL SOCIETY OF NEW YORK

909.093
P945

Lord Baltimore Press, Baltimore
Walker Engraving Co., New York

To

KITTY PAULINE PRICE

WHO HELPED TO GATHER
IN THE TROPICS
THE MATERIAL FOR
THIS BOOK

CONTENTS

vii

LIST OF ILLUSTRATIONS

FOREWORD

This book could not possibly have made its appearance at a more opportune time than the present. It may well serve a greater purpose than even Dr. Price himself foresaw when he undertook the painstaking task of correlating past history with the accumulating knowledge that is gained as the various sciences gradually unfold. Today more than ever before understanding and clear thought are needed concerning areas suitable for receiving refugees from Europe. It now seems certain that because of intolerance many people must soon find homes in a new environment.

Dr. Price has traced the record of many types of white settlements in the tropics and has deduced the known facts and outlined the uncertain theories. He shows certain splendid achievements in recent history; he also shows that the future lies in scientific investigation and that political and economic policies will never succeed unless based on the facts so established.

While others have dealt with particular aspects of the problem and with specific regions, no one before, I think, has attempted as comprehensive a synthesis as has Dr. Price. Not, of course, that he makes any pretension to completeness. That would hardly be possible in a pioneer work upon a problem whose components are as yet but barely resolved. One need do no more than glance at the numerous bibliographical references to sense the scope and complexity of the problem—and these references represent merely a selection from an immense specialized literature, historical, economic, social, administrative, medical, climatic, geological, and geographical. The book, however, derives its outstanding value from the author's broad outlook. To cover so wide a range requires judgment and a type of courage that many specialists lack.

My own experience has been in the Netherlands East Indies and Malaya, where for many years I was occupied in the development and operation of rubber plantations. I have studied soil, climatic, economic, and labor conditions in Siam, Indo-China, the Philippines, India, Ceylon, the West Coast of Africa, Brazil, and Central America, though I have been concerned with these problems as they are related to the white "sojourners" rather than to the "white settlers." Such men and women expect to spend perhaps twenty or twenty-five years in the tropics, relieved only by occasional visits to their homes in the temperate zone. Science and improved communications are gradually increasing the length of tropical service of these people, and in time many white "sojourners" may develop into "white settlers" desirous of establishing permanent homes.

Dr. Price was born in Adelaide, South Australia, and was educated at the University of Adelaide and at Oxford. He has been Master of St. Mark's College, University of Adelaide, since 1925. He is the author of "The Foundation and Settlement of South Australia" (1924), "South Australians and Their Environment" (1921), and "The History and Problems of the Northern Territory, Australia" (1930). This, his most recent book, "White Settlers in the Tropics," gains authenticity from his personal familiarity with the Australian tropics and from his research work in Panama, Costa Rica, the West Indies, the United States, and Europe.

Students of the problems of settlement in the tropics will find Dr. Price's book a practical guide and a stimulus to thought.

H. STUART HOTCHKISS

Member of the Council

American Geographical Society

ACKNOWLEDGMENTS AND EDITOR'S NOTE

Both the author and the American Geographical Society join in acknowledging with sincere thanks the assistance and courtesies rendered by many persons in the preparation of this work. Among those who have read the manuscript, either as a whole or in part, and have offered valuable suggestions the following may be mentioned: Professor J. A. Prescott and Dr. James Davidson of the University of Adelaide, Dr. Jarvis Nye and Mr. W. Wynne Williams of Queensland, Dr. E. G. Malherbe of South Africa, Professors G. C. Shattuck and C. K. Drinker of the Harvard Medical School, and Dr. Ellsworth Huntington of Yale University. The author visited the Caribbean region and the United States in 1932-1933 on a Research Fellowship of the Rockefeller Foundation, to which institution an especial debt of gratitude is due.

At the request of the American Geographical Society and with the consent of the author, Mr. Robert G. Stone of the Blue Hill Meteorological Observatory, Harvard University, has contributed many additional data in the form of notes, appendixes, bibliographical references, diagrams, and a few passages in the main body of the text. In the text and Notes Mr. Stone's material, which deals mainly with questions of climate, health, and acclimatization, is enclosed in square brackets and identified by the initials "R. G. S."

Half the circumference of the earth separated the author in South Australia and the editor in New York while this book was in press. Galley proofs of the text were sent to the author and revised by him, but this was not done in the case of the Notes and Appendixes, as the date of publication would have been unduly delayed thereby. Likewise to avoid delays the editor has compiled the foregoing list of acknowledgments, from which he hopes there are no serious omissions.

EDITOR

PART I
NATURE AND HISTORY OF THE PROBLEM OF WHITE SETTLEMENT IN THE TROPICS

CHAPTER I

THE PROBLEM OF WHITE SETTLEMENT IN THE TROPICS

Science is unveiling many mysteries. Almost daily man learns the underlying causes of some phenomenon before which his ancestors stood mystified. Yet, when the layman asks the scientist why the white races,[1] particularly the northern races, have in general failed to colonize the tropics and when he seeks to know if the future is more hopeful, it is the scientist who stands perplexed.

The problem may be stated in three short questions. Why in general have the whites failed? Are they beginning to make progress? Can they hope for ultimate success? Scientists are unable to agree on any of the three questions. Some authorities assert that settlement failed owing to the so-called tropical diseases, that science is now controlling these diseases, that the whites are making steady progress, and that the future offers every hope. Others state that the whites failed through many, and in some cases unalterable, causes, such as certain climatic factors, that the recent victories of science are illusory, and that the whites can never establish working communities in the tropics.

Hitherto the medical scientist has tended to regard the problem as his peculiar field. Yet, although the question is largely medical in character, it has many other aspects. If the white man is to probe to the root of his difficulty—if he is to settle permanently in parts of the tropics—the statesman, philanthropist, economist, historian, geographer, engineer, and medical scientist must all coöperate.

Definitions

At the outset it is necessary to define "white," "settlement," and "tropics." The term "white man" will be used in a broad sense. The inquiry will deal primarily with white races of north European ancestry, but it will touch on tropical communities of Mediterranean origin, for much can be learned from such countries as Costa Rica and Puerto Rico, where the great majority of the inhabitants are whites or near-whites of south European descent. In dealing with white races of European ancestry this book will adopt one important distinction in order to save confusion and space. Avoiding the much abused term "Nordic," it will call the peoples of north European ancestry "northern whites," and the peoples of south European ancestry "Mediterranean whites." [2]

The term "settlement" may be defined as permanent colonization, under which the incomers and their descendants follow all the usual

---

[1] The notes will be found at the end of the book.

routine of life, including manual labor, maintain their standards of health, energy, civilization, and culture, and raise families that do not exhibit mental or physical degeneracy. This definition excludes officials, soldiers, missionaries, and traders, who go to the tropics for only a part of their lives. They are sojourners, not settlers.

The term "tropics" requires a longer explanation. Geographers have advanced many and varied definitions, owing to the fact that the parallels of latitude 23½° north and south, which bound the "mathematical tropics," are no true delineation. In certain areas highlands, cool winds, and cold ocean currents carry temperate conditions far into the tropics, while in other areas lowlands, hot winds, and warm ocean currents carry tropical conditions beyond the mathematical limits.

Supan in 1896[3] suggested the mean annual isotherm of 68° F. (20° C.) as a suitable boundary for the tropics. Köppen (1900)[4] took as the criterion a temperature exceeding 68° for all twelve months of the year. Supan's classification made the tropics too extensive and Köppen's too limited. Köppen subsequently (1918 and later) extended his definition to include areas where the temperature of the coolest month is over 64.4° (18° C.). Austin Miller[5] and Ellsworth Huntington have recently defined the tropics by the annual isotherm of 70°. This seems fairly satisfactory and will be adopted here.

Within the boundary of the 70° isotherm there are several different types of tropics, and in broad outline we may distinguish between the equatorial tropics, the trade-wind coasts and islands, the "wet-dry" (including the monsoonal) areas, the deserts, the mountains and plateaus, and the marginal zones. In each of these regions controls, such as temperature and humidity, vary greatly and create many "local climates." These "local climates" undoubtedly exercise great influence on white settlement, but the matter has been little examined or discussed.

Importance of the Problem

A decade or so ago the nations viewed with apprehension a tremendous rise in world population. Owing to the progress of medicine and other causes, numbers grew between 1905 and 1911 at such a rate that it appeared that in sixty years the population of the world would have doubled.[6] It was apprehended that in little more than a century mankind might number 6,600,000,000, the maximum figure that the earth could be expected to feed,[7] and it was jestingly prophesied that by 3000 A.D. the notice "standing room only" might be up.

In these circumstances the eyes of the nations turned to the tropics with their "vast undeveloped potentialities." From the time of Humboldt to that of Gorgas scientists had been drawing attention to the huge resources of the Amazon Basin and other tropical regions. Here, they thought, lay immense virgin reservoirs of foodstuffs and raw materials, awaiting only the enlivening energies of the exploitative and colonizing whites. A decade ago the growth of world population quickened this interest. G. T. Trewartha, for example, stated in 1926 that the question of food supplies had created a renascence of interest in the tropics.[8] "When the great valleys of the Amazon and Congo are occupied by a white population," he quotes General Gorgas, "more food will be produced in these regions than is now produced in all the rest of the inhabited world." As late as 1930 R. DeC. Ward wrote that the future looked more and more to the tropics and that it was for the white man to decide the course of events.[9]

Recent developments have modified this outlook. War, famine, influenza, the living standard, industrialization, city life, birth control, and possibly biological factors have retarded the increase in many countries. In the long view the outlook is more hopeful, and such authorities as Kuczynski believe that "as matters stand there is no real danger of overpopulation."[10] In the short view, however, the future is less cheerful. Although in many countries—particularly in white countries—the rate of increase is declining, in others the drop is not yet evident, or it is operating at a very slow rate. Italy, India, the U. S. S. R., and Japan, for example, still show an immense growth. The Italians are augmenting their population at the rate of 500,000 and the Japanese at 900,000 per annum, and in these countries the same rate of growth is likely to continue for several decades.[11] Medical science is greatly increasing the length of life, and neither the medical scientists nor the great organizations supporting them appear to have any plans for the solution of the difficulties they are helping to create. The problem is complicated by the fact that the white peoples, who number only one-third of the earth's inhabitants, rule eight-ninths of the globe. Moreover, a few white nations, with England and France in the lead, control the most promising zones of colonization and dominate many tropical lands. On the other hand, Germany, Japan, and Italy rank as the "have nots," and between the two groups lies the great colonial conflict.[12]

The tropics must figure in such a conflict. Already Italy has annexed the tropical plateaus of the Ethiopian Empire. If she can fill these with white colonists—which remains to be seen[13]—and exploit their resources, she will loom over the growing British settlements in the East African tropics and threaten the main British trade route to the tropical East. Similarly, the Japanese are rapidly developing their Pacific mandates, and their expansion definitely threatens the isolated Australians, who are slowly colonizing with whites the few good parts of their generally arid tropics.

The situation is less dangerous in the American tropics, where racial amalgamation seems inevitable, but even here there are echoes of the racial conflicts that afflict the Eastern Hemisphere.

CONTRADICTORY OPINIONS

The widely differing opinions of leading authorities indicate that the subject is complex. The pessimists hold that the whites have established no great civilizations or cultures in tropical countries, that white races in the tropics are beyond their natural or optimum environment, and that, under these conditions, they will always prove less efficient than colored peoples. These authorities consider that the whites have failed, not through uncontrollable diseases, but from eternal and unchangeable factors that will always prevent white acclimatization. They believe that the advances of white communities in marginal regions, such as eastern Queensland, are too recent to be significant, that the high plateaus produce nervous conditions, and that the whites will never defeat disease and heat, particularly in the low humid tropics, which, according to past theories, should be the most productive areas of the world.

On the contrary, the optimists believe that man originated in the tropics and that he evolved great civilizations and cultures there. They consider that the tropics are the natural home of the white races and offer the greatest future for the whites. Disease, they say, formed the only real barrier to white settlement, and they are certain that the whites can now defeat sickness, particularly if they exclude or rigidly control colored races of a lower standard of life.[14] The young communities in the marginal regions should be permanently successful. The white man, with his marvelous powers of invention and his control of modern science, should conquer the tropics as he has conquered the subtropical zone.

Of the writers on the basic problems of climate and acclimatization, Ellsworth Huntington has put forward theories of history and of climatic optima and limits that are generally regarded as pessimistic, although certain optimistic views of Dr. Huntington will be noted in Chapter XIV.[15] Castellani and Ward admit that "the basis of the largest proportion of illness and death in the tropics is imperfect sanitation, and not climatic influences," but they have "always believed that tropical climate per se has a deleterious influence." Castellani thinks that a damp, hot climate, when endured for years, diminishes physique, energy, fertility, and resistance to disease and has a markedly deleterious effect on the nervous system. "A permanent colonization of the low-lying regions of the tropics, with equable, hot, moist climate and no cool season, by the white race . . . is not possible."[16] R. DeC. Ward believed that the future of the white man in the tropics depended upon acclimatization and that few more interesting problems awaited medical investigation. After an able summary of the evidence, he reached the conclusion that life in the tropics would become safer and more comfortable and that there would "be a slow and limited settlement." He feared, however, that in the light of existing knowledge acclimatization in the sense of white men and women living for successive generations in the tropics and reproducing their kind without physical, mental, or moral degeneration—that is, colonization in the true sense—was impossible.[17]

Dr. Andrew Balfour—perhaps the greatest authority on the subject—reached the following conclusion on the low tropics: "So far as the race is concerned, I am persuaded that the hot and humid Tropics are not suited to white colonization and never will be with our present knowledge, even if they were rendered as free from disease as England."[18] This, on investigation, seems to be the general opinion of British medical scientists in Burma and the Malay States and of the Rockefeller doctors and scientists in the West Indies and Central America. Views differ in the moderate tropics of Queensland, but many Australian scientists are pessimistic.

More hopeful was the outlook of the Manson, Sambon, Gorgas, Guiteras school of medical scientists, who put forward the theory that the tropical climate per se has no deleterious effect on the whites and that, with proper sanitary and other measures against disease and with care in the matter of food and drink, the European can live healthily even in the low tropics.[19] After a careful study of the records of Cuba, Guiteras wrote: "The tropical climate is compatible with the most elevated manifestations of human activity, and the acclimatization of the white race to the tropics has been effected with complete success."[20] Gorgas, elated with American progress in Cuba and Panama, thought that the whites could colonize the Congo if malaria and sleeping sickness could be stamped out.[21]

It would seem that these scientists greatly underestimated the difficulties of the tropics and entirely misjudged the conditions of progress (Chapter XI). During the last few years white successes in Queensland have led Sir Raphael Cilento and other medical scientists to reaffirm the views of Gorgas and his followers. Cilento attributes the historical failures of the whites to tropical diseases. Like R. B. Vance, a sociologist of the southern United States,[22] he lays great weight on the white successes in the subtropics. He affirms, with the support of Queensland statistics, that the tropical climate per se has no deleterious effects on the morality, nervous system, physique, energy, or fertility of white settlers, and he puts forward the revolutionary thesis that it is essential for the whites to engage in manual work, a view now generally held among medical men.[23] Huntington and other authorities have strongly criticized Cilento's opinions, but the optimists are receiving support, particularly from those who hold great hopes of the successes that science may achieve. The well-known economic geographer, J. Russell Smith, for example, believes that man may solve the vital problem of tropical comfort by air conditioning, for engineers are now in a position to make a perfect indoor climate in any part of the world.[24]

Dr. Björn Palm, former Swedish Consul-General in Guatemala, who has lived in the tropics, particularly in Sumatra, for many years, regards white colonization as practicable if certain technical problems can be solved. "If the colonist," he writes, "after a day's work in the tropical heat could retire into a home of normal temperature and normal humidity, a real revolution in living conditions in the tropics would thereby be accomplished." [25] Unfortunately economic conditions in the tropics would rarely support air conditioning without subsidies, even for the whites alone.

Opinions on other aspects of white settlement in the tropics are as contradictory as those on acclimatization and climate. Very little is known, for example, about human biology or about the relative suitability of the white races as tropical settlers. Chapter XII, on racial problems, outlines certain aspects of this question.[26] Here, again, opinions differ greatly, and an immense amount of detailed research must be carried out.

Narrowing the Field of Inquiry

Before commencing this inquiry we may limit the field by excluding certain tropical regions that are totally unfit for white occupation. No race, be it white or colored, can closely settle tropical deserts, like those of Africa or Australia, except on oases or islands of irrigable land, though temporary towns spring up where there are mineral deposits. Again, as indicated above, many eminent authorities doubt if the whites will ever occupy the humid equatorial lowlands, which, according to some writers, offer the highest potentialities for the production of raw materials and food. Eliminating the tropical deserts and humid equatorial lowlands, there remain the tropical highlands, and wet-dry monsoonal regions, the trade-wind coasts and islands, and the marginal lands. We shall discuss the advantages and difficulties that each presents and shall see that in each of these environments white communities—even northern white communities—have at least survived.[27] Once again, however, the argument may disregard extensive areas where such factors as poor soil, unsatisfactory rainfall, or great isolation make the conditions unsuitable for settlement.

A further limiting influence, one that has received but scanty attention, is the density of colored peoples of low economic standard in many of the richest parts of the tropics. This population barrier is not a purely climatic one, yet scientists usually brush it aside as a secondary control resulting from climate. This reasoning seems at fault. While admitting that negroes and other colored peoples may be more tolerant of tropical climates than are the white races, it must also be remembered that the whites have failed to settle permanently in Japan, China, and other temperate countries where dense indigenous populations also exist. Combined with this is a social factor, the living standard required by each particular community or race. Here we can almost glimpse the operation of a racial Gresham's law. A people prepared to accept a low standard of living and the discomfort of large families will usually drive out or absorb peoples of a higher standard, unless the latter increase their numbers through immigration or protect themselves by political supremacy, social barriers, or laws. The progress of the central and southern Europeans and of the Jews in the United States, of the Indians in Central and South America, of the negroes in South Africa and the West Indies, and of the Italians in Queensland, are examples that illustrate the process among many races and in many types of climate. Contrary cases are the successful stands made by the white Americans against the negroes and by the white Australians of the fifties against the flood of Chinese immigrants. These successes were largely due to political supremacy, but they led, as usual, to the numerically greater people expelling or absorbing, or tending to absorb, the less.

These racial factors, which will be discussed in later chapters, again limit the potential areas of white colonization by excluding all regions of dense colored settlement. There remain only the trade-wind coasts and monsoonal regions of Australia and a few areas in Africa, the Americas, and the West Indies. Even in some of these regions the whites face absorption by colored peoples of lower economic standard, and in every area white settlement, if it is to be successful, demands the most careful watching and control.[28] Behind everything lies a question of ethics. The white races command vast and sparsely settled areas of temperate country. Have they any moral justification for attempting to occupy the tropics as well? This question is particularly important in view of some recent developments in national and international ethics, a case in point being the policy of the "Dual Mandate" adapted by British governments of late years for parts of Africa.

METHODS OF ATTACK

Means for examining the problem of white settlement in the tropics are found in historical, statistical, and laboratory research. Although the technique and results of these methods may at present be questionable in points of detail, in combination they cast considerable light on the subject.

The Historical Method

Why have the whites failed so repeatedly in the tropics? White races have invaded these regions from remote ages, and they have established some civilizations therein, although the glowing accounts of tropical cultures are often inaccurate, as the examples quoted generally refer to the subtropics.[29] As early as the golden age of Greece leading thinkers were evolving scientific reasons for the white disasters. Aristotle, for example, believed that the climate was unfavorable, that the influence of Asia was enervating, and that the barbarians had the nature of slaves.

Geographers and historians—Professors Ellsworth Huntington and A. J. Toynbee, for example—have attempted to apply modern views to ancient historical data, but their efforts, although stimulating, leave the matter in doubt. If modern scientists are unable to agree on the causes of the present difficulties in the tropics, how can the historian ascertain with any assurance the factors that defeated the white invasions of the remote past?

Coming to later history, the population movements of the last four centuries provide some definite data, but the underlying causes of the repeated white failures are still obscure. Until recently most historical research was directed towards "cabbages and kings," with the emphasis upon the kings. A few comparatively recent theses, such as Keller's history of colonization, Carter's history of yellow fever, and Heiser's "An American Doctor's Odyssey," [30] glimpse the racial and cultural contacts, the medical problems, and other phenomena that are of basic importance. Yet many of the latest research works—for example, several on West Indian history—neglect the central problem of the causes of white failure, contain no references to the vitally important diseases, and leave the reader tangled in a skein of minor controls. Research in the archives of Spain, Portugal, France, Holland, Britain, and other colonizing nations and of institutions such as the Roman Catholic Church, if directed towards the really important factors, would doubtless throw new light upon the question. Yet, as indicated above, it is doubtful if the truth can be discovered by historical research alone.

A further difficulty arises from the fact that recent scientific discoveries have greatly reduced the value of past interpretations, and writers, such as General Gorgas and Sir Raphael Cilento, claim that history is no longer a guide. It is true, of course, that modern transport, diet, housing, comfort, sanitation, and medicine have greatly mitigated the hardships of tropical settlement, but throughout the greater part of the tropics many of the old obstacles remain. Experience has shown that the hopes of the Gorgas school were illusory, and overoptimism is still causing disappointment, expense, and harm. In these circumstances we cannot wholly ignore the historical facts and the historical method that interprets them.

The Statistical Method

The second line of attack—the use of statistics—has been ably developed by Dr. Ellsworth Huntington and other scientists, but, in the present state of statistical knowledge, this method, like the historical, is far from perfect. Huntington's theories, which are set out in Chapter XIV, postulate that there are climatic limits and optima for human

beings and all other forms of life and that the tropics are beyond
the climatic optima and possibly near the climatic limits for whites.
From this it follows that climate per se and its secondary effects, such
as "tropical" parasitic diseases, are destructive to the mental, moral,
and physical energies of white settlers.[31] Sorokin, Vance, Cilento, and
others have vigorously attacked Huntington's theories and statistics,
but it is fair to say that they have failed to disprove his central
thesis that there are climatic optima for the white races and that the
tropics may lie beyond these limits.[32]

Nevertheless, several weaknesses in the statistical method are apparent. There is still a great want of data, and such data as exist
have been collected under many systems and are by no means uniform.
Statistics are few for some of the most important elements in climate,
as, for example, air movements. Professor Griffith Taylor writes, "It is
a counsel of perfection to advise the meteorologist to allow for *wind
velocities* in his study of comfort as controlled by climate." [33] Yet, as
we shall see in the chapters on Florida, the West Indies, and Queensland, air movements have great influence on tropical settlement. Local
climates, too, are particularly significant, but here again there is a difficulty in the meagerness of the statistics available for the tropics.

Another difficulty lies in the increasing probability that white settlement in the tropics is a far more complicated question than is generally
believed and that it may be influenced by factors on which we have no
statistics or even knowledge. Climatologists and physiologists have long
recognized that there are many weather elements of possible or probable
importance to the life of man. While the statistical and experimental
investigation of the occurrence and effects of these elements has lagged,
there are nevertheless many data available that have not been utilized as
they might be. Climatologists have not as a rule obtained observations
of the type needed for medical studies, since the medical men have not
clearly indicated what was wanted. "The solution of the general problem of climate and health requires extensive studies of the effects of
many other elements (than temperature), such as atmospheric ionization, sunshine, barometric pressure, precipitation, wind, frost, and perhaps other factors, all of which may have an important bearing on
health." [34] The truth seems to be that white settlement in the tropics is
a vast and complicated problem, which demands the collection of far
more data if an unchallengeable solution is to be reached by statistical
research.

The Laboratory

The third and most hopeful line of attack is the laboratory.[35] This
offers a means of analyzing with accuracy the effects of a number of
factors that clearly influence white settlement. Here, however, the
scientist faces two difficulties. First, laboratory investigations have only

limited scope. They can make soil analyses. They can explain tropical diseases. They can discover certain results of racial mixture. They may disclose important physiological changes in the whites. But the laboratory cannot explore many basic phenomena. It cannot touch a vast mass of environmental, racial, economic, and political factors, nor can it as yet explain important psychological and moral changes.

A second disadvantage is the difficulty and expense of investigation in tropical countries. D. B. Dill, C. P. Yaglou, and others who have carried out researches on such problems as the effects of varying temperatures and humidities on manual labor themselves recognize the impossibility of producing all the effects of outdoor climates in laboratories and agree that this and the process of acclimatization make their results so far unreliable for the tropics.[36] Breinl and others have experimented under better conditions in the Institute of Tropical Research at Townsville (Queensland) and in other tropical centers, but many of their results are indefinite and contradictory and touch but the fringe of the problem.[37]

In the chapters that follow the methods of historical, statistical, and laboratory research will be discussed in detail and some of the results will be examined.

CHAPTER II

PRESCIENTIFIC INVASIONS OF THE TROPICS

The progress of science is revolutionizing tropical life, but lessons may still be gained from what may be called the "prescientific" era, which lasted until about the beginning of the present century.[1] From the early sixteenth century white settlers poured into the tropics, to be defeated in most cases by the indigenous races, climate, disease, diet, isolation, maladministration, and faulty economic policies. Unfortunately, the existing knowledge is fragmentary. Historians have paid but slight attention to many fundamental aspects of the invasions, and rare treasures may await those future scholars who will synthesize the records of the great colonizing nations and of the Roman Catholic Church, in efforts to explain the real causes of the white failures and to evaluate the various controls.

From 1500 onwards the Portuguese, Spaniards, Dutch, English, French, Danes, and other Europeans poured into tropical Asia, Africa, America, and Australia. In both hemispheres the invaders wrought profound biological changes. In both they conquered indigenous races. In both they exterminated the natives in many places, where the latter were few in number and weak. At the outset the invasions were overwhelming and spectacular. Quickly and irresistibly, however, the tropical climates, diseases, and peoples began to take their toll. The millions of Asia gave the invaders little footing for settlement, and their status remained that of sojourners and aliens. In the western tropics colored races absorbed most of the white communities even where they had established themselves on favorable islands and plateaus.

Perhaps even the political supremacy of the whites is transitory. In the Americas rulers of mixed or native blood have often risen to prominence after centuries of white dominion. In Asia native races are seeking self-determination. In "darkest Africa" doctrines such as the "Dual Mandate" and the development of the negro are filling white settlers with strongly grounded fears.

Many historians have outlined the causes and course of the invasions that the whites conducted from 1500 until the beginning of the twentieth century. The nations of Europe had long assimilated energy from infusions of barbarian blood and from the pressure of Asiatic and African races on the eastern and southern frontiers. From the fifteenth century, led by Portugal and Spain, European sailors swept around the geographical barriers of the arid or tropical coasts of western Africa to conquer India and the East Indies. Others drove across the Atlantic to dominate the American tropics by a series of swift blows. Two facts are significant. In the first place, the early successes were won by peoples who occupied advantageous geographical locations. The southwestern Europeans had reached advanced stages of civilization, were accustomed to warm climates, and were in close contact with peoples of northern Africa. In the second place, no little of the success of these so-called prescientific invasions was due to an elementary knowledge of science. In navigation, in map-making, in ship-building, in the use of gunpowder, the peoples of southwestern Europe were beginning to utilize science in their conquest of tropical lands.

For Da Gama the goal was "Christians and spices." For Portugal and for her European competitors, however, the period of exploration and spasmodic trading soon evolved into that of commercial empire. The Portuguese entrenched themselves on the coasts of Africa, India, the East Indies, and Brazil. The Spanish conquistadors also established themselves in the East Indies, but their great work was the founding of settlements in the highlands of the American tropics and in favorable islands and strategic positions on the coasts of the New World. To the Eastern and Western tropics flowed two great streams of sojourners and settlers. The Dutch, English, French, Danes, and many others quickly followed for trade, settlement, and loot.

THE EAST

From the outset a dissimilarity in the character and effects of the currents that flowed to the east and to the west is noticeable. In both hemispheres the invaders found almost all types of tropical environment, but the density of the indigenous populations, their cultural development, and their wealth were by no means the same. We cannot examine here the wide range of factors that operated on the whites in the many and varied localities. In general, however, the incomers were able to establish white working communities in parts of the American tropics, whereas in tropical Asia and Africa they remained alien sojourners from generation to generation. As Meredith Townsend writes of India:

Not only is there no white race in India, not only is there no white colony, but there is no white man who purposes to remain. . . . No ruler stays there to help, or criticize, or moderate his successor. No successful white soldier founds a family. No white man who makes a fortune builds a house or buys an estate for his descendants. The very planter, the very engine-driver, the very foreman of works, departs before he is sixty, leaving no child, or house, or trace of himself behind. No white man takes root in India.[2]

Only those who revisit, after a very few years' absence, an eastern station in countries such as India or Burma can realize how rapidly the entire white population changes.

A. J. Toynbee believes that Europeans could not make themselves at home in the Indian climate and that in any case the existing native population "was too numerous and too far advanced in civilization to be exterminated, even if our British Israelites had ever contemplated

treating the Canaanite in India as they treated him in America." [3]
Thus, in the eastern hemisphere, India contained in 1921 only 156,637
whites in a population of 319,000,000, and of these whites only 45,000
were women. The Eurasians numbered the small total of 113,000.

A report of the Statutory Commission [4] gives an excellent summary
of the position of whites and Eurasians. Of the whites it states:

While the British connection is continuous and deeply rooted, the British individual is
a sojourner, who, after spending his working years in India, looks forward to retiring
to that country which is his real home. Only a small fraction of those who go out for
the purposes of business or employment settle down in India permanently, and the
European community does not grow.

Of the Eurasians the report notes:

The community has played an honourable part in developing the country and in supporting the forces of order. . . . But it is, generally speaking, a poor community. . . .
It is domiciled in India and must make India its home and it now finds itself, largely
as the result of . . . the progress of Indianization, exposed to the danger of falling
between two stools.

The same facts are true of the whites and Eurasians in Dutch Java
and in British Malaya. In the latter country 17,768 British composed
in 1931 only 0.4 per cent of the population, while the Eurasian element
was even less.[5] As regards the Dutch, according to the census of 1930,
the Netherlands Indies contained 60,727,233 people of whom only
240,417 were white.[6]

The Portuguese in the East

The story of the Portuguese illustrates the factors that defeated the
whites in the eastern hemisphere. This race was particularly fitted for
tropical settlement by environmental experience and racial history, and
it succeeded in establishing important colonies in the Western tropics.
Yet in Asia and the East Indies the Portuguese failed before colored
populations of teeming millions, while in the African tropics they faced
hot, humid coastal climates and tropical diseases and for centuries were
unable to do more than found a few slaving stations, penal settlements,
and halting places for their ships. They taught the African negroes
"a hundred arts and industries," and checked famines by the introduction of European, Asiatic, and Brazilian animals and plants. But they
made no real progress and established no real settlements until they
developed Angola in the nineteenth century and Brazilian Portuguese
began to settle its interior plateaus.

The rise and fall of the commercial empire of Portugal is a remarkable story. A tiny nation challenged and overthrew the Arab power
that had brought the whole Indian Ocean under Islam. History, ancient
or modern, records no achievement so brilliant or so politically fruit-
ful. Yet, although Vasco da Gama did not reach Calicut until 1498,
by 1515, when the great governor Albuquerque died, the Portuguese
power was already on the wane.

The fundamental cause of the decline was the insignificant numbers of the invaders as opposed to the vast mass of the indigenous peoples. Albuquerque himself recognized this and proposed to recruit the Portuguese armies and navies by deliberately breeding a Portuguese-Indian race. He extended special favors to Portuguese who married Indian women. He encouraged them to engage in industrial pursuits. He made them a special class with privileges, offices, and lands. Nevertheless, the attempt was "totally unsuccessful." With the absence of regular infusions of European blood the mixed race tended to revert toward the Indian type and fell before invasions of hardier European stocks.[7] It is a striking fact that the Portuguese themselves preferred the native auxiliary to the blend which they were trying to create.

Poor in its products, the Portuguese system also undermined the morals of the conquerors. The unbridled passions of the lower types of invaders, who included outlaws and prostitutes, brought scandal upon the Portuguese name. As few European women came out to India, miscegenation was common, and even the higher classes degenerated. The first governor to have his wife with him in Goa was Cabral, 1549, and even Albuquerque had a son by a negress. In such circumstances life in Goa became orientalized. The whites left all hard work to slaves and fell into luxury, vanity, and sloth. The customary evils of this type of society followed, and the whites adopted the enervating doctrines that trade disgraces a man and domestic work is beneath a woman's social status. These evils are still rampant in British India, as in most of the Eastern tropics where the Europeans hold sway.

With the decline of Portuguese society even greater evils appeared. The whites became savagely cruel, and the Inquisition was introduced. Administrative ability deteriorated. The governors became unjust. Monopolies, prohibitions, parasites, corruption, and the sale of offices ruined the empire. Prices rose and population declined. The king's confession of 1614 "stands as one of the most remarkable state confessions of utter demoralization." [8]

Another basic cause of the Portuguese failure was the geographical environment, although it is impossible to estimate how much of the trouble was due to the climate and how much to secondary factors such as disease. Keller states that, in spite of their familiarity with warm climates and their proverbial temperance, the Portuguese were so demoralized and so ignorant of the laws of health that they could not accustom themselves to their surroundings.[9] Hence disease took a frightful toll. In addition to losses in India the invaders suffered grievously both on the long ocean voyage and in the African ports. It has been estimated that "not 60 per cent of the men who left Portugal for India reached their destination." [10] The only way that so small a country could free her nationals for Eastern service was to replace them by imported slaves.[11] Thus in Portugal herself national life and national homogeneity declined, and her empire fell at a touch.

The Successors to the Portuguese

Holland, France, and Britain, the nations that followed Portugal, possessed the man power and resources to build up sovereignties of greater capability, strength, and morality, and of longer duration than the empire of the Portuguese. Yet none of these nations established permanent communities of white workers in Asia or the East Indies, but relied, and still rely, on various plantation systems operated by indigenous labor. In recent years the political power of the Europeans has steadily weakened in the Far East, and many authorities consider that the white sojourner-rulers must see the writing on the wall. According to De Kat Angelino, the general tendency in the East is obviously to create continuous and self-governing communities, although Western leadership must remain until the foundations have been laid.[12]

On the African plateaus and in the Australian tropics European nations have established white communities, some of which include manual workers. With a few small exceptions these important developments are very recent and fall within the period of scientific invasion discussed in Chapter IV.

THE WEST

While European nations were building commercial empires in the Eastern tropics, the tide of white settlement rolled west. Sir Charles Lucas writing in "The Cambridge History of the British Empire" outlines the story of the English invasions in terms that illustrate the general trend:

In India the trade motive was entirely dominant, and along the African coast only a few scattered forts and factories were set up to carry on the slave trade. The real course of empire for Englishmen in the seventeenth century flowed westward. . . . Nor were the new homes to be found only on the mainland of North America or in Newfoundland. The tropical heat of the West Indian islands did not prevent them from becoming abiding places for the British race, real plantations of Britons, as witness the thousands of resident white citizens of Barbados in the middle of the seventeenth century.[13]

Apart from the trade motives mentioned by Lucas, there are three basic reasons why the Western conquest differed from that in the East. First, the dense populations of the Western tropics, in preference to the hot, humid lowlands, occupied the higher and cooler plateaus. Here the whites could settle permanently, enslave the natives, create ruling castes, and in some regions build up settlements of white or near-white workers. Secondly, the whites found some fertile regions such as Costa Rica, Cuba, or St. Christopher very lightly settled or even uninhabited. As they quickly exterminated the indigenous peoples by slavery, disease, and cruelty they were compelled to introduce white workers in various regions, and white working settlements were the result. Thirdly, the European peoples wrought a biological revolution and insured their own disappearance from many regions, when, for motives of economic

3

profit, they introduced the negro and later the Asiatic. The elimination of the whites was hastened, as these peoples, particularly the negroes, brought with them serious types of tropical disease, notably yellow fever, smallpox, typhus and influenza.

As in the Old World, the morale of the white invaders declined from the enslaving of the natives, from the caste system, from miscegenation, and from laziness. Hence history discloses a conquest of the conquerors by the tropical peoples, by tropical diseases, and possibly by climate per se.

When the Spaniards and Portuguese invaded the American tropics they wrought these profound racial changes with amazing rapidity, and the English, Dutch, and French, who followed, continued the process with almost equal speed. The conquerors absorbed or exterminated the natives of the West Indies so quickly that by 1503 they were importing negro slaves. On the mainland great groups of aborigines were destroyed by slavery or were cruelly slain, but there the Indians were too numerous to be obliterated. Professor A. J. Toynbee puts forward the theory that the Protestant whites were soaked in the savagery of the Old Testament and that they exterminated the colored Philistines more ruthlessly than did the Catholics.[14] It is true that the cruelty of the Catholic nations—the Portuguese and Spanish—has been exaggerated by Protestant historians. In his "Negro in the New World" [15] Sir Harry Johnston gives examples of ferocious brutality on the part of the Protestant Dutch in the eighteenth century. Nevertheless, the deciding factor was the density of the indigenous inhabitants rather than the cruelty of the immigrants. Miscegenation also saved the conquered. All the incoming peoples bred with them, but, as both the Portuguese and Spaniards were of mixed race and did not bring their own women, they cohabited freely with Indian and negro women and rapidly built up a conglomeration of mixtures. The chief groups to evolve were the mestizos (European-Indians), now the dominant class in most of the Latin-American Republics, and the mulattoes (European-negroes), who are now of great importance in the continental lowlands and the West Indies. It is unnecessary to trace the history of these intermixtures. The rapidity of the process is indicated by Professor Mark Jefferson's examples from Chile, where married men in Valdivia had up to 30 concubines each, and where in one frontier post 60 children were born to 160 Spanish soldiers in the space of a single week.[16]

It is impossible to estimate the exact numerical strength of the pure white communities that escaped the general mixed breeding and survived the advance of the Indian and negro. The classification of race in the republics of tropical America is unreliable, and many of the so-called whites are of mixed blood. Table I presents, however, the best available statistics of the whites or near-whites as contrasted with the other racial groups.

If we consider this table in the light of environmental controls the following facts appear: the whites or near-whites still predominate in two northern islands of the West Indies, Cuba and Puerto Rico, and in certain parts of the high mainland plateaus, such as Costa Rica and southern Brazil. There are considerable numbers of whites in other

TABLE I—TROPICAL AMERICA: PERCENTAGE OF MAIN POPULATION
TYPES TO TOTAL POPULATION*

	EUROPEAN	INDIAN	MESTIZO	NEGRO	MULATTO
SOUTH AMERICA					
Brazil............	35	15	30	..	20
Bolivia...........	10	50	40	..	..
Colombia.........	10	15	40	..	35
Peru.............	10	50	35	..	1
Venezuela	10	11	70	..	9
Ecuador..........	6	65	23	..	5
CENTRAL AMERICA					
Costa Rica.......	80	1	14	4	..
Mexico...........	17	28	55	..	..
Nicaragua........	17	5	69	10	..
Honduras.........	about the same as Nicaragua, with more Indians and fewer negroes				
Salvador..........	as for Nicaragua				
Guatemala........	1	64	35	..	..
WEST INDIES					
Puerto Rico.......	73	..	..	4	23
Cuba.............	72	..	..	28	
Barbados.........	9	..	..	91	
Jamaica..........	2	..	..	98	

*Statistics mainly from C. F. Jones: Economic South America, in A. C. Wilgus, edit.: Modern Hispanic America (Studies in Hispanic American Affairs, Vol. 1), Washington, 1933, pp. 139–169, and R. R. Hill: Geographic and Historic Background of Central America, in A. C. Wilgus, edit.: The Caribbean Area (ibid., Vol. 2), 1933, pp. 210–227. Owing to the omission of minor groups these figures do not always add up to 100 per cent.

parts of the high continental plateaus, although it is generally believed that the Indians and mestizos are absorbing them.[17] On the continental lowlands and in almost all the larger West Indian islands, except Cuba, Puerto Rico, and Santo Domingo, the numerical supremacy of the negro is overwhelming and the whites have almost disappeared. Is race or place the cause of these phenomena? In the chapters that follow an attempt will be made to analyze the factors that have produced or maintained substantial white populations in some of these tropical lands.

CHAPTER III

BRITISH FAILURES IN THE WEST INDIES

The preceding chapter outlined the factors that debarred the European nations from colonizing tropical Asia and most of tropical Africa. More important for our purpose is the history of the Western tropics, where the Europeans did establish white working communities. Excellent research on the West Indies by British and American historians makes it possible to enumerate and examine some of the reasons for the failure of a number of these settlements.[1]

The discovery of the West Indies by Christopher Columbus in 1492 was followed by a great burst of Mediterranean colonization, so that by 1502 there were 12,000 Europeans in the island of Haiti. But Spain was not left for long in her monopoly. France was in the field before the middle of the sixteenth century. In 1562-1563 John Hawkins brought England into the slave trade, and from 1586 onwards Dutch and Flemish ships traded in the Caribbean. Colonization followed. In 1607 the French attempted to grow tobacco in Cayenne. English efforts to settle Guiana failed, but in 1623 Thomas Warner established in St. Christopher the first English colony in the Caribbean. In 1625 an English expedition occupied Barbados. The deluge of northern whites had begun.

The following years, 1625-1637, were vital in West Indian history. "Swarms of English and French colonists poured like flies upon the rotting carcase of Spain's empire in the Caribbean."[2] By 1643 there were 37,200 whites in Barbados, a population of more than 200 to the square mile. The whole island was divided into plots of from five to thirty acres, upon which small white planters and their white servants raised tobacco or cotton. St. Kitts and Nevis were densely populated by small planters, each holding a few acres and cultivating them with the help of white servants.[3] The north European settlement of Jamaica came later, but events moved on similar lines. When the English captured the island in 1655 it was estimated that the population of the capital was "half Spanish and Portuguese or their descendants, and half slaves."[4] Owing to deaths from yellow fever and dysentery, the English had difficulty in populating the island, but, according to Bryan Edwards, there were, by 1673, 7768 whites as contrasted with 9504 negroes.[5]

For reasons to be discussed in detail the ensuing period saw a fall in white population. In some islands this fall was absolute, and in all islands ruled by north Europeans it was relative to the number of negroes. Table II, of the white, black, and colored population in Barbados, St. Kitts, and Jamaica, illustrates the decline.

CHARACTER OF THE IMMIGRANT PEOPLES

A great mass of evidence indicates that the experiment of establishing north European workers in the West Indian tropics failed, at any rate in the British islands, partly through the poor quality of the workers and their inadequate numbers. The period of the "Great Emigration," 1618-1648, saw many Englishmen of good type cross the seas to avoid the tyranny of the Stuart kings; but when the Civil War broke out in 1642, the tide ceased to flow. Further, North America proved more attractive to the best English immigrants than did the Caribbean, to which flocked adventurers and persons of low character,

TABLE II—BRITISH WEST INDIES POPULATION TYPES: HISTORICAL*

	BARBADOS		ST. KITTS		JAMAICA	
	White	Black or colored	White	Black or colored	White	Black or colored
1640–1643	37,000	6,000	20,000 to 30,000	....	....	....
1667–1678	20,000	40,000	1,897	1,436	8,500	9,500
1786–1791	16,167	62,115 835 half castes	1,900	20,435	23,000	260,093
1807–1809	15,566	69,119	....	....	15,000	356,070
1911	....	....	1,348	24,935	....	....
1921–1922	15,000	180,000	....	....	14,476	817,643

*Statistics mainly from V. T. Harlow: History of Barbados, Oxford, 1926, Appendix B, p. 338; C. S. S. Higham: The Development of the Leeward Islands under the Restoration, Cambridge, 1921, p. 145; L. J. Ragatz: The Fall of the Planter Class in the British Caribbean, 1763-1833, New York, 1928, pp. 30 and 124.

who were anxious to make money rapidly by any legal or illegal means. In the words of Ragatz:

No considerable body of persons inspired by motives higher than the desire to extract the greatest possible amount of wealth from them in the shortest possible time ever reached the smiling shores of the Caribbean colonies. Save during the civil wars of the sixteen hundreds, no haven of refuge from persecution was sought there. Few landed to establish homes and to raise their station in a new world. Instead, the islands became the goal of spendthrift bankrupts, eager to recoup their wasted fortunes, of penniless younger sons of gentility desirous of amassing means sufficient to become landed proprietors in the homeland, and the dumping-ground for the riffraff of the parent country.[6]

Like the Spaniards, the English on some islands at first attempted to utilize Indian labor, but the Caribs soon died out under slavery, and the estate owners turned to white labor and to negroes. White servants came from three sources—rebellions, kidnapping, and indentures—but in almost all cases these servants were little better than slaves. It was a disgraceful policy, shamefully executed, and it filled the British West Indies with undesirables from the motherland, with foreigners from any European country that would offer a supply, and with negroes. "As could only be expected in such a community, all ideas of a decent colonial society, of a better and greater England overseas, were swamped in the pursuit of an immediate gain." [7] To quote Whistler's "Journal of the Barbados" (1655), "This Illand is the Dunghill wharone England doth cast forth its rubidg." [8] About the same time Venables described the planters as "fearful, prophane, debauch'd persons." Later writers, such as Pitman, Higham, Harlow, and Ragatz, drew sad pictures of a selfish, ill-educated, and cruel planter aristocracy tyrannizing over a poverty-stricken mass of enslaved white servants.

Nor were many of the officials and military much better. During the administration of Governor Ricketts in Barbados a comely negress reigned at Government House and enjoyed most of the privileges of a wife.[9] The rank and file of the West Indian regiments consisted of the lowest grade of men wearing the British uniform. Governor Valentine Morris of St. Vincent wrote in 1777 that "those which have been sent out these last twelve months, are in general the very scum of the earth. The Streets of London must have been swept of their refuse, the Gaols emptied . . . I should say that very Gibbets had been robbed to furnish such Recruits . . . literally, most of them fit only to fill a pit with." [10]

TREATMENT OF WHITE LABOR

While the character of the white workers in the West Indies was so unsatisfactory as to render failure likely, the treatment that many received was sufficiently scandalous to render that failure almost assured. Contemporary eyewitnesses, such as Ligon in Barbados, give examples of the most barbarous undernourishment, cruelty, and overwork.[11] Governor Russell, writing from Barbados in 1695, stated that the whites were "domineered over and used like dogs, and this in time will undoubtedly drive away all the commonalty of the white people and leave the Island in a deplorable condition." [12] Harlow, Pitman, and others who have used the original documents, consider that "brutal treatment and miserable conditions were prevalent" and sketch a ruinous labor regime. Conditions seem to have been similar in the French islands. Du Tertre (1667) notes that the French, who colonized Guadeloupe and Martinique, experienced a heavy mortality owing to famine, sickness, and the cruelty of the overseers who treated the enfeebled colonists "worse than the slaves in Barbary," driving them "by blows and by severity to work in clearing the woods in all weathers." [13]

Returning to the subject of the British islands, one finds that there was a general agreement among contemporary writers that the European servant was in a less favored position than the negro.[14] A slave was a permanent possession, and it was to the advantage of the master to preserve him. On the other hand, a white laborer was available only for a restricted period, during which a master might work him to death in order to avoid paying him the stipulated amount of sugar at the end of his time. Contemporary records show that cases of murder and torture were not infrequent and that sick servants were turned off and left to perish miserably.

There were, of course, good masters and conditions, and diet improved when the governments and planters became alarmed at the growing preponderance of negroes and attempted to increase the ratio of whites to blacks by the so-called Deficiency Laws, which compelled every master to keep a proportion of white servants. Yet, as late as 1695, Governor Russell noted that there was a great dearth of white servants owing to neglect and sickness. Servants received no encouragement, as they were paid only 40 shillings when their time expired. In contrast, the other colonies offered much greater inducement, and servants left Barbados as soon as they were free. The Governor advocated that white peasant proprietors should receive votes in the Assembly, in the belief that planters would "sometimes give the poor miserable creatures a little rum and fresh provisions and such things as would be of nourishment to them . . . in the hopes of getting their votes." [15] But matters were beyond remedy. As Jeaffreson wrote from St. Kitts, the terms offered failed to attract "a sufficient number of honest immigrants," for, whereas the early planters had had a superabundance of European recruits of the best quality, the rage for adventure had by then diminished, and petty tradesmen and peasants of the old country had received discouraging reports of the insecurity of life in islands "infested by pirates, destructive fevers and bloody wars." [16] Hence, the planters had to look for labor to African slaves or to English convicts, while the free immigrants went to New England, where life was more orderly, decent, and devout than in the unhappy West Indies, from which one governor could write that for forty orthodox parishes he had one drunken orthodox priest, one drunken sectary priest, and one drunken parson who had no orders.[17]

From circumstances such as these, the Deficiency Laws failed to raise the ratio of white to black. Even when groups of white settlers were brought in, as after Emancipation (in 1834), they received no preferential treatment over the negro and were quickly absorbed. On the whole, one can fully agree with Harlow that "generally speaking . . . the weight of evidence proves incontestably that the conditions under which white labour was procured and utilized in Barbados" (and one could add other islands) were "persistently severe, occasionally dishonourable, and generally a disgrace to the English name." [18] One can, perhaps, go further and say that under such a policy and treatment it was almost impossible for white workers to succeed.

WAR AND BUCCANEERING

A third cause of the white decline was international warfare and private buccaneering, which ruined several of the islands and assisted in giving the West Indies their bad name. Higham, for example, writes:

The French War of 1666-7 marks a turning point in the history of the Leeward Islands; before the war the islands had progressed steadily, and had been largely settled; by the French successes the islands were practically ruined, and had to start their economic life anew. The exodus from St. Christopher is estimated by Du Tertre at 8,000, but probably the number was about 5,000 exclusive of slaves.[19]

At this time, Barbados, "the principal pearl in his Majesty's crown," was almost bankrupt of men and money, while Surinam had fallen to the Dutch. Buccaneering also discouraged good immigrants and induced the bad to take up that profitable profession. A contemporary wrote of the Scottish Jacobites sent to the West Indies in 1716: "The greatest part of them are gone and have Induced others to go with them a Pyrating . . . the few that remains proves a wicked Lazy and Indolent people." [20] Jeaffreson's remarks, quoted above, indicate how greatly warfare and buccaneering conspired together to give the West Indies a bad name.

ECONOMIC AND ADMINISTRATIVE FACTORS

A fourth cause of the failure of the whites lay in the administrative mistakes, both of the island authorities and of the English government, which controlled their destiny from outside. In Barbados and the Leeward Islands the rapid increase of white population quickly exhausted the soil and forced out the small white settlers who could not afford expensive fertilizers.[21] The same thing occurred in Jamaica, where small planters were driven off the land—cattle and sheep appearing in their place. Heavy taxes, costly provisions, high risks, and the low prices for produce accelerated a process under which the large proprietors gobbled up the small planters, and many families emigrated to North America to avoid debt. The class of big planters, which then arose, consisted in many cases of absentees who frequently left their servants to cruel and extravagant bailiffs. Even the sons of resident planters were estranged by education in England and comparatively few returned. Nor was the English government sympathetic or helpful to their white subjects in the Indies; for the motherland crippled them by a 4½ per cent duty on exports and other taxes, by the Navigation Acts, by the slaving monopoly of the Royal African Company, by the engrossment of all patronage by the king's ministers, and by the quartering of troops.[22]

Harlow's research on the documents of Barbados emphasizes the importance of economic and administrative factors in causing this decline.

The decrease in the white population was chiefly attributable to the concentration of land into the hands of a few great landowners and the ousting of white labour by black.

A writer of 1667 gives a striking picture of the tide of emigration from Barbados: "At least 12,000 former landholders and tradesmen have gone off, 'wormed out of theire small settlements by theire more suttle and greedy neighbours'—between 1643 and 1647 to New England 1,200; to Trinidad and Tobago, 600; between 1646 and 1658 to Virginia and Surinam 2,400; between 1650 and 1652 to Guadeloupe, Martinique, Mariegalante, Grenada, Tobago and Curazoa 1,600; with Colonel Venables to Hispaniola and since to Jamaica 3,300." More than 5,000 left Barbados on the various expeditions to the Leeward Islands during the wars with the French and Dutch, very few of whom ever returned. After 1667 the exodus of time-expired servants and others to Carolina and elsewhere consistently outnumbered the arrivals in Barbados from the Mother Country. In 1670 no less than 2,000 colonists left Barbados for other plantations.[23]

Other islands experienced the same drift. Governor J. Hart of Antigua wrote in 1724: "The real cause why there are so few White People is, that the wealthy Inhabitants of this Island have Ingross'd such vast Tracts of Land that there is not Room for a Number of poorer Inhabitants to invite them to Settle amongst You." [24]

The same trend appeared in Jamaica, although at a later date. Richard Harris told the Board of Trade (Mar. 20, 1724/5) "The decrease of Small Freeholds, was by reason of the greater Eating up or buying out all the lesser planters and keeping vast tracts of Land unoccupied." [25] The rural aristocracy of the West Indies came from the class that created a similar depopulation in England. The small white landholders gradually disappeared, and in their place came cattle and sheep pastures, vacant land, or great sugar estates.[26]

DIET, HOUSING, CLOTHING, AND SOCIAL CONDITIONS

While servants faced conditions of life and labor that almost ensured failure, the upper classes showed a calamitous inability to meet the tropical environment in vital matters of housing, clothing, and diet. Most of the settlements were located so as to fulfill the agricultural and shipping requirements of the planters and, consequently, stood on the hot coastal plains. In the early years nearly all the houses were of wood, and fires were frequent and destructive. Even as late as the latter half of the eighteenth century many of the buildings were miserable, thatched hovels, hastily put together with wattles and plaster, damp, unwholesome, and infested with every species of vermin." [27]

Then again, the planter's table was one of rude plenty and contrary to every law of modern tropical diet. Drunkenness was prevalent and gambling a consuming vice.[28] Many a young West Indian immigrant of good family drank himself to death. Friends notified his parents that he had died of "fever," and that good old whipping horse, the tropical climate, took the blame. Clothing was equally unsuited to the tropical conditions. In the words of one writer, "Our English Belles . . . do

not scruple to wear the thickest winter silks and satins; and are sometimes ready to sink under the weight of rich gold or silver brocades. . . .
The winter fashions of London arrive here at the setting in of hot
weather. . . . Surely nothing can be more preposterous and absurd
than for persons residing in the West Indies to adhere rigidly to all
the European customs and manners which . . . are certainly improper,
ridiculous, and detrimental in a hot climate." [29]

While the diet and clothing of the planter class were excessive, the
poor suffered from the reverse. Ligon states that the Barbadians of
1650 worked their white servants from 6 a. m. to 11 a. m. and from
1 p. m. to 6 p. m. on potatoes mashed in water, or on loblolly, which
consisted of crushed Indian corn. "The servants," he wrote, "[had]
no bone meat at all unlesse an Oxe dyed." He paints a sad picture
of their housing: "Their lodging at night [is] a board, with nothing
under, nor any thing a top of them. . . . If they be not strong men,
this ill lodging will put them into a sicknesse: if they complain, they
are beaten by the Overseer; if they resist, their time is doubled." [30]
Some of the planters, of course, were more humane, particularly in
later years. Yet, inadequate housing, clothing, and diet continued to
produce great harm.

The Negro

A fundamental cause—perhaps the main cause—of the failure of
white settlement in the Caribbean was the importation of the negro.
It is usually said that the introduction of this race was due to the
necessities of the environment and that the negro was a hardy exotic,
admirably equipped for the tropics, whereas the white was a tender,
unsuitable plant. Yet other factors enter the picture. The planters
could force the negro to work at an economic and social level that en-
tailed the degeneracy or emigration of white workers, and for the first
few centuries the black was sufficiently backward, weak, and docile to
suffer this exploitation.

The English were interested in the Caribbean slave trade from the
time of John Hawkins' voyage of 1567-1568, but they delayed the
wholesale introduction of black slaves, owing to the scarcity of negroes
and the hope of securing white labor. When, for example, the French
captured and ruined the Leeward Islands in the war of 1666-1667, the
slaves on the English part of St. Christopher numbered only about
400, although the English occupation had lasted more than forty
years.[31] As early as 1651, however, Barbados contained 20,000 negroes,
for the planters visited Brazil to learn sugar planting from the Dutch
and purchased slaves from them. Great prosperity rewarded the new
economic and racial policy, but the result was tragic to the whites. By
1667 no less than 12,000 "good men" had left the island for other plantations, the 11,200 small holdings of 1645 had been included in **745**

large estates, and the negroes had increased to 82,023.[32] The sufferings
of the displaced whites were terrible. Faint echoes reached England
and Scotland, and men began to realize that the most cruel fate for
political prisoners was to be "barbadoed." [33] Twenty years before, the
West Indies had been the goal of hopeful emigrants. They were now
the dreaded haunts of black slavery, savage cruelty, and vice.[34]

The Leeward Islands and Jamaica quickly followed the Barbadian
example, with the same results. The usual evils of *latifundia* appeared
in absenteeism, a decreasing white population, a fluctuating one-crop
industry, and the growth of a class of degenerate poor whites. In the
past the small planters and their time-expired servants had formed a
sturdy yeomanry, which increased the white population and provided
a valuable militia and a variety of crops. Now the islands were devoted
almost entirely to the one-crop sugar industry, worked on large estates
for absentee capitalists by overseers and negro slaves. As the proportion of blacks increased and the Deficiency Laws failed, the planters
inevitably became more oppressive. Slave rebellions were crushed with
fiendish cruelty. In many cases negro leaders were burnt alive. Nevertheless, the slave trade continued on a vast scale. In a report to the
Privy Council, Liverpool merchants estimated that British ships carried
38,000 negroes annually. Between the years 1744 and 1760 Jamaica
alone purchased more than 100,000 slaves. Owing to the low cost of
upkeep the planters began to train the negroes as artisans, so that
slaves invaded the field of skilled labor. In the words of one observer,
"I have seene 30, sometimes 40 Christians, English, Scotch and Irish
at worke in the parching sun without shoe or stockin', while theire
negroes have bin at worke at theire respective Trades in a good
condition." [35]

The growth of the plantation system brought two customary but
damning evils: a half-caste element in the population and a class of
poor whites. In a few striking sentences Edwards traces the tragic position of the browns—social outcasts, hated and envied by the natives
and lorded over by the dominant race. "Their spirits," he wrote, "seem
to sink under the consciousness of their condition." The whites forced
good-looking women to be their mistresses and then, refusing to marry
them, accused them as a class of incontinency. "The unhappy females
here spoken of, are much less deserving reproach and reprehension
than their keepers, . . . excluded as they are from all hope of ever
arriving to the honour and happiness of wedlock, insensible of its
beauty and sanctity; ignorant of all christian and moral obligations;
threatened by poverty, urged by their passions, and encouraged by
example, upon what principle can we expect these ill-fated women to
act otherwise than they do?" [36]

We cannot tell how soon the negro immigration produced a typical
poor-white stratum, but later occurrences show that the evolution is

usually swift and inevitable, even when the whites are not debased by semislavery, cruelty, and neglect. In most of the island communities white men of the upper classes ravished the slave women, while the lower class of whites came into economic competition with the negroes, were riddled with negro diseases, and sank rapidly to the negro standard of life. Here and there white groups, such as the "Redlegs" of Barbados, the "Chachas" of St. Thomas, or the British-Dutch of Saba, refused to mingle and maintained their racial purity, but miscegenation and absorption went on in almost every community and is gradually coloring the white groups that still survive. The "Black Irish" of Montserrat and of Jamaica are typical communities in which the "negrodation" of the whites is complete. The German community of Seaford, Jamaica, is an excellent example of the process in operation and indicates how far it can proceed in less than a hundred years.[37]

HEALTH

It is the basic argument of Gorgas and other apologists for tropical climates that the white failures have been due to tropical diseases and that, with the progress of scientific medicine, the white man can thrive as strongly in the tropics as in the temperate zone. This vital problem has received little attention from West Indian historians. Nevertheless, there peeps from the pages of their histories a story of tropical sickness, which was undoubtedly an important cause of the British decline.

The whites introduced many diseases to the topics, either from Europe or through the importation of African slaves. How terrible could be the mortality among non-immune persons when confronting exotic diseases two examples will show. In 1520 a sick negro in the train of Narvaez introduced into Mexico an epidemic of smallpox so appalling that it broke the resistance to Cortez.[38] In St. Louis, Mauritius, an epidemic of malaria killed 22,231 persons out of 80,000 in 1867-1868 and might easily have depopulated the island in the same way that the disease is believed to have devastated ancient Greece and large tracts of Italy and Spain.[39] Among white immigrants to the West Indies the mortality was very grave. When, in 1635, the French colonized Guadeloupe and Martinique with *pauvres engagez* from Dieppe, they experienced a heavy mortality from the sickness that followed upon famine and overwork.[40] The British, too, complained greatly about health. Ligon wrote that in Barbados, about 1650, the inhabitants and shipping "were so grievously visited with the plague, (or as killing a disease,) that before a month was expired, after our Arivall, the living were hardly able to bury the dead." [41] The voyage, said the same author, "takes many passengers," as did "ill dyet" and "strong waters," through which many brought diseases on themselves. The men suffered particularly. Ten men died for every one woman, for the men were "the greater deboystes" (debauched). Barbadian dispatches in the "Calendar of State Papers" contain numerous laments such as the following: "Sickness and bad weather have been very prevalent, and we have lost many from small-pox and violent fevers." [42]

Among the military forces in the tropics the mortality was nothing short of frightful. Of 19,676 men sent to the British West Indies in 1796, no less than 17,173 died within five years, and departure for Caribbean service was viewed as a voyage to the grave. To this many factors contributed. Physically the soldiers were of poor stamp. Primary laws of hygiene and diet were ignored. Barracks were generally located on waste land near marshes, and yellow fever took its toll. Quarters were neither roomy, airy, nor clean. Bathing was infrequent. The authorities forced men to wear the traditional scarlet, designed for use in European climates, and issued salt meat five times a week under the standard Old-World rationing. Lastly, new rum, a veritable poison, formed the customary drink. Under such conditions the home governments were appalled by shocking death returns and in 1795 sought to solve the problem of West Indian defence by organizing negro companies, recruited through purchase from among the best-conditioned slaves. [43]

CLIMATE

So far we have traced a variety of factors that contributed to the failure of the whites in the British West Indies. There remains the fundamental and most mysterious problem of all—the question of how far the collapse was due to the tropical climate per se.

There is a vast amount of evidence in West Indian history that appears to indicate that the climate affected the whites unfavorably and prevented them from engaging in hard work. Pitman believes that the English moral constitution broke down under a tropical sun and that by the second generation it became apparent that only African slaves could withstand the tropical conditions. [44] Ragatz considers that "climatic conditions made an economic system based on free European workers impossible." [45] Yet, as we have seen, the white settlement of Barbados was extensive and vigorous before it was ruined by war, capitalism, overcrowding, soil exhaustion, and the introduction of the negro with his diseases. Landowners, such as Christopher Jeaffreson of St. Kitts (1676-1686), made no complaint that the white workers were unsuitable or ineffective, but demanded more white servants, even of the criminal class. [46] About the same date Colonel Codrington of St. Kitts emphasized the greater superiority of the colonial troops over soldiers from England. In his opinion "a hundred disciplined men enured to hardships will be worth four hundred of mere new-raised men; . . . for we in these parts are generally accustomed to a hardy and active kind of life." [47] The island regiments were specially selected for severe mountain work, and they acquitted themselves well.

One hundred years later, in 1788, when negro slavery was all-important, a Committee of the Lords and Commons made an extensive survey of the West Indies, in order to ascertain whether the sugar industry could be worked with white labor or with freed negroes. As might be expected, the evidence, which was largely that of the planters, was strongly against any liberation of the slaves. European witnesses stated almost unanimously that under such a climate the whites could not carry out the hard labor of the sugar industry, however well they were fed. "As far as experience can determine," they wrote, "the same exposure to the sun which cheers the African is mortal to the European. Nine in ten of them would die in three years." [48] French planters expressed the same belief.[49]

Yet, amid a welter of condemnation from biased sources comes the significant opinion of a small planter in Barbados. It was "very possible," he said, that free negroes could cultivate canes, while Europeans, inured to common labor and not unduly proud, "might also cultivate their lands well," especially for cotton, where the labor was much lighter than for canes. "The constitution of the human body, when brought up to hard labour, soon accustomed itself to the climate by opening the pores to easy perspiration, but men of debauched habits of mind or body would seldom live to a second year." [50]

As previously indicated, a number of communities of north European peasant workers have survived in the West Indies until the present time, and some of these show less deterioration than one would expect, considering their fight against isolation and other factors not purely climatic in type.

TROPICAL WHITES

Writing about 1793, Bryan Edwards, the Jamaican historian, gives some views on West Indian planters that are extremely important for the light they throw on the evolution of tropical whites. Edwards thought that the West Indian climate displayed its influence more strongly on the persons of the native-born than on their manners or on the faculties of their minds. They were obviously a taller race than the Europeans but in general not proportionately robust. They were all distinguished by freedom and by suppleness of joints, which enabled them to move with ease and agility and gracefulness in dancing. They also excelled in penmanship and in the use of the small sword. Their eye sockets were deeper than among the natives of Europe, which guarded them against the continuous glare of the sun. Their skin felt cooler than that of the European, which proved that nature had contrived some peculiar means of protecting them from the heat. Possibly the climate increased their sensibility, which contributed to create an impatience of subordination. On the whole this attitude was beneficial as awakening frankness, sociability, benevolence, and generosity. Though the method of living differed in no respect from that of the European residents, they were rarely liable to those inflammatory disorders that frequently proved fatal to the latter. The women lived calm and even lives, marked by habitual temperance and self-denial. They took no exercise, except dancing, and had no amusement or avocation to compel them to much exertion of either mind or body. Their diet was abstemious to a fault, and lemonade was their strongest beverage. Their food at the principal repast was a vegetable mess, seasoned with cayenne pepper. Their mode of life and the hot oppressive atmosphere produced lax fiber and pale complexions. They seemed to have just risen from a bed of sickness. Their voices were soft and spiritless, and every step betrayed languor and lassitude. Eminently and deservedly applauded for heart and disposition, no women on earth made better wives or better mothers.

Under the climate the children's mental powers developed early, exceeding those of European children of the same age in a degree that was unaccountable and astonishing. Subsequent mental acquirement did not keep pace with early progress, but that might be due to the want of proper objects for exercizing the faculties. The climate undoubtedly encouraged early and habitual licentiousness, which was against mental improvement. Among such of the native-born as escaped the contagion and enervating effects of youthful excesses were found men of capacities as strong and permanent as among any people whatever. Edwards strongly denied that the Creole whites in general possessed less capacity and stability of mind than Europeans or that they had less quality of heart. Frank, kindly, and truthful, they treated the slaves far better than did the adventurers from Europe. Indolence was too predominant, but it was rather an aversion to serious thought and deep reflection than due to slothfulness and sluggishness of nature. When the springs of the mind were set in motion both sexes had warm imaginations and high spirits.[51]

Although Edwards is describing a planter aristocracy which obviously suffered from isolation, insufficient exercise, and contact with a substratum of negroes, we shall see that his description is applicable in certain respects to the present generation of north Queensland whites, and that here, too, a tendency to conserve muscular, heat-producing energy is appearing, which possibly forecasts some decline.[52]

CAUSES OF FAILURE

The history of these British West Indian Islands has been closely examined in order to enumerate and examine the complex controls that caused the failure of most white settlements in the western hemisphere.

In Barbados, St. Kitts, and Jamaica the British established for a considerable period flourishing groups of white workers, which were ultimately destroyed by war, faulty economic policy and administration, bad housing, diet and liquor, cruelty, the influx of workers of a lower economic standard, the plantation system, the exhaustion of the soil, diseases, and possibly climate per se. The historical method, ably applied by experienced students, has listed factors that produced the British failures, but what scientist would dare to evaluate from this evidence the relative importance of the various controls? Nevertheless, two outstanding and incontestable factors deserve emphasis. First, the prescientific invasions showed that white races, both northern and Mediterranean, could survive in favorable parts of the tropics for many generations in the face of stupendous difficulties and without modern scientific aids. Second, there were very few examples of the white man's successful resistance in the tropics to the competition of races of lower economic and social status.

CHAPTER IV

THE SCIENTIFIC INVASIONS OF THE TROPICS

Some four centuries after the opening of the prescientific invasions a less ambitious but more promising era ensued. Scientific discovery began to bring revolutionary assistance to white sojourners and settlers by improving transport, medicine, and sanitation, and by lifting the clouds of abysmal ignorance that enshrouded such matters as housing, clothing, and diet. No specific date marks the transition, for the change was gradual and even yet has had slight effect on the more remote white settlements. In 1927-1928, for instance, the Peruvian Expedition of the American Geographical Society visited an isolated, prescientific German community at Pozuzo.[1] In most regions, however, the revolution has already had a profound effect on the lives of sojourner and settler alike.

In this chapter we shall deal briefly with two prominent aspects of the scientific advance: the developments in transport and in medical and sanitary science. These, as well as other phases of the subject will also be examined in later chapters, especially those on Florida, Queensland, and Panama.

PROGRESS OF TRANSPORT

The steamship, the railway, the motor, and the airplane have brought necessary comforts and foodstuffs to the white communities of the tropics. They have opened new markets for produce. They have made it possible for many sojourners and settlers to recuperate in the comparatively cool tropical highlands or in the temperate zones. A detailed discussion would entail the writing of a history of modern transport, but the following illustrates the trend of events.

The question of transport has become of vital economic importance to the white communities of the tropical plateaus. It was primarily the American railway builders who put Costa Rica on the economic map. Similarly, in early days the journey to Bogotá on the plateau of Colombia took weeks of toil up the Magdalena River and over the mountains, and seriously endangered the health of the travelers. The river steamer and the mountain railway made the journey reasonably safe and rapid. The airplane reduced it to a few hours. It is this scientific transport that has brought the white inhabitants of remote highlands in touch with modern progress. In the economic sense, at least, they owe a boundless debt to men such as the railway builder Minor Cooper Keith and to organizations such as the United Fruit Company for constructing plateau railways and applying scientific transport to the banana trade.[2]

4

Again, as we shall see, the young white communities of Florida and eastern Queensland owe much of their progress to the scientific communications. Their products can now be carried swiftly to great centers of population in more temperate lands.[3]

Similar facts are in evidence where white communities are struggling for a footing in the wet-dry regions. In the monsoonal belt of north Australia the summer rains prevented communication between the port of Darwin and its hinterland until the coming of the railway. In the outback, arid country of central Australia the cattleman used to await for months the arrival of the camel train with necessities that the telegraph and motor truck now secure in a few days. Until the invention of the airplane these isolated pioneers and their womenfolk were beyond all reach of medical assistance. Today an S. O. S. by portable wireless secures a doctor, nurse, and airplane-ambulance within a few hours.[4]

The American whites at Panama in the hot, wet tropics provide another instance of the beneficial effects of scientific transport. Situated as are these communities at a center of world communications, the steamer and airplane bring a wealth of amenities and foodstuffs and provide rapid transport for leave in the temperate zone.[5] In Panama we saw a striking instance of the efficiency of scientific communications in the tropics. It was necessary for Rockefeller medical scientists to visit Nicaragua, Salvador, and Costa Rica. Even by rail and steamer the journey from Panama involved some weeks of traveling. By airplane these doctors visited three isolated countries, completed their tasks, and returned to Ancon within a few days.

Of course, scientific progress is not always beneficial. While modern transport gives the American of Panama one of the best and most varied of diets in tropical stations, it brings the unhappy Puerto Rican, who suffers under a one-crop industry, a deleterious "tin-can" sustenance of fish and beans.

Medical Progress

The most striking and generally quoted features of the scientific invasions are the advances in medicine and sanitation that have crowded the last forty years.[6] In the final quarter of the nineteenth century medical scientists began a series of epoch-making discoveries and paved the way for the formulation of fundamental generalizations on the so-called tropical diseases, which are a principal barrier to the progress of the whites. They developed, for example, the great concept that there is a geography of disease. In the words of R. B. Vance, "the prevalence of many diseases conforms to a spatial pattern, and the intensity of many diseases is completely seasonal."[7] In the second place, research workers found that the list of diseases is always larger in humid regions, where heat and moisture favor the multiplication of microorganisms.[8] A third great discovery was that many important diseases are due to parasites and that the geography of these diseases is a biological fact, existing in the limitation by temperature and moisture of the range of the parasite. Sir Patrick Manson wrote "the more we learn about these diseases the less important in its bearing on their geographical distribution, and as a direct pathogenic agency, becomes the rôle of temperature *per se,* and the more important the influence of the tropical fauna." [9] Finally, it has been proved that certain diseases reflect the incidence of the social and economic, as well as of the geographical, environment. Differences in sanitation, diet, or medical services produce widely different standards of health. Unfortunately the tropics contain vast numbers of poor, illiterate, and badly governed folk, whose low standard of living makes them a prey to malnutrition and disease.

As indicated above, the great era of scientific discovery in tropical medicine opened during the closing quarter of the last century. In 1877 Manson, a Britisher, discovered that filaria undergoes development in a mosquito. In 1880 Laveran, a Frenchman, found the parasite of malaria in Algeria. In 1893 Kilborne and Smith, Americans, showed that the protozoa in the shape of Babesia could be transmitted by ticks. In 1895 Bruce, a Britisher in South Africa, associated trypanosomiasis of cattle with the tsetse fly. In 1897 Eijkman, a Dutchman in Java, discovered that fowls took polyneuritis when fed exclusively on decorticated rice. In 1897 Ross, a Britisher in India, demonstrated that human malaria parasites commence to develop in malaria mosquitoes. In 1898 he proved the whole cycle of bird malaria in culicines. In 1899 Grassi, an Italian, confirmed Ross's work on human malaria. In 1901 Looss, a German in Egypt, demonstrated how the hookworm infection occurred.[10]

The opening of the twentieth century saw the great fight against yellow fever—a private war conducted by medical scientists with the support of philanthropic and business interests. In 1900 Major Walter Reed found that the mosquito, *Aëdes aegypti* (or *Stegomyia fasciata*), a house mosquito, was to blame. His work was carried further by Dr. H. R. Carter and General W. C. Gorgas, who in three months cleaned up Havana by mosquito control. After that Gorgas went to the Panama Canal, which was regarded as a death trap, and, in spite of violent criticism, was assured of success by May, 1905. The International Health Board of the Rockefeller Foundation then went south and largely cleared Mexico, Central America, and the west coast of South America of yellow fever, and the Board has recently been active in northern Brazil.

If the Rockefeller Foundation has played the most conspicuous part in the eradication of this scourge, governments and other agencies have also had a large share in it, and the Health Section of the League of Nations has contributed toward the international coördination of the work.[11] The elimination of yellow fever in Africa is now probably only a question of time.

Researches by innumerable observers in all parts of the world are enabling medical scientists and sanitarians to work wonders throughout the tropics and to make certain regions comparatively or completely safe for the whites. Two examples will suffice. In the Queensland tropics advances in medical science and in hygiene, facilitated by a high living standard and the expulsion of the Kanakas, raised the expectation of white male life at birth from 41.3 years in 1881-1890 to 54.2 years in 1901-1920. Moreover, the crude death rate in Queensland (8.32 for 1928-1932) became the lowest in Australia, and in 1929-1933 the death rate of tropical Queensland (8.37) was lower than the death rates in warm-temperate Queensland or in the Australian Commonwealth as a whole.[12] Similarly in the Panama Canal Zone the Americans, under General Gorgas and his successors, reduced the combined death rates for white and colored persons from 29.8 in 1905-1909 to 7.86 in 1926-1930.[13]

Unfortunately, some of the medical scientists have exaggerated their successes. After their achievements in Cuba and Panama General Gorgas and his followers became convinced that the Anglo-Saxons could live as healthy lives in the tropics as in the temperate zone. They fondly imagined that in two or three centuries the whites would gradually fill those tropical lands that offered high potentialities for foodstuffs and raw materials and that the tropics would become the chief centers of population, culture, and wealth. Sir Raphael Cilento, using the recent and important data of the Queensland successes, wrote in 1933: "Australia is really a tropical and sub-tropical land, cleverly coerced into the production of temperate climates, free to a large extent from endemic diseases, and increasingly populated by a white race of high standards and culture, which, during three generations, has demonstrated its fitness for residence in the tropics. It seems to me that we may look forward with confidence to successes in the tropical North equal to those which have so transformed the sub-tropical South." [14]

Subsequent history indicated that Gorgas was overoptimistic. The medical scientist has not yet conquered malaria, and this disease alone can defeat, in the humid tropics, the progress of the whites. Cilento's opinions ignore the basic facts of geography. Much of southern Australia is not subtropical. It is very different from the Australian tropics or subtropics, and success in the south is, unfortunately, no criterion that the whites will succeed in the north. Also, the Australian tropics vary greatly in different localities. The advance in the well-watered trade-wind areas of coastal Queensland is no criterion of similar progress in the arid or wet-dry regions of the north and northwest.

SCIENCE AND SETTLEMENT

Science has brought great assistance to white sojourners and settlers throughout the tropics. It is strengthening long-established communities like those of Costa Rica, and it is enabling the whites to penetrate and to settle in a few virgin zones. In Florida the white population increased from 678,000 to 1,026,000 between 1920 and 1930 and now includes thousands of genuine settlers engaged in manual labor. In the Queensland tropics the white population advanced to 184,831 by 1933 and now consists of a working community engaged in the hard manual labor of the sugar and other primary industries. There are some 90,000 British on the plateaus of the Rhodesias and East Africa, although these whites rely very largely on negro labor. The plateaus of southern Brazil contain thousands of white settlers, many of whom are recent immigrants. H. G. James estimates that in a Brazilian population of 40,000,000 more than 60 per cent are of white descent.[15] There are about 600,000 Italians and 400,000 Germans, many of whom are pure white.[16]

The above communities are colonizing the marginal tropics or the high, cool plateaus. In the wet-dry regions—even in white Australia—settlement has made little progress. In a few favorable parts of the humid equatorial lowlands, however, the whites have succeeded in establishing posts, of which Panama is the outstanding instance. It is true that special geographical and economic circumstances make this experiment unique. Nevertheless, a number of white Americans have lived in Panama and have engaged in hard manual labor for many years. Even more significant is the fact that in a few instances the Panamanian-born children of these white Americans are following in their parents' footsteps. As, however, this community rests on a substratum of negro labor and as most of the Americans make comparatively frequent visits to the temperate United States and return there on retirement, we must regard Panama as a quasi rather than as a genuine tropical settlement.[17]

BARRIERS TO SCIENTIFIC PROGRESS

The scientific invaders of the tropics still face three great obstacles: disease (as we have seen), climate, and the colored races.

Climate still constitutes an unsolved problem. The white communities in the margins in Florida and Queensland, on the plateaus of East Africa, and in Panama are very recent, and, despite the improvement in health, the position is uncertain. Cilento himself admits that the Queensland whites are undergoing physiological changes.[18] Although these communities differ widely from those that failed in the West Indies, we cannot wholly ignore West Indian history and must still face the possibility of later generations of whites deteriorating in the hot climate.

The third obstacle is the colored people. The progress of science has not strengthened the political position of the sojourner in the tropics. On the contrary, his status has declined. Scientific food production, medicine, and sanitation are increasing the populations of many colored nations, and education is elevating them. Modern means of communication are enabling them to place their points of view and demands for self-determination before the citizens of such white democracies as still survive. In these circumstances the grip of the sojourner-ruler is loosening. The freeing of the Philippines and the trend in India indicate that some of the colored races of the tropics will soon secure freedom, even though such freedom may immediately expose them to the domination of a new set of races, perhaps even colored races, from the temperate zones.

For the white settler who lives among colored peoples there also seems little hope. Science is increasing not only the numbers but the mobility of the colored folk. In American tropical countries, such as Costa Rica, modern industry has poured the negro along the edge of the white man's territory, and he and malaria are creeping up the plateaus. In the Brazilian melting pot and in other South American regions the white colonist faces gradual but inevitable absorption in an Indian-white or Indian-negro-white race. In the African tropics the progress of the negro peoples makes the white foothold insecure. In the United States the whites will doubtless long continue to control the negro. Hence, the white penetration of Florida has hopeful prospects, although racial mixture is in evidence. In the long view tropical Australia is perhaps the only large area where pure white settlers can keep to themselves the results of scientific progress, for in Australia alone the whites have "liquidated" the aborigines in the closely settled regions and have imported no colored peoples to take their place. As yet, however, the Australians show little real appreciation of the fact that they occupy an isolated and defenseless outpost in a western Pacific now completely dominated by the Japanese, who are rapidly expanding westwards and southwards under population pressure at home. Apart from all questions of climate, health, and soil, racial and economic problems in the Pacific make the future of the white man in the Australian tropics far from certain.

PART II
SOME WHITE SETTLEMENTS IN THE TROPICS
REGIONAL STUDIES

CHAPTER V

THE TRADE-WIND MARGINS: I. FLORIDA

The opening chapters stated the problem, outlined some of the history of the white invasions of the tropics, and indicated from the Portuguese failures in India and from the British failures in the West Indies the complexity of the factors that appear to produce disaster or success. We shall now discuss a number of tropical communities that are making progress, or at least have survived, and can, therefore, be examined *in situ*. Space forbids a detailed analysis of more than a few of these white communities, but one or two groups in each of the main types of tropical environment will be discussed. Of the examples selected Florida and eastern Queensland are situated in the marginal tropics and in trade-wind zones. Puerto Rico, Saba, and the British West Indies are trade-wind islands. North Australia is a wet-dry region. Costa Rica and East Africa are high plateaus. The coasts of Panama are almost equatorial. It must always be remembered, however, that, although its "regional" location is of great importance to each community, white settlers face many more influences than those of the immediate physical environment. Chapter XII amplifies this point. We do not suggest that this detailed study of some typical settlements can solve the problem. It may, however, bring the underlying factors into clearer light.

GEOGRAPHICAL FACTORS

Florida lies outside the mathematical tropics, yet its low elevation, the warm Gulf Stream, and the trade winds bring the southern section of the state within the boundaries of the tropical zone. Even the central and northern areas experience greater heat and humidity than many white settlements on tropical plateaus. Allowance must, however, be made for the fact that Florida lies between two belts of water and receives a considerable number of cyclonic storms in winter. Australian writers are apt to claim that the Queensland coast provides the most important example of a northern white penetration of the tropics. In point of fact the invasion of Florida by white Americans is of greater magnitude than the Australian effort. In many respects it is not dissimilar, and it teaches equally important lessons.

The state, which embraces an area of 54,861 square miles, is thus described by Vance:

Florida is not a coral reef but possesses an interior whose basis is a limestone of marine origin. This flat, low-lying sandy table extends south by east into the Atlantic Ocean. . . . On the basis of both topography and vegetation the region may be divided into

TABLE III—FLORIDA: CLIMATIC DATA, WITH DATA FOR COMPARISON WITH OTHER REGIONS*

STATION AND LENGTH OF RECORD	LAT.	ALT. (feet)	TEMPERATURE (degrees Fahr.)		RAINFALL (inches)		RELATIVE HUMIDITY	WIND (miles per hour)
			Mean ann.	Range[a]	Mean ann.	5 months dry per.		
Tampa 1840–1920 (Central West Florida)	27°55′N	130	72.0	20.4	50.19	11.76	83% 8 A. M.	6.7
Okeechobee 1913–1920 (Central Florida)	27°20′N	27	72.4	18.7	45.82	8.77	…	…
Miami 1855–1920 (Southern Florida)	25°70′N	83	75.1	15.0	59.94	12.69	78% 8 A. M.	8.9
Homestead 1910–1920 (Southern Florida)	25°40′N	13	74.2	13.4	62.75	10.62	…	
Key West 1932–1920 (Southern Florida)	24°30′N	16	76.9	13.6	37.29	7.65	46% noon	9.7
Basseterre 1899–1927 (St. Kitts)	17°20′N	29	79.0	4.9	46.60	14.00	76% 24 hours.	9.5
Balboa 1907–1926 (Panama)	9°0′N	98	78.5	2.6	68.00	1.85	83%	7.6
Darwin 1893–1928 (Northern Terr., Australia)	12°20′S	98	82.5	8.4	61.00	1.42	73% 9 A. M.	…
Innisfail 1881–1928 (Eastern Queensland)	17°32′S	22	73.8	13.5	142.61	22.16	81% 9 A. M.	…
Mackay 1907–1928 (Eastern Queensland)	21°09′S	35	72.3	17.2	74.50	9.50	74% 9 A. M.	…

*Data for Florida stations from U. S. Weather Bureau: Summaries of Climatological Data by Sections, Bulletin W, Vol. 3; for other stations from the Köppen-Geiger "Handbuch der Klimatologie" and Commonwealth of Australia Council for Scientific and Industrial Research, *Pamphlet No. 42.*

[a]Range between mean temperatures of warmest and coldest months.

pineland and swamp. The 30,000 square miles of pine land are set off by relief into dunes, rolling sand plains, flat land and rock ridges. The dunes lie near the coast in ridges flanked by rolling sand plains. Between these and the Everglades lie the imperfectly drained pine flat lands. That great saw-grass morass, the Everglades, may be thought of as a huge series of shallow, connected sinks without either soil or surface drainage. In this region of "grassy water a difference of two feet in topography may mean the difference between a shallow lake and dry land for hundreds of square miles." The poor drainage of interior Florida is due to the youthfulness of its surface with lack of time for a system of drainage to become organized, the absence of relief or a dominating slope, and the dissolving effect of ground water on limestone in opening passages for underground drainage without regard to surface features.[1]

The essential point in this physiography is the difference between the pine lands and the swamps, although both are included in the humid, subtropical crop belt of the United States Department of Agriculture's map.[2]

The climate of Florida varies from subtropical to tropical. Miller, Thornthwaite, and other authorities class the southern division with the moderate tropical lands.[3] The annual temperatures range from about 78° F. in the extreme south to 67° in the west. The rainfall is high and well distributed throughout the year. It varies from about 40 to 70 inches, the average for the state being 52.65 inches. The humidity is also very high, being about 80 per cent at 8 a. m. for the state. The wind velocity is about 10 miles an hour at places such as Tampa, Miami, and Key West. Residents of the last-named place consider that this wind control has a very beneficial effect. Of fundamental influence on agriculture is the fact that there have been only three or four disastrous freezes in the last one hundred years. The Florida Keys are probably the only frostless places in the United States.[4]

Table III gives the most important statistics for various meteorological stations. Comparative figures are added for the West Indies, northern Australia, and Panama. The effects on population and industry will be noted later, but it is clear that in the agricultural areas, such as Okeechobee and Homestead, the annual temperatures, temperature ranges, and dry-period rainfalls correspond closely with those of the white agricultural settlements on the Queensland coast.

HISTORY

The history of Florida from its discovery in 1513 demonstrates that various combinations of environmental factors have played an important part in its development over successive periods. At the outset strategic location, frontier problems, and a restricted English colonial policy, which demanded the production of raw materials, permitted little settlement save at a few fortified posts along the coast. Later generations added village strongholds along the northern and western boundaries, and these spread down the interior of the peninsula as the Indians were subdued. A third period saw the development of agriculture, predominantly cotton and tobacco, to supply the demand in England and the New England states.[5]

After the Civil War a population, then less than 200,000 in number and almost wholly centered in the north, expanded with astonishing rapidity until it exceeded more than a million and a half. Here, again, new factors were evident: the improvement in communications, the growth of the fruit and vegetable industries for the supply of the great northern markets, the campaign against disease, the discovery of the state as a tourist resort, and the appreciation and utilization of a climate that had previously been regarded as malignant to the whites.

We can disregard the early history of Florida under Spain and Britain, for little progress was made until the United States purchased the territory in 1819. It is believed that the Seminole Indians originally migrated south, following the line of least resistance on the higher parts of the peninsula. The whites followed the Seminoles about the beginning of the last century, building forts which became permanent settlements, although in the southwest the lines of communication were so tenuous and the swamps so vast that civilization failed to take hold.[6] One of the most remarkable of the few early settlements in the south was Key West. This island town was surveyed in 1829 and by 1860 contained about 3000 people, of whom only 600 were negro slaves. Here many of the old families have survived [7] in spite of a mean annual temperature of above 78° F. Even during a brief visit we observed the beneficial influence of the trade winds.

Until the opening up of the state for the agricultural and tourist industries, progress was very slow, and in 1880 the population numbered only 269,493, or 5 to the square mile, and was centered almost wholly in the northern plantation belt. Governor W. D. Bloxham sold 4,000,000 acres of land bordering Lake Okeechobee in central Florida to Philadelphia capitalists at 25 cents an acre. H. M. Flagler built the Florida East Coast Railway. H. B. Plant constructed the Atlantic Coast Line to Tampa and the west coast. The pioneers of modern medicine destroyed the menace of yellow fever and mitigated the ravages of hookworm and malaria. In the peninsular part of the state, which had long been regarded as a sandy desert fit only for hunting and fishing, great coastal cities sprang up as tourist resorts, and the whites utilized fertilizers to cultivate the sandy soils. Although the severe freezes of 1890 and 1899 frightened the orange growers, the center of population for the state moved steadily south. By 1925 it was located at Hernando in the citrus area, 75 miles north of Tampa and 140 miles south of the center of 1830.

WHITE POPULATION AND INDUSTRY

As in the Queensland tropics, the movement of population towards lower latitudes was accompanied by a great numerical increase. In the single decade 1920-1930 the population of Florida rose from 968,470 to 1,466,625, in the latter year the whites numbering 70.6 per cent and the colored 29.4 per cent. In this period the number of permanent residents rose by half a million, and Florida was second only to California in percentage increase.

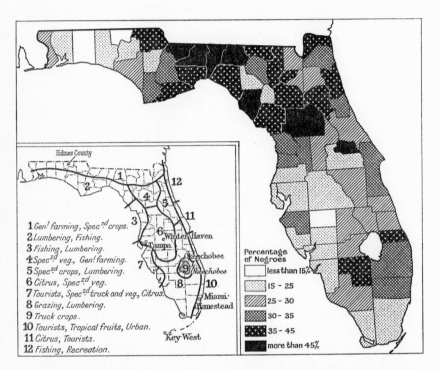

FIG. 1—Map of Florida (scale: 1:7,600,000; 1 inch = 120 miles) showing percentage of negroes in total population by counties, 1930 (based on U. S. Census). The inset shows the principal occupations in 12 regions.

Atwood notes three leading points in the penetration: changes in the character of the population, in its regional distribution, and in the industries in which the people engage.

The most striking change in the character of the population has been in the increase of the whites. In 1920 the ratio of white to negro was 66 to 34 per cent.[8] In 1930 it was 71 to 29 per cent, and no less than 80 per cent of the total increase in population was white. The birthplaces of the Florida population, however, indicate how young and uncertain is the experiment. In the western, eastern, and southern areas from 28 to 75 per cent of the white population was born outside Florida, a large percentage coming from cool-temperate states.

From the regional point of view the white penetration of Florida is also striking. Of the total increase 97½ per cent has occurred in the peninsular area shown as areas 3 to 10 in Figure 1. By 1930 these divisions contained 77 per cent of the people of the state. It is true that most of the growth is urban. In the ten years the number of persons engaged in the tourist industry has doubled; those employed in manufactures have advanced 30 per cent, while agriculturalists have increased only 7.8 per cent. Yet, as Atwood points out, these figures mask an amazing development in farming. During the period the total production of citrus crops grew from 13,200,000 to 26,500,000 boxes, and some 90 per cent of this production came from the orange and grapefruit groves within 60 miles of Winter Haven, where the whites number some 70 per cent and where the average annual temperature is about 74° F. Atwood notes:

The area is a gently rolling region with literally thousands of lakes around which are clustered the orange and grapefruit groves. The northern limit of successful citrus production has steadily migrated south until now it coincides with the December 1st line for the last killing frost in autumn. The vast majority of the orange and grapefruit groves of Florida are located within the area having 255 to 305 frost free days. This area has an annual rainfall of about 50 inches, 70 per cent of which comes in the summer and early autumn. It should be noted in connection with this industry that the people engaged in caring for citrus groves usually live in the cities and towns and would therefore not be listed as rural population.[9]

In regard to vegetables the total acreage more than doubled during the decade 1920-1930 and reached 150,000 acres in 1930. The production is highly localized and is controlled by topography, soil, temperature, and transport facilities. Owing to the presence of tremendous areas of fertile muck soils in Florida, the factors of temperature and transportation are most important. The state has the heaviest crops of fresh fruit and vegetables during spring when the competition is weakest and the demand strongest. This time element is vital. As a general rule, the crops are available for market a fortnight earlier in the season for every hundred miles they are farther south. Florida, like eastern Queensland, is nearer its principal markets than are its competitors. The location and topography offer great facilities for sea and land transport, and the products are sufficiently varied to meet a wide range of demand. The vegetable industry is practically confined to areas 5, 7, 9 and 10 of Figure 1. In all these divisions there is a large excess of whites.

From the point of view of white settlement in the tropics it is very significant that the whites greatly exceed the negroes in the southerly agricultural areas around Lake Okeechobee and even at Homestead in the extreme south. While visiting Florida our attention was strongly directed to the fact that the proportion of negroes is highest in the cooler north and lowest in the warmer center and south. Holmes County, which was formerly 50 per cent negro, is now 96 per cent white owing to the migration of the negro following the decline of the cotton crop [10] (Fig. 1). In the scientific farming of Florida, however, the negro has never been conspicuous, and the whites have never been less than 70 per cent. Of 59,219 farms in Florida no less than 47,205 are tilled by white farmers, and 45,608 of the proprietors are white. Authorities state that negroes are used for about 90 per cent of the labor in the sugar industry, for about 50 per cent in vegetables, and 10 per cent in citrus fruits.[11] In their opinion the whites could now dispense with the negro in every type of work except the cutting of cane. Even this last stronghold of negro labor seems likely to disappear with the improvement in cane-cutting machines.

As in tropical Australia, the difficult environment has led to a number of mistakes. Too much swamp land has been drained, and peat fires, together with shrinkage, have taken their toll. Experience has shown the necessity of soil analysis in the selection of suitable lands for the sugar and other industries. Fortunately, the farmers can now secure highly expert advice. Scientific research has also had good results in the cattle industry, and it is expected that dipping will eradicate the tick. There are comparatively few sheep in Florida owing to dogs and to internal parasites, although the latter can be removed by drenching. The authorities are progressively attacking the chief stock problems under a complete scheme of animal husbandry.

The tourist and manufacturing industries are wealthy and support many whites. They are, however, less important to the student of northern white communities than is agriculture, for the tourist industry is seasonal in character, and many of the manufacturing industries, such as cigar manufacture, employ Cubans and southern Europeans. Nevertheless, both the tourist and manufacturing industries have created a large and permanent population of northern whites, largely centered in a long coastal string of cities, towns, and villages.

White Settlement, Energy, and Health

Like the Australian advance on the Queensland coast, the white penetration of Florida represents a penetration of the tropical margins and forms a battleground for scientific optimists and pessimists. Students such as R. B. Vance and A. N. J. den Hollander, who have worked in the American southeast, refuse to admit that the warm climate is deleterious and either deny the alleged inferiority of subtropical whites or attribute any inferiority to diseases such as malaria, hookworm, and pellagra, or to diet. Vance, for example, writes that "much of the inefficiency and comparative lack of energy attributed to the climate of the South may be laid with justice at the door of the so-called concealed diseases. With their passing, no doubt, the so-called ' poor whites ' will pass into the realm of legend and myth. . . . The once neglected or ridiculed boils and risings, spring sickness, the feared rheumatism and the dreaded pellagra are, no doubt, indices of dietary maladjustment. As the diet imposed by the frontier and the cotton system recedes before the knowledge gained by science, we may expect a release of the energies of southern people comparable to that in sections which have conquered hookworm and malaria." [12]

Den Hollander, Dutch research student of the Rockefeller Foundation, is even more optimistic. He writes:

> Whether the southern climate may be regarded as a contributing cause of the "poor whites" of the region is . . . a question of a very general nature. Insofar as climate is indirectly one of the greatest single factors shaping the culture of a particular region, numerous but not very elucidating relations can of course be established. One might point out, for instance, the softening of the struggle for life incident to a mild climate and the promotion of easy going habits by a hot and long summer. Especially, however, the demands of a subtropical climate for systematic sanitation, careful hygiene, and a well-adapted diet should be given weight. When these requirements have to be met by a section where the population is preponderantly rural, generally poor, inadequately educated and the masses have . . . a badly balanced, monotonous diet . . . ill-adjusted to life in these lower latitudes, it means that the climate puts the section as a whole at a disadvantage, but especially the poorer rural people. Malaria and hookworm are in their distribution largely determined by climate; in late years pellagra has been shown to be a deficiency disease generally following the boundaries of southern poor folk's food habits. . . . We can only conclude, therefore, that so long as really convincing evidence is not brought forward, there seems to be no reason to assume that any part of the white population of the South is any more inherently inferior than comparable classes in other sections of the United States.[13]

On the historical side the writers on the southern states make a good case against a pessimistic outlook, and their claim that white degeneracy is caused by disease, diet, and the evil influences of slavery [14] is supported by evidence from the West Indies and from the Queensland coast. It is doubtful whether any writer has analyzed satisfactorily the factors that created the slave system in the United States, but it is clear that the general trend closely resembled that in the West Indies. In the early days some of the southern states made good progress for long periods with white labor, although this labor was of a poor type. Later the negro was brought in from the West Indies to remedy a labor shortage, and, although his foothold was not assured for fifty years, he ultimately proved inexpensive, docile, and particularly suited to crops such as cotton and rice. Exploited under the plantation system, the negro undercut the white and produced the same poor-white problem as evolved in South Africa and the West Indies. U. B. Phillips traces "a great increase of slave imports and a dwindling influx of servants." [15]

Den Hollander has pointed out that even in the ante-bellum white society the dual picture of an aristocratic colonial planter and the degraded poor white was a myth created by Olmsted and other northern travelers, who followed the tourist route through the poorest areas of the lower pine woods and who did not see, or who ignored, the largest numerical group--the white yeomen farmers with few, if any, slaves. The differences between the southern and northern farmers were not due to any lack of essential qualities, as is proved by the physical and moral records of the South in the Civil War. The truth is that in the

Fig. 2—Negro housing, Gainsville, Florida. Note the attempt at screening windows.

Fig. 3—A negro house of an unusually good type: the home of a janitor, Gainsville University, Florida.

Fig. 4—White housing, Waldo, Florida. Note the screening.

South the small whites were the victims of a system that involved
export crops, absentee profiteers, and negro slaves. Yet, although
negro slavery ruined many of the whites by economic competition,
drove them to the pine woods and mountains, degraded them by isolation and lack of educational facilities, and riddled them with hookworm and malaria, the majority did not sink to any such degree as
northern writers loved to paint. In den Hollander's impartial opinion
the southern whites suffered from northern propaganda against everything in the slave regions.

Yet the South owes something to the North, for the Civil War
emancipated the southern poor whites, although more slowly than it
freed the slaves. Recent years, however, have seen a rapid advance,
and the whole tenor of southern life has changed. Artificial fertilizers
have extended the culture of cotton and tobacco. Truck farms, orchards,
and winter resorts have appeared. Lumber and turpentine have developed the pine barrens. Railways, highways, towns, and schools have
spread throughout the land. New immigration is infusing new blood.
Campaigns against hookworm and malaria are eliminating most of the
listless hunters and fishermen who formed such a large part of the poor
whites. Although the grave problems of the share croppers and cotton
tenants are still unsolved, in den Hollander's opinion, "as a specific
class with definite limits 'southern poor whites' exist chiefly in the
non-southern imagination." [16]

So much for the claims of the southerners and of unbiased research
students who have worked in the South. What light do the vital and
other statistics cast on the present and future? Tables IV, V and VI
present the mortality, the birth rate, and the excess of births over
deaths for white and colored persons in Florida as compared with
Queensland and with the registration area of the United States.

These tables indicate that the death rate for Florida whites over
the years 1927-1929 (11.4) was but little higher than that of the
registration area of the United States (11.3), although it is alleged
that many old people seek the mild climate of Florida in their declining years and die in the state. The Florida death rate was, however,
greatly above the death rate in tropical Queensland (8.37). Moreover, the negro death rate (17.7) was higher than that of the whites
or than the negro death rate in the registration area (16.8).

As regards births, the white rate for Florida (21.7 in 1927-1929) was
considerably higher than that of the registration area (19.5) and
slightly higher than that of tropical Queensland (21.2). The white
birth rate is falling rapidly, but this is a general tendency and is no
doubt emphasized in Florida by the urbanization of population and
the growth in the use of contraceptives, which are advertized openly
and extensively in cities such as Miami. As regards the excess of births
over deaths, the rate for whites in Florida is more than double that

5

TABLE IV—SELECTED REGIONS: DEATH RATES PER 1,000*

REGION		1920	1925	1927	1928	1929	1932
Florida...................	white	11.5	11.9	11.7	11.8	10.8	10.4
	colored	17.6	17.4	17.9	18.2	17.1	15.7
U. S. Registration Area.....	white	12.6	11.3	10.9	11.5	11.4	
	colored	17.9	17.6	16.6	17.1	16.9	
Tropical Queensland........	white						8.35
Panama Canal.............	white employees	1927–1931		6.36			
	colored "	1927–1931		10.02			

TABLE V—SELECTED REGIONS: BIRTH RATES PER 1,000*

REGION		1920	1925	1927	1928	1929	1932
Florida...................	white		23.7	25.7	21.3	18.2	17.4
	colored		24.0	25.4	22.0	20.1	19.2
U. S. Registration Area.....	white	23.4	21.2	20.4	19.5	18.6	
	colored	26.9	25.4	23.6	22.2	21.3	
Tropical Queensland........	white						20.14
Panama Canal.............	white employees	1928–1932		9.39			
	colored "	1928–1932		14.96			

TABLE VI—SELECTED REGIONS: EXCESS OF BIRTHS OVER DEATHS PER 1,000*

REGION		1920	1925	1927	1928	1929	1932
Florida...................	white	11.8	14.3	14.0	9.5	7.4	7.0
	colored	6.6	5.1	7.5	3.8	3.0	3.5
U. S. Registration Area.....	white	10.8	9.8	9.5	8.0	7.3	6.5
	colored	9.0	7.8	7.1	5.1	4.4	6.8
Tropical Queensland........	white						11.79
Panama Canal.............	white employees	1928–1932		3.03			
	colored "			4.94			

*Data for Florida and the U. S. registration area from Statistical Abstract of the United States, 1932, 1934; for tropical Queensland from A. B. C. of Queensland Statistics, 1935; for Panama Canal from Report of Health Dept. of the Panama Canal for 1931, 1933.

for negroes and is considerably above that of the registration area. These figures indicate that the population is youthful and that education is a vital necessity.

To the visitor the white workers of Florida look healthy, although, as in many white countries, the artificial coloring of the women makes observation difficult. Most of the people minimize the problems of tropical sickness or degeneracy. Some residents, however, admit the presence of malaria and hookworm in spite of the health campaigns, and many feel that the negro forms a reservoir of disease and tends to lower the living standard and prolong the poor-white problem. The matter will remain very grave until the whites raise the negroes to their own standards of living and health.

The Report of the State Board of Health 1923-1932 summarized the general position. The hookworm situation had improved. The first 7500 tests made in 1910 showed an infection of 57 per cent. Of 250,000 tests made in 1931 only 25 per cent were positive. Nevertheless, malaria and hookworm were still the outstanding factors that retarded the economic development of the rural communities, particularly in the principal farming area—the northwest. In addition, venereal diseases presented an appalling problem.

The diet question also remains serious, although matters have improved from the days when a frontier diet pattern was responsible for the deficiency disease, pellagra, and when the extensive consumption of alcohol made serious inroads on health. A nutritional study of white school children in five representative counties of Florida (1930) [17] gives a very favorable showing of children free from defects. It indicates, however, that less than 25 per cent of children receive adequate diet, that for a given age the children up to the age of 14 are in general below the average in height and weight, and that more than 45 per cent of children have hookworm infestation, abnormal tonsils, or carious teeth. Nevertheless, diet is improving both in Florida and throughout the South, in spite of a lack of milk in the coastal districts. Vance writes that the trucking areas furnish a healthful, varied diet during off seasons. Much has still to be achieved, but there is no doubt that Florida with her urban and trucking regions is leading the South in the realization that a bitter price has been paid for the consumption of ardent spirits, salt meat, corn, and pork, and that the remedy for a tropical or subtropical people lies in a greater proportion of milk, eggs, green vegetables, and fruit.[18]

CHAPTER VI

THE TRADE-WIND MARGINS: II. QUEENSLAND

At a superficial glance the Australian tropics appear to offer some of the highest potentialities for white settlement in the world.[1] The region of 1,149,320 square miles[2] is vast and unoccupied. The terrific summer heat and the heavy summer rains of certain areas are offset by a comparatively mild and dry winter climate. Above all, there are no teeming millions of colored people to absorb white settlers, and the "White Australia" policy of "a continent for a nation" has so far excluded those colored races that have timidly sought an entry. Outside observers, in most cases completely ignorant of the Australian tropics, have frequently made violent attacks on the Commonwealth for an alleged "dog-in-the-manger policy." Such criticisms are largely unjust. Australia has not been unmindful of her tropics. If anything, she has been rash and overstrenuous in some of her attempts at development, while in Queensland she is conducting one of the most successful white penetrations in the tropical world. Of equal danger to the Commonwealth is the Australian critic, usually a superoptimist or a superpatriot, who fears invasion by a colored race. Such persons frequently publish fallacious or exaggerated statements on "vast empty spaces," "huge undeveloped potentialities," "the medical conquest of the tropics"—statements that supply ammunition for outside critics and sometimes lead to hasty and unscientific efforts that have generally produced disastrous results.

Overoptimistic Views Regarding the Australian Tropics

In the past it has been considered shamefully unpatriotic to speak unfavorably of the Australian tropics, and bitter attacks have been made on able and impartial observers like Professor Griffith Taylor, as on the first American scientists who have been brave enough to say that the people of the southern United States suffered from hookworm and pellagra. The Federal failure in the Northern Territory has, however, chastened the national outlook. Three arguments are particularly unscientific and obnoxious. The first is the danger of an empty north Australia, an argument usually accompanied by a map comparing the vacant Australian tropics with the crowded countries to their north. Such comparisons neglect the facts that Asiatic regions (such as parts of Arabia or even of India) are as empty as north Australia for similar geographic reasons and that if Asiatic powers desired a footing in this continent the well-watered southeast, the coal of Newcastle, or the iron of Iron Knob would be their goals.

The second fallacy put forward is that Australians will settle their tropics as soon as it becomes desirable, partly because of the progress of tropical medicine and partly because the nation is gradually occupying the continent. Probably as time goes on Australians will utilize more of the tropics, but success in the south is no argument that they must necessarily succeed in the north. The progress of tropical medicine is only one factor in the problem. The climates and soils of tropical Australia differ fundamentally from those of the temperate areas of the continent.

The third fallacy is that Australians can work the north with colored labor. The Northern Territory plantations failed completely with Chinese labor. In 1876-1877 the Japanese rejected an invitation to settle, and, although the Kanaka, or South Sea Islander, proved useful in the best regions of Queensland, he also proved a reservoir of disease, and the whites have done far better since he was expelled. W. Wynne Williams of the Bureau of Industry, Brisbane, has recently obtained important information on the environmental controls that affect colored settlement in certain dry areas of India, Nigeria, and the East Indies. The information from the two former regions stresses the value of dry farming and Zebu cattle and the extremely small output required to support the mixed farmer of India or Nigeria. The Director of Agriculture, Ibadan, Nigeria, considers that "millions of coloured people are living in less favourable natural conditions" than in Australia and that, if Nigerian families could be established in the Australian tropics they could farm profitably. A great deal of scientific work must, however, be done upon the climate and soils of tropical Australia before it is proved that this region (other than eastern Queensland) would be of value to any colored race.[3]

Climatic Subdivisions of Northern Australia

Climate, soil, and communications are the chief controls of white settlement in the Australian tropics, together with the very low altitude of almost the whole region. We may divide the region into three zones, although the exact boundaries must remain undetermined until the continent contains more meteorological stations.

The first division is the "Uniform Region" shown on Professor Griffith Taylor's rough generalization (Fig. 5). This includes 94,000 square miles of eastern Queensland. Even in this area the country suitable for close white settlement covers only a very limited extent of coast lands and plateaus near the coast. Figure 6 shows that in these localities the rainfall is heavier and has a better seasonal distribution than in the remainder of the Australian tropics. Andrews' map (Fig. 7) indicates, however, that the reliability of this rainfall is low.[4]

The second division is the arid rainfall region shown on Figure 5. This huge area probably covers some 600,000 square miles of country

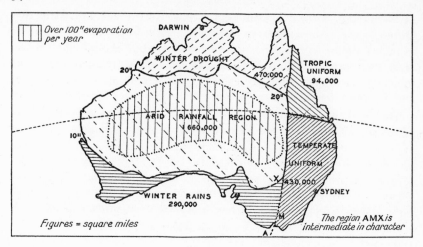

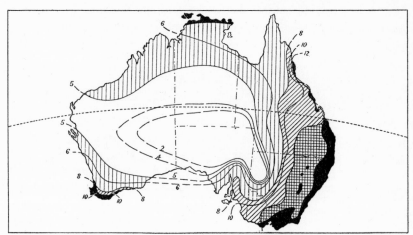

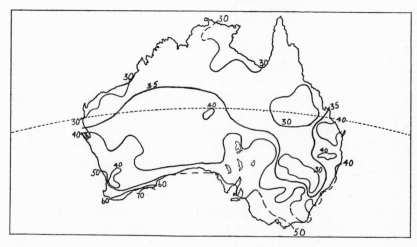

Figs. 5-7—Climatic maps of Australia (scale 1:55,000,000). For explanation see foot of opposite page.

in the interior of the continent that receives 10 to 15 inches of rainfall. Owing to the high evaporation of summer rainfall the division extends in places almost as far north as the 20-inch isohyet, although in other areas there are good summer grazing lands south of this line. Figure 6 indicates the deficiency of the rainfall during the long winter drought, and Figure 7 shows its unreliability.

The third division is the northern and northwestern region of summer monsoonal rains and winter drought, an area estimated by Taylor as covering 470,000 square miles. Here the rainfall varies from 20 inches on the southern boundary to 60 inches in the extreme north, but the primary control over close settlement is the winter drought shown in Figure 6 and for Darwin in Table VII. Figure 7, again illustrates the unreliability of the rainfall, which, according to Andrews, is far more variable than in the closely settled southern regions of the continent.

Table VII gives the details of temperature and rainfall in seven typical stations in the Australian tropics. Miami (Florida) and Balboa Heights (Panama) are added for purposes of comparison. These statistics will be discussed later, but several points of general importance are clear.

First, of the seven typical Australian stations only two (Innisfail and Mackay on the east Queensland coast) appear to be in regions suitable for close agricultural settlement unaided by irrigation. In the five remaining stations the rainfall is less than the 10-inch minimum deemed necessary during the dry season in a hot climate, while evaporability exceeds rainfall during eight to twelve months of the year. Even in Panama, where there are agricultural difficulties in the dry season, the dry-season rainfall is as high as 9.4 inches. If these five Australian stations are typical of the monsoonal and arid regions of the Australian tropics there appears to be little hope for close white settlement over most of the zone.

Second, as regards temperature the three east Queensland stations have a far lower average annual temperature than the four monsoonal or arid stations, although in eastern Queensland the relative humidity is greater and, from the point of view of white settlement, more severe. Herberton, at an elevation of nearly 3000 feet on the Atherton Tableland, has an annual temperature of only 67.5° F., and this tableland seems suitable for whites. Even the town of Mackay, in latitude 21.1° S., has a cooler climate than the American holiday city of Miami, although

EXPLANATION OF FIGURES 5-7.

FIG. 5—The rainfall regions of Australia. (After Figure 2 in Griffith Taylor: The Agricultural Regions of Australia, Installment 1, *Economic Geogr.*, Vol. 6, 1930; pp. 109-134.)

FIG. 6—Rainfall uniformity in Australia. (After Griffith Taylor: The Australian Environment, Melbourne, 1918.) The lines show the number of months receiving more than 1 inch of rainfall each. The black areas receive more that 2 inches during each of 7 months.

FIG. 7—The reliability of rainfall in Australia. The higher the index number, the greater is the reliability. (After Map 3 in J. Andrews: Rainfall Reliability in Australia, *Linnean Soc. of New South Wales*, Vol. 57, Pts. 1 and 2, 1932.)

TABLE VII—TROPICAL AUSTRALIA: CLIMATIC DATA, WITH DATA FOR COMPARISON WITH OTHER REGIONS

STATION AND REGION	ALT. (feet)	LAT.	TEMPERATURE (degrees Fahr.)			RAINFALL (inches)		REL. HUM. (%)	DRY MONTHS (%)[a]	NO. OF MONTHS EVAP. EXCEEDS RAINFALL
			Mean ann.	Hottest month	Coolest month	Mean ann.	Dry season (May-Oct.)			
Roebourne, W. A., Arid West Coast	40	20°40'S	80.4	90.8	67.2	11.85	3.1	44	50	12
Darwin, N. T., Monsoonal Belt...	97	12°28'S	82.6	84.1	77.3	60.45	3.44	68	32	8
Tennant's Creek, N. T., Arid Cent.	1075	19°34'S	77.3	87.1	63.7	14.72	1.69	36	43	12
Camooweal, Q., Monsoonal Belt..	738	19°57'S	76.9	87.5	62.8	15.31	1.79	41	41	12
Innisfail, Q., East Coast..........	22	17°32'S	73.8	80.5	66.5	142.61	35.58	81	3	5
Mackay, Q., East Coast..........	35	21°09'S	72.1	79.6	62.0	67.34	12.40	74	6	5
Herberton, Q., East Plateaus.....	2890	17°23'S	67.5	73.6	59.5	42.99	5.63	74	33	8
Balboa Heights, Panama..........	118	9°0'N	78.6	78.7	78.2	68.8	9.4 (Dec.-Apr.)	83.6	25	
Miami, Florida, Trade Wind, Tropical Coast..............	83	25°70'N	75.1	82.0	67.0	59.94	12.69 (Nov.-Apr.)	76.5	0	

*Data on Australian stations from Commonwealth of Australia Council for Scientific and Industrial Research, Pamphlet No. 42; for Balboa Heights from the Chief Hydrographer, U. S. Canal Zone; and for Miami from United States Weather Bureau, Summaries of Climatological Data by Sections, *Bull, W*, Vol. 3.
[a]Percent of months having less than 10 points (one inch) of rain.

both are coastal towns and the latter is some 4 degrees farther from the equator. It appears that there are strong climatic reasons for the failure of white settlement in northwest and north Australia as compared with the successful white invasion of the east Queensland coast lands, and this fact is supported by history and by present-day statistics. About 70 per cent of the present white population and about 70 per cent of the total production of tropical Australia are concentrated in the 22,894 square miles of the east Queensland coast lands and all but 4½ per cent of the remaining white population is in the rest of the Queensland tropics. The whole white population of the central and western tropics of Australia does not exceed 10,000 souls. Between the census of 1921 and that of 1933 the population of Australia as a whole increased 22 per cent, the population of tropical Queensland increased by nearly one-third, yet that of the central and western tropics was stagnant.[5]

Northeastern Queensland: Geographical Factors

The story of white settlement in Queensland is remarkable and offers lessons that should be known to all nations who are attempting to develop the tropics.[6] The Australian experience is the direct reverse of that of the West Indies. Where in Barbados, to take one example, the northwestern European workers began promisingly but later suffered deterioration and "negrodation," the Australians of Queensland at first suffered health deterioration in the presence of colored peoples, and later passed on to apparent success. Furthermore, with the exception of southern Florida, Queensland is probably the only region that has recently seen the establishment of a large working population of northern whites in a tropical coast climate. It is true that the region of white occupation is, like Florida, a marginal area with exceptional advantages. Nevertheless, the Australian effort can genuinely claim to be a successful penetration of the tropics.

The region of the east Queensland tropics, as depicted by Professor Griffith Taylor, embraces an area of 94,000 square miles, of which the coast lands comprise 22,894 square miles, but this uniform division includes, as we shall see, a great deal of country that is unsuitable for white settlement.

Taylor's generalized region, which he calls the "Townsville Division," embraces the greater part of the Queensland highlands and the narrow strip of plains along the east Queensland coast. As shown in Figure 15, most of the area lies inside the 20-inch isohyet, for it possesses both a monsoonal summer rainfall and a rainfall that is due to the constant southeast trades. The scarp of the Atherton Plateau presents to these winds a barrier 3000 feet in height and creates the heaviest rainfall in Australia (Innisfail 142.61 inches). Nevertheless, the precipitation falls off rapidly across the plateau and in the rain shadow to the west. Herberton, close behind Innisfail, has a rainfall of only 42.99 inches and a dry-season precipitation of 8.98 inches in spite of an altitude of 2890 feet. Altitude, with corresponding cooler temperatures, makes the tableland a thriving dairying region, in spite of its situation in latitude 17° S. Farther west the rainfall decreases rapidly, and Georgetown (990 feet) on the western slopes of the highlands has a rainfall of only 31.97 inches with a very low precipitation of 2.8 inches in the dry season (April-October). Farther south in the rain-shadow rainfalls are even lower. Hughenden (1074 feet) has only 19.26 inches. Andrews' (Fig. 7) gives the reliability of this rainfall an index of 30, which is low. Dr. James Davidson shows that the rainfall exceeds the evaporability for seven months of the year in two small districts around Innisfail and Mackay, for from one to four months in the highlands, and for no months at all in the southwest. Davidson's work thus indicates that the area of tropical Australia that can be classed as humid is remarkably small, a fact of great significance as regards close agricultural settlement.[7]

The control of climate is stressed by W. H. Bryan:[8] he notes that the eastern geological region, which he calls the Tasman geosyncline, coincides closely with Taylor's area of uniform rains (Fig. 8). This region contains the chief agricultural and pastoral industries (Figs. 10, 15). Very important is the close association of the highlands with the coastal agricultural zone. The Atherton Tableland, immediately behind Innisfail, has an area of 12,000, and the Clarke Range near Bowen, Bloomsbury, and Mackay, an area of 2000 square miles. In general the edge of the highlands rises steeply from the east coast and slopes gradually to the west. The east-coast rivers, such as the Fitzroy and Burdekin, are important, and it has been said that the valley of the Fitzroy may become one of the most populous parts of Australia, although Wynne Williams disputes this in view of the poor rainfall of the dry season. The best soil occurs in patches, the richest being found in flats of deep alluvium. Hence the agricultural areas are scattered along the coast, particularly along the river bottoms. Andrews gives an excellent summary of the topographical conditions that govern sugar, the principal industry (Fig. 8):

The growing of cane in Queensland is confined very definitely to the coast, usually in the river valleys and on the slopes of the smaller hills within a few miles of their mouths. Inland in the middle and upper courses of the rivers the country is usually too rugged for cultivation, and cattle may take the place of crops. The most important cane areas are the valley floors, with their fertile alluvial soils, which are very often the product of the weathering of the volcanic rocks under the conditions of heavy rainfall and luxuriant plant life. [Fig. 11.] These soils, however, are not by any means continuous along the coast, for many areas have very poor soils in close proximity to those of the richest type. The main agricultural regions form a series of basins connected only by the coastal railway from Brisbane to Cairns; this disconnected arrangement of centres of population being characteristic of the Queensland coast, but unusual in Australia. Almost the whole of the coast from the N. S. W. border to Cape York receives more than 40 in. of rain per annum, the 40 in. isohyet running roughly parallel to the coast from Brisbane to Cairns. There are two centres of much heavier rainfall, one near Mackay, where a small area receives over 70 in., and the other centering around Hervey Creek, just south of Cairns, with a maximum of 160 in. Innisfail receives approximately 140 in., and Cairns 90 in. The tropic cuts the coast at Rockhampton, and temperature increases steadily to the north to some 80 deg. F. at the base of Cape York Peninsula. From the map of the distribution of cane, then, we may say that the main part of the crop is grown within the tropics in those areas where the most favourable

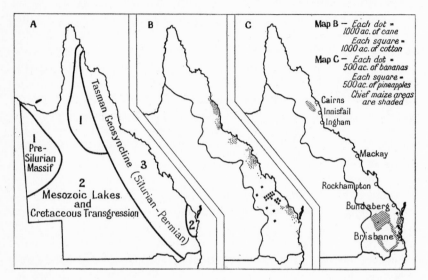

FIG. 8—Queensland: A, geological regions (after map on p. 49 in W. H. Bryan: The Geological Basis of Queensland Industry, *The Australian Geographer*, Vol. 1, Pt. 4, 1932, pp. 48-57); B, distribution of cultivation of cane and cotton; C, the chief banana, pineapple, and maize districts (B and C after Figs. 2 and 3 in John Andrews: Tropical and Sub-Tropical Agriculture in Coastal Queensland, *ibid.*, Vol. 1, Pt. 3, 1931, pp. 62-68). (Scale of maps: 1: 32,500,000, 1 inch = 500 miles.)

conditions of rainfall and soil coincide. The densest areas at Mackay, Ingham and Innisfail-Cairns are well shown. There has been since the beginning of the century a marked increase in the acreage devoted to the crop in the tropical areas, with a corresponding decrease in the southern districts. Most of the cane is milled near the growing area, and there were in 1928 35 mills, employing over 6000 people. It is then carried either by ship or by rail to the central markets.[9]

The heavy rainfall of parts of the area produces the only tropical rain forests of the continent, more especially on rich basalt soils. The principal forests lie between Cooktown and Ingham and reach their optimum in the Cairns district. There are many valuable timbers.[10]

HISTORY OF NORTHEASTERN QUEENSLAND

The early history of northeastern Queensland falls within the final stages of the prescientific invasions of the tropics. The southern part of the colony was "rushed" in the early sixties. In 1866 one of those financial crises so frequent in Australia developed as a result of the customary overborrowing and overspending, but disaster was averted, as often happened, by the discovery of minerals, in this case gold. The tropical coast lands invited attempts to cultivate sugar, and favorable geographical conditions led to success. Like the whites of the American tropics, the Australians introduced colored labor, and did so well in sugar planting with indentured South Sea Islanders that as early as 1868 Queensland contained more than 2000 Kanakas, and by 1871 there were 27,000 colonists north of Dawes Range (lat. 24° S.). The discovery of gold and silver in the inland areas and the northward rush in the coast lands insured a rapid growth. By 1872 the colony met its own needs in rum and sugar and in that year exported these commodities to an annual value of £37,803. Mackay and other settlements began to flourish. By 1880 the value of sugar exports had reached £286,222. In spite of low prices due to the growth of beet sugar in continental Europe, the Queensland sugar industry continued to expand with little or no tariff protection, owing to cheap labor, fertile virgin soil, and the adoption of the central-mill system for crushing the ripe cane.[11]

A remarkable state of affairs now developed in Queensland. An important section of the Australian people had established a plantation system, like the old one of the southern United States and the West Indies, on a basis little removed from slavery, and nothing but favorable geographical conditions had prevented a cancerous growth of the system throughout the Australian tropics. The effective resistance of southern Queensland, aided by the British government, alone prevented the secession of the northern sugar lands. Only the paucity and weakness of the north Queensland population and the concessions made by southern Australia averted a crisis such as preceded the American Civil War.

From the point of view of the Australian nation there were two fundamental arguments against the colored labor system in Queensland: the undercutting of white labor and the appalling incidence of disease and death, which afflicted the Kanakas and through them the whites. From the outset the laboring classes of white Australians struggled against Kanaka labor, which they rightly saw was incompatible with the white standard of living and with free democratic ideals. Also, the rates of disease and death soon became deplorable. From 1875 to 1878 the average mortality of Polynesians in the colony was 70.9 per 1000. Although this mortality rate fell greatly in the later years of the system, it was 47.74 in 1892 and 52.57 in 1893, about four times that of the whites. Also, as in Florida, the effect on the whites was severe. "The unhappy kanakas died in great numbers, bequeathing their diseases to their masters; the expectation of life among white males at birth was only 41.3 years, a figure more than 12% less than that of the average for Australia; and the actual crude death rates for Queensland were enormously in excess of those of other States, in one year (1884) there being an excess of as much as 50%."[12] "The dreadful eighties" saw the peak of disease in tropical Australia.

The truth was that history, the history of the West Indies and the southern United States, was repeating itself. The island continent, which might have remained a protected human laboratory for the white races, had opened its doors to malaria, filariasis, hookworm, leprosy, and other forms of tropical disease.[18] Altogether the whites brought some 46,000 or 47,000 Kanakas to Australia. In addition, by 1887 60,000 persons, or one-fifteenth of the entire Australian population, were Chinese. The unique feature of Australian history is that the young Australian nation saw the dangers to the economic status and health of her white citizens and carried out a long and difficult purification, despite the fight waged by north Queensland for the Kanakas and by the British government for the Chinese. Even before Federation, Queenslanders had begun to replace the Kanakas with white labor. In the fifteen years prior to Federation the islanders decreased from 10,775 to 8826, although the production of sugar rose from 55,000 to 123,000 tons. The number of small white farmers increased in the south, but as late as 1889 a Royal Commission reported that opinion was unanimous that white men could not cultivate cane. When Federation came in 1907 colored labor still grew 86 per cent of the sugar cane.

During the following decade the Commonwealth gradually enforced the "White Australia" policy, but it encouraged white-grown sugar by means of bounties during the difficult period of transition, with the result that, although the Kanakas were repatriated, the industry was not destroyed. British, Australians, and Italians took over all the processes of production and by 1912 produced 96 per cent of Australian sugar. At a later date "protection" and "embargoes" supplanted the bounty system, and Queensland discovered that these safeguards, together with a division of labor that separated growers, millers, and refiners, made the industry as profitable as in the old plantation days. Prior to the world depression the efficiency of white labor and of the Colonial Sugar Refining Company had reduced production costs to very nearly those of colored-labor countries.

Since the crisis the cost of sugar within the Commonwealth has been far above world parity in spite of the great efficiency of the industry, and southern Australians naturally grumble at the cost. At the same time most of the people recognize that the nation must maintain the white standard of living for its tropical workers and that the tropical industries are no more uneconomic than most of the tariff-propped industries of the temperate parts of the continent. It can be said in favor of the Australians that they are consistently supporting their sugar workers and are not endangering their own creation as the British are endangering the sugar industry of their West Indian islands and as the Americans may endanger the Cuban sugar trade.

We have centered this historical sketch around sugar, not because other industries, such as mining, pasturing, and dairying, are unimportant, but because sugar created the Kanaka question and is still the key industry of close white settlement. Figure 8 illustrates the present distribution of the agricultural occupations, their scattered distribution and their proximity to the coast. This figure is particularly interesting as indicating the paramount importance of cane in the lower latitudes. Figures 9 and 10 show the distribution of sheep and cattle.

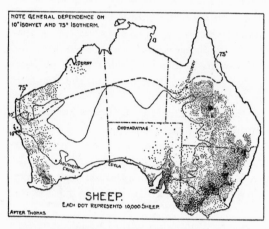

FIG. 9—Australia: Distribution of sheep (after Fig. 7 in Stephen H. Roberts: History of the Pioneer Fringes in Australia, *in* Pioneer Settlement, *Amer. Geog. Soc. Special Publ., No. 14*, 1932, pp. 392-404).

THE QUEENSLAND EXPERIMENT

Optimistic Views

Is the penetration of Queensland by northern whites proving satisfactory, and will the experiment achieve permanent success? Certainly up to the present the Australians have made remarkable progress. They have established a population of 185,000 in northeastern Queensland, largely in the agricultural industries of the tropical coast lands, and they have shown that northern whites can engage in all the laborious operations of field work, although sugar experts in Florida and the West Indies still feel certain that such work would be fatal to the whites. This success of the whites in manual labor appears to support the view of Sir Raphael Cilento and other Australians that, if white men and women are to remain healthy in the tropics, they must engage in hard manual work. When we see the superior health of white men over white women in all parts of the tropics we wonder whether the difference between the sexes is due to the fact that white men in such regions as India, Panama, or Saba engage in hard outdoor sports or manual labor, while northern white women throughout most of the tropics undertake comparatively little sport or work.

Sir Raphael Cilento once summed up the position in a conversation: "The woman," he said, "who does hard physical labor, such as scrubbing offices, remains healthy in the Australian tropics. The sedentary worker, like the typist, deteriorates, and the woman who does nothing becomes sick."

In 1924 a scientific investigation of certain Queensland towns yielded remarkable results. The inquiry explored representative centers in the coastal plains, on the plateaus, and in the dry rain shadow of the west. It examined white women and children of the laboring classes for mental and physical development. It also thoroughly investigated the sociological and environmental conditions. A fixed percentage of the total houses in each area was taken at random. Persons of extratropical birth were used as a control series, and a further control series was taken from figures for English, Australian, and American standards. Contrary to all previous beliefs, white residents, even of the second and third generations, seemed to be strong and healthy. Tropical native-born women averaged larger families than immigrant women from the cool-temperate zone. The most healthy people were those who did hard manual work. These results were obtained in spite of the fact that many of the homes were totally unsuited to the tropics

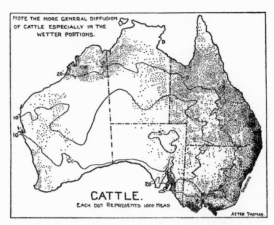

FIG. 10—Australia: Distribution of cattle (after Fig. 8 in Stephen H. Roberts: History of the Pioneer Fringes in Australia, *in* Pioneer Settlement, *Amer. Geog. Soc. Special Publ. No. 14, 1932, pp. 392-404*).

and conditions in many cases were sufficiently primitive to cause what Cilento calls "kitchen neurasthenia."

The examination of 2080 school children disclosed no signs of mental deterioration. At all ages tropical-born children of the second generation were as far advanced as the immigrants, although drawn from the poorest classes and suffering from faulty hygiene and sanitation and from other environmental disadvantages. In weight they were almost identical with English and American normals,[14] and they were from 1 to 3 inches taller.

Other evidence supports similar conclusions. The researches of the Institute of Tropical Medicine at Townsville gave satisfactory results. In 1920 the Australian Medical Congress at Brisbane declared: "The opinion of the medical practitioners present was overwhelmingly in favour of the suitability of North Queensland for the successful implantation of a white working race." Tests amongst the cane cutters appeared to show that British gangs were at least equal to any others. "Expert opinion, supplemented by the actual records kept by some of the mills, is to the effect that the best British cane-cutter can more than hold his own in speed and stamina against any other race, white or coloured. Some of the records achieved in this particular class of work under the piecework system are almost incredible"[15] (Figs. 13, 14).

The physiological experiments made by Breinl and Sundstroem on Queensland wharf lumpers support these tests.[16]

TABLE VIII—AUSTRALIA: SELECTED POPULATION AND SOCIAL STATISTICS*

	TROPICAL AUSTRALIA[a]				NON TROPICAL AUSTRALIA	Q'LAND	N. S. W.	VICTORIA	TASMANIA	AUSTRALIA
	Tropical W. A.	N. T.	Tropical Q'land	Total						
Population, Mean 1935..	3,324	4,870	184,831	193,025	6,437,590	945,706	..	..	..	..
Birthrate per 1000 of mean population, 1929–33........	13.14	14.35	21.20	20.88	18.31	19.47	23.4	17.87 (1928–1932)	21.72	18.38
Death rate per 1000 of mean population, 1929–33........	12.61	14.28	8.37	8.95	8.85	8.55	8.44	9.30 (1928–1932)	9.12	8.81
Infantile death rate (under 1 year) per 1000 births, 1929–33..	50.36	69.03	44.54	45.03	44.2	41.12	49.10	47.39	50.95	44.26
Serious crimes in Magistrates Courts per 100,000 people, 1927–31....	..	156	..	..	..	34.2	46.7	21.6	32.7	..
Drunkenness, convictions per 100,000 people, 1927–31............	..	294.56	..	..	..	130.98	136.58	37.64	14.98	..
Illegitimacy, per cent of total births, 1929–32..	8.9	20.17	4.9	..	..	5.1	5.24	4.39 (1932)	5.57	..

*Statistics kindly supplied by the Commonwealth Statistician.

[a]J. Brigden and W. Wynne Williams in "Tropical Settlement in Australia" give the Queensland Government Statistician's figures for the non-aboriginal population of tropical Australia as follows: Queensland, East Coast: 140,318; Queensland, other: 60,478; Northern Territory: 4,182; Western Australia: 5,328; Total: 210,306.

Fig. 11—Sugar lands near Cairns, northern Queensland.
Fig. 12—White workers in sugar lands near Cairns.

FIG. 13—British Australian white sugar gang, Cairns, northern Queensland.
FIG. 14—Italian cane cutters, Cairns.

Table VIII gives some vital and social statistics for tropical Australia, including Queensland. It indicates that the natural increase is satisfactory in tropical Queensland and that the birth rate is higher than for the nontropical parts of the continent. The death rate (1929-1933) for tropical Queensland is lower than that for nontropical Australia or for the Commonwealth as a whole.[17] The infant death rate for tropical Queensland (except for 1933) compares satisfactorily with the figures for temperate Australia. As far as tropical Queensland is concerned we can say that recent figures support the theory that the Australian experiment is meeting with success.

Critical Examination of the Experiment

So much for the hopeful aspects of white settlement in northeastern Queensland. We must now examine the experiment more critically. Even this comparatively small region of 94,000 square miles contains several different zones, and we must differentiate the tablelands and dry western plains from the coast lands, which contain the bulk of the white population.

The Tablelands, Rain-Shadow Plains, and Coast Lands

Since visiting in 1936 the Atherton Tableland (latitude, 17° S.; altitude, 2000-3000 feet) and securing medical and economic evidence, I have had little doubt that northern whites in these small highland regions can continue as a healthy farming population for an indefinite period of time. Although these tablelands are hot and humid in summer, the winters are quite cool. Both adults and children seem intelligent, energetic, and healthy, even though much of the housing is poor and many children are forced to combine school work with home duties that are described as little short of child slavery [18] (Fig. 17).

Similarly in parts of the dry outback areas of the Queensland tropics, a sparse population of white pastoralists can probably maintain themselves permanently. Dr. C. V. Watson Brown, who works at Longreach, a center of 4500 inhabitants in latitude 23.27° S. and 420 miles from the coast, writes: "Had nature wished to stage a human experiment in avitaminosis, calcium deficiency and superabundant sunshine, her choice of our central districts would be ideal." Yet he feels "confident in stating that this experiment in colonization can be wholly successful," provided that it receives "sympathetic consideration from the government and education of the public in proper methods of housing as well as proper hours of work and adequate diet.[19]

The position is more uncertain in the coast lands where we found medical scientists, teachers, sugar workers, and others frank and helpful but extremely divided in their views. Several points are, however, clear. First, it is undeniable that the coastal region is, for a tropical area, peculiarly favorable to white settlers. The soil is fertile. Important

6

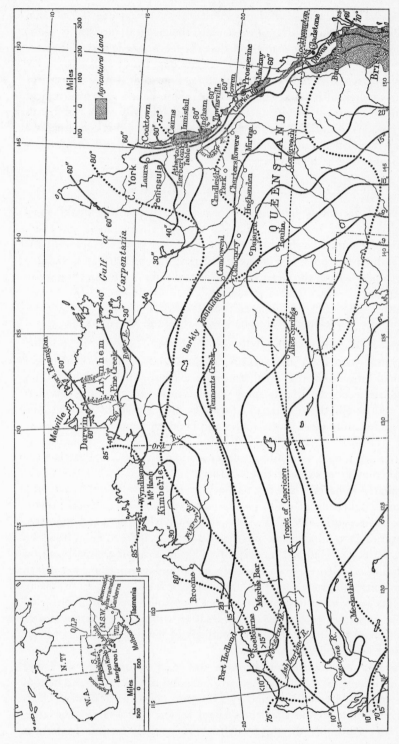

Fig. 15—Map of northern Australia (scale: 1:21,500,000). The dotted lines are isotherms showing mean annual temperature and the solid lines isohyets showing mean annual rainfall (from W. Köppen and R. Geiger: Handbuch der Klimatologie, Band IV, Teil S, pp. 5II, 528). The solid black dots (e. g. Cairns) indicate stations where the dry season rainfall (May 1–Oct. 30) exceeds 10 inches and the percentage of months on record with less than 0.1 inch of rain is less than 10 (see p. 74). These data and agricultural areas from map in W. W. Williams: "The Settlement of the Australian Tropics," *Econ. Record*, Vol. II, 1935, p. 23.

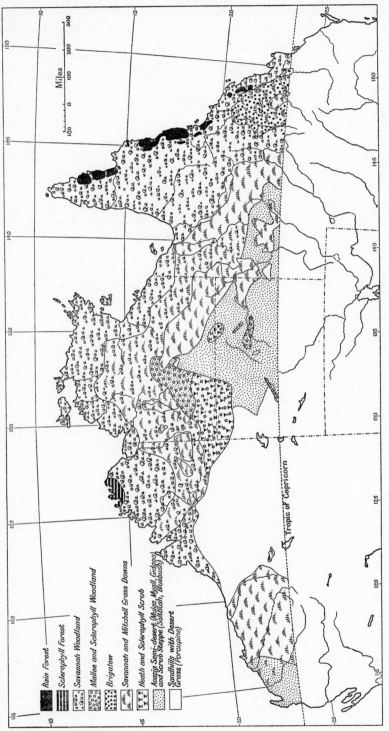

FIG. 16—Vegetation map of Australia north of the Tropic of Capricorn (scale: 1 : 21,500,000). Based on map accompanying J. A. Prescott, The Soils of Australia, *Commonwealth of Australia, Council for Scientific and Industrial Research, Bull. No. 52*, Melbourne, 1931.

markets are reasonably near. The temperatures and humidities are low for the tropics (lower, for example, than in most of the West Indies), and the winters are remarkably cool. Thus, to take minimum figures, Cairns (lat. 16.55° S.) has a mean July temperature of 69.9° and a humidity of 66 in October. Innisfail (lat. 17.32° S.) has a July temperature of 66.5° and a November humidity of 75, and Mackay (lat. 21° S.) a July temperature of 62° and an October humidity of 66. Even in May we found that the heat was not oppressive in the coast lands, and we saw shops displaying heavy woolen clothing for the winter. It is clear that, although the hot rainy summer is trying, the comparatively cool winter gives the white settlers an annual spell of inestimable importance and value. Then again, considerable areas benefit from the trade winds, which blow off the ocean. I was informed that comfort in the towns varied greatly according to their opennesss to the trades and that the heavy labor of sugar cutting and loading would be almost unbearable in some districts, were it not for these winds.

Another peculiarly favorable point in northeastern Queensland is the close proximity of the towns and sugar country to the mountains, which in many places run right down to the sea. Thus the people of Cairns have Kuranda (1100 feet) only a little more than an hour away by rail and such places as Yungaburra and Atherton (2466 feet) only a few hours by motor or train. Good roads also connect the Innisfail, Tully, and Townsville districts with the tableland, and even closer hill resorts are being opened up in the Townsville hinterland. One feels, however, that in parts of the Queensland tropics the people have shown insufficient appreciation of the importance of location in tropical regions and could learn an immense amount from the Americans at Panama. Towns such as Cairns and Townsville, to take only two examples, are low-lying and largely shut off from the prevalent winds. Hills, which could provide accessible, cool, and airy suburbs, are partly or wholly neglected, and the demands of the tropics are largely overlooked in the planning both of buildings and towns. Paradoxically, this fact may offer hope for the future. If the Australian has done so well by unscientific, slapdash methods, he will do far better when he adopts scientific plans.

Recent Penetrations

British Australian Settlers

A second point of great importance in estimating the permanency of white settlement in Queensland and the significance of the experiment to other tropical countries is the fact that the penetration is so recent that it provides no proof that the tropical climate will not cause degeneracy in later generations. On this point authoritative opinions vary greatly on the northeastern coast. As noted above, the mortality statistics are excellent, as is general health. The men keep southern hours,

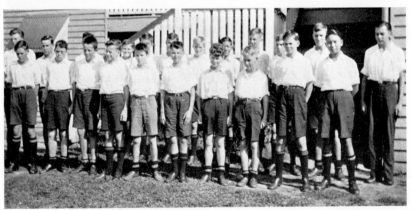

FIG. 17—Children at rural school, Malanda, Atherton Tableland, northern Queensland.
FIGS. 18 and 19—Boys and girls of similar grade and ages, High School, Cairns, northern Queensland.

FIG. 20—British Australian white girls, natives of northern Queensland. Townsville.

FIG. 21—British Australian boy, Cairns, northern Queensland. Both parents and two grandparents were natives of the Australian tropics.

FIG. 22—Boys at Cairns.

yet perform all types of labor. Manual workers, such as wharf laborers, appear to retain their vigor, but I was told that cane cutters do not average more than eight years of work. The evidence on intellect varies. Some residents stated that they suffered from tropical memory; others considered that permanent residence produced no intellectual harm. The same may be said of vitality. Some doctors consider that there is no degeneracy. Others believe that there is a loss of vitality and "tone" and a slowing up of muscular activity. The northern communities share the general Australian love of outdoor sport and undertake very strenuous exercise in swimming, cricket, tennis, hockey, basketball, and rugby football at all seasons of the year (Figs. 20, 22). Like the men, the women do all the usual types of work, particularly as domestic servants receive high wages and are hard to secure. Most doctors are, however, less satisfied with the women than with the men. They consider that women age rapidly, lose vitality, and in the drier areas suffer from dehydration of the tissues. Several medical men informed me that they could at once tell on examining a woman whether she had lived her life in the coastal areas of the Queensland tropics, in the arid interior, or in the temperate south. Some doctors state, however, that there is very little anemia and no more neurasthenia than can be expected from poor housing and hard domestic work. As in most tropical communities, the wealthier women seek recuperation in the temperate zone at intervals of from one to three years. Several doctors noted cases of young women who grow extremely fat, suffer from suppressed menstruation, and do not have children unless sent for some years to cooler climates, when matters right themselves.

Opinions vary greatly on the children. Dr. Anton Breinl considers that the average intelligence is high and the physique good. Some doctors and educationists are of the same opinion; others are less satisfied. Most of the educationists whom I consulted said that the children were of high intellectual standard. The Queensland Director of Education thought that the north gave the best results in the state and that children in the northern mining camps were exceptionally bright. It was significant, however, that several high-school masters believe that the tropical children show a marked falling off in intellect after sixteen. Experienced authorities generally agree that the children develop rapidly and are of good physique, tall, highly strung, excitable, and sexually advanced.[19a] Even a visitor can see that the girls develop early and more quickly than the boys. The latter appear small, stringy, and lean, whereas the girls are said to be heavier and taller than girls in the south and to be fully developed women by seventeen. Several of these points are supported by the photographs (Figs. 18, 19, 20). Except on the tableland, the children lack the complexions of southern Australians, but they appear as energetic and as fond of vigorous games, and they rarely exhibit the peculiar pallor so common among whites in many parts of the tropics. Teachers disagree as to whether these tropical children show less vigor and interest than southern Australians, but they concur that the attitude of the children varies definitely with the weather and that they are more vigorous on wet days. It seems that in this direction lies a valuable field for research. Well-to-do parents commonly send their children to boarding schools in Brisbane or Charters Towers, a town situated at an elevation of 1019 feet on the tablelands in latitude 20° S. These children develop fine physiques and have excellent intellectual ratings.

North Queensland still contains a number of Chinese and aborigines, and one sees their children of pure or mixed blood in the schools. The teachers informed me that the Chinese-whites were almost always of high and the aborigine-whites of low intellectual ability. The aborigines and aborigine-whites are, moreover, very frequently reservoirs for hookworm and venereal disease, another instance of the danger created for white settlers by the presence of a colored people of lower social standard. Venereal disease, however, is not prevalent among the whites, possibly because Queensland, alone of Australian states, maintains legalized prostitution under government supervision. As already noted, the northern Queenslanders seem to have conquered hookworm, although it is practically impossible for children to wear shoes in the rainy season in the wetter areas. There is little malaria, but on the tableland the children in certain districts suffer from sores. Disease is more common in the dry than in the wet season. For this the doctors blame the dust and southern tourists, who bring in epidemics such as influenza.

The high standard of living produces a fair diet compared with that of some parts of the tropics, but not enough milk and green vegetables are consumed. The coastal regions could certainly procure milk in greater quantities from the tablelands. One is told that the climate and soil are not favorable for vegetable growing, as the humus has been washed from the soil and the grasses are low in proteins. Nevertheless, one is inclined to think that the main barriers to the extension of truck farming are the high returns from the sugar lands and the prevalent feeling that vegetable growing is beneath the dignity of the whites. As a result Townsville and other towns are primarily dependent for their vegetables on southern imports or on Chinese gardeners. On the whole, it seems fair to say that the diet of northeastern Queenslanders still leaves much to be desired and that great improvement would follow the introduction of home education and of dietetic clubs on American lines. Brisbane doctors are conducting a diet campaign (1936), and the new medical school of the Brisbane University will no doubt take matters in hand. As in every tropical country one visits, the abuse of alcohol seems an unmitigated curse. I have not secured the figures for drunkenness in tropical Queensland, but those for the state as a whole are much higher than the statistics for Victoria and Tasmania, although lower than those of New South Wales (Table VIII).

FIG. 23—Housing of the best type, Townsville, northern Queensland.
FIG. 24—Government school, Cairns, northern Queensland.
FIG. 25—Cairns, Street, with church and usual type of wooden bungalow.

FIG. 26—Bungalow with detached iron kitchen, Townsville, northern Queensland.
FIG. 27—Iron bungalow in sugar lands, Innisfail, near Cairns, northern Queensland.
FIG. 28—Italian housing in sugar lands, Innisfail.

Housing is improving greatly, but still leaves much to be desired. Everywhere extensive use of "the satanic galvanized iron" is seen, and many houses have insufficient ventilation and no ceilings between the roofs and rooms. The law now demands that stoves must be placed in recesses, and this and the fairly general use of wide verandas and open rooms are probably helping to combat the kitchen neurasthenia noted by observers in the past. At the same time, too few houses are designed on really tropical lines, and little effort is made to take advantage of the prevalent winds. Residents say that, owing to storms and cyclones, they cannot use mosquito screens, but one feels that enormous benefit would result from the adoption of the American methods that are so successful in Panama. The cost of housing in tropical Australia seems inordinately heavy. Timber is expensive and wages very high (Figs. 23-28).

The dress of northern Queenslanders is also unsatisfactory. It is good to see a number of Queensland house-wives working in open-neck shirts and shorts, but it is unfortunate that many people of both sexes still cling to southern Australian dress. The heavy British helmet has, however, been discarded, and many of the men wear no headgear even in the hottest weather and suffer no apparent ill effects.[20]

On the whole one feels that northeastern Queensland is clearly a young and vigorous community, at least equal to southern Florida in living standards and development and inferior only to Panama, where the population includes comparatively few white manual workers who are permanent residents and where economic conditions are unique. The northeastern Queensland experiment is, however, too immature for an estimate to be made of the ultimate results. I could find no individual who could claim that all grandparents had been born in the tropics, although I met several who had one or two tropical grandparents and many adults with parents of tropical birth. Some of these tropical settlers had large and healthy families. One teacher was a member of a family of nine, all born in the tropics, and had a family of ten very fine children, ranging in age from 23 years to 7 months (Fig. 21). A doctor had been called in for sickness only once.

On the other hand, one was surprised to find in districts such as Innisfail the low percentage of children with tropical-born parents. It is clear that over much of northern Queensland the experiment is very recent, and one finds considerable support for Ellsworth Huntington's contention that the population of these coast lands is young, migratory, and select. Cilento and the late Commonwealth Statistician C. H. Wickens vigorously attacked this criticism, but there is no doubt that Huntington put his finger on an unpalatable truth. Wickens may have been right in maintaining that the women of tropical Queensland showed no decline in vitality and fertility and that statistics for Queensland-born women were particularly good. Yet, there is undoubtedly a great deal of natural selection. Many Australians refuse to go to the Australian tropics if they can avoid doing so.

Then again, there is no doubt that a substantial proportion of the population is migratory, as is particularly evident in the much-advertised sugar gangs. The Census of 1933 gives the population of the Queensland tropics as 240,000 on June 30th as against a mean of 185,000. In this winter influx it is difficult to separate tourists from workers, but of 28,737 men engaged in the sugar industry at the peak period of the year 1930, 7684 were cane farmers and 6823 field workers in regular employment—a total of 14,507 permanents—while 8142 cane cutters and 6088 mill workers were seasonal employees.[21] Evidence was given that a number of these cane cutters were drawn from the southern states and that as soon as the crop was harvested they returned to the south to engage in work such as apple picking in Tasmania or to live at home on the dole. There has, however, been an increase in permanent and tropically resident labor during the last decade. In the far north the greater part of the labor required is recruited from the region, and there are many married men and home owners not only among the mill employees but among the cane cutters as well.

There is very little doubt that, although part of the white workers of tropical Queensland are migratory, the proportion of permanent residents has increased.

The Italian Penetration

Another argument against the ultimate success of the northern whites in tropical Queensland is particularly significant. This is the rapid growth of an Italian element, particularly in the northern sugar lands. It is true that the Committee of Enquiry (1931) came to an optimistic conclusion, but the figures presented by them are by no means satisfactory. They stated that the Committee was convinced that the whole Italian problem was passing through a transitory stage and that satisfactory communities would eventually be evolved out of the new settlements in the far north. At the same time, they considered that only the action of the Commonwealth in restricting Italian immigration had prevented the dilution of the British personnel engaged in the sugar industry and a growth of foreign control in the settlements, which would have been "a matter of some concern." [22]

The student of British settlement in the tropics must view this story of Italian penetration far more seriously than did the Committee. The statistics show that the central and southern districts (Nos. 2 and 3) contained an average of 2.3 per cent of foreign employees and 4 per cent of naturalized. In district No. 1, however—the northern sugar areas, which produce 60 per cent of the crop—the percentage was 23.4 foreign and 20 naturalized. The Committee gave the number of foreign workers in the three districts as 2488 foreign and 2130 naturalized. The Census of 1933 stated that 5336 males and 2112 females gave Italy as their birthplace, and 3100 males and 818 females claimed Italian nationality.

The living standards of the aliens, the greater part of whom were Italians, were lower than those of the Australians, and this, together with the fact that many farms were passing from British owners to Italians, created considerable alarm from 1925 onwards (Fig. 28). In spite of preference agreements, which have favored the British cane cutter, farms are gradually being transferred from British to non-British owners. Furthermore, the position of the British field laborer is said to be weakened because two or more aliens often combine to purchase a farm and to furnish the labor among themselves. We found impartial northern Queenslanders genuinely alarmed at the steady Italian penetration, which is still in progress. The Italian works harder and for longer hours than the British Australian, and he disregards trade-union regulations or dodges them by faked pay rolls, dummying, and coöperation. Northern employers informed me that it was untrue that Italian cane-cutting gangs were inferior to the British (Fig. 14). Like the American, the Queenslander regards the northern Italian as a good, honest citizen but considers the southern Italian a national menace. Nevertheless, most Italians rapidly acquire Australian characteristics. Small Italian boys in Innisfail have been heard refusing to play with new Italian arrivals on the ground that they were not going to associate with "bloody Dagos."

The student of white settlement may well ask whether this ousting of British by Italians is due to race, to economics, or to climate. One feels from the foregoing study and from the evidence as regards northern Europeans in the West Indies that the primary factors are economic and that the north Queensland tropics, which are marginal lands of peculiar suitability, can probably be developed by the British race. It is well known that the Italian method of penetration is to live economically, work extremely hard, save, buy a farm, and then to import relatives. If Australians are determined to maintain a numerical supremacy of northern Europeans, it is essential that they should safeguard their living standards in occupations that are just as worthy of support as are the vast mass of protected and assisted industries in the south.

The Future: White Population

Although at present the outlook is favorable, the future of the British whites in the Queensland tropics must remain for some generations a matter of doubt. Cilento states:

There is, indeed, beginning to be a very definite type of North Queenslander, or tropical-born Australian . . . He is tall and rangy, with somewhat sharp features, and long arms and legs. Inclined to be sparely built, he is not, however, lacking in muscular strength, while his endurance is equal in his own circumstances to that of the temperate dweller in his. This North Queenslander moves slowly, and conserves his muscular heat-producing energy in every possible way. One can pick him out in the streets by the fact that, as a general rule, he walks more deliberately. In the women this becomes a gracefulness of movement that reminds one of those nations of the East that live in similar environments.

The hair colour is darkening, black, dark-brown, and red hair being increasingly frequent in long-settled localities. There is, moreover, a pallor of the skin, which has been referred to previously, which produces most perfect feature-types in dark-haired women, though it is unkind to the fair-haired, and gives them a freckled and faded appearance. The race is in a transition stage, and it is very apparent that there is being evolved precisely what one would hope for, namely, a distinctive tropical type, adapted to life in the tropical environment in which it is set.[23]

It is pertinent to ask whether the conservation of muscular heat-producing energy to which Cilento refers may not indicate some loss of vitality and some degree of physical decline.

While the evidence from Queensland, Saba, and Florida gives some hope for white evolution in the marginal tropics, it is of vital importance to scientific knowledge, to Australia, and, not least, to the white settlers of tropical Queensland that the experiment in this region should be watched closely. It was nothing short of a tragedy to science and to the Australian nation that the Commonwealth government cut off the investigations of Breinl, Young, and others by closing the Townsville Institute, and it is to be hoped that the new medical school of the Queensland University will reopen the work. Periodical examinations should be made, particularly of children, and research conducted into the bases of acclimatization, as the waste of millions in money and of thousands in lives might be prevented if means could be discovered to show what type of people acclimatize best. In this respect the Commonwealth might well coöperate with the Americans if they establish a tropical experiment station at Panama. There is also the problem of improving sanitation, housing, and similar necessities. The removal of the Kanakas and the medical campaign against hookworm and other diseases have worked wonders, but much remains to be done.

Future Industries

The Queensland tropics undoubtedly possess a future in agriculture, pastoral industry, mining, and manufacture. The state has splendid coal resources and may also develop water power. Yet a great extension of close white settlement based on agriculture seems unlikely, particularly as the nation will probably confine the sugar output to the demand within the Commonwealth. Many north Queenslanders expect such an eventuality. They realize that, although Australians as a whole may be willing to pay a high price for Australian sugar in order to maintain a reasonable standard of living in north Queensland, they may well refuse to pay for the support of sugar exports. W. Wynne Williams has analyzed the situation and concludes that agriculture cannot prosper in any region where the dry months (May-October) have less than 10 inches of rainfall and where more than 10 per cent of the recorded months have had less than 0.1 inch of rain. The areas not included in such a category are limited to comparatively small districts on the coast of Queensland and are already largely occupied by the whites (Fig. 15). Beyond these limits agriculture has failed, and irrigation settlements have either proved unsuccessful or are being maintained at great expense. Even on the Atherton Tableland (a few miles from Cairns, and only eight miles westward of the mist-covered coastal range) agriculture has failed, except with the wet-season crop of tobacco, owing to the fact that the dry-season rainfall is only 2 inches and the percentage of dry months 21. Professor Griffith Taylor and other experts consider that some of the drier areas offer possibilities for crops such as wheat, millet, cotton, maize, and tobacco, but even in these cases the economic and administrative difficulties are great. The failures in the Northern Territory indicate the complexity of the problem. Summer floods, winter droughts, poor soils, and pests (such as the white ant and rat) have defeated the efforts to grow sugar, India rubber, coffee, cinchona, and peanuts, even where Chinese labor was utilized. In the words of Wynne Williams, "Beyond this narrow fringe of coastal scrub-land [in Queensland] there is only one locality in the whole of the Australian tropics, viz., the tip of Cape York, with a recorded dry season rainfall greater than 4 inches and a lesser percentage of dry months than 18 per cent." [24] Except in this small area of coastal Queensland "any attempt to foster agricultural settlement beyond the meteorological limits which have bounded it hitherto needs to be scrutinised with the gravest apprehension because . . . disaster will follow in its train." [25]

The pastoralist also faces great difficulties, with results that will be enumerated in Chapter VIII. The climate confines sheep to relatively small sections of the Australian tropics and places the cattle industry under grave handicaps as compared with competitor countries such as the Argentine.

Manufactures offer some hope for the future, for Queensland has splendid coal fields [26] and the northeastern tablelands have potentialities for water power. One feels, however, that the latter may prove disappointing. North Queenslanders are disappointed with the Barron Falls scheme and its high costs. This is unfortunate, for it is clear that the future of the white settlers in north Queensland depends upon the diversification of industries, as does the progress of Costa Rica and other tropical countries of similar type. Development in this direction is gravely hindered in this part of the Australian tropics by the great value and returns of the sugar lands and by high wages and other heavy costs. One point is outstanding as regards wages. If the north possesses, as is claimed, a healthful climate entirely suited to white settlement, is there reason for the sugar worker to be paid a special tropical rate? One recalls the words of Sir George Buchanan in his important report on the Northern Territory: "It is obvious that, if the young pioneer is to be paid a special isolation allowance . . . all attempts to develop that country had better be abandoned." [27]

All things considered, this chapter on the white settlers of north-eastern Queensland must end with a question mark. Up to the present, with an adequate living standard supported (and justly so) by the whole Australian nation, the progress of this tropical penetration has been excellent. But past successes are no certain proof of further advances, and the people of Australia, who are making substantial contributions toward one of the most important experiments in world history, should see that while the national government treats north-eastern Queensland with sympathy and kindness it at the same time subjects the area to continuous and vigorous scientific research.

CHAPTER VII

THE TRADE-WIND ISLANDS OF THE WEST INDIES

The West Indian survivals of the prescientific invasions are of considerable interest. The Spanish peoples of Cuba and Puerto Rico indicate that in favorable circumstances Mediterranean whites can establish white working settlements for indefinite periods in the moderate tropics and resist and absorb even the negro peoples. The numerous groups of northern whites show that these peoples can remain in the moderate tropics for hundreds of years in spite of grave difficulties.

TABLE IX—WEST INDIES: CLIMATIC DATA FOR CERTAIN STATIONS*

STATION AND LENGTH OF RECORD	LAT.	ALT. (feet)	TEMPERATURE (degrees Fahr.)		RELATIVE HUMIDITY (per cent 24 hours)	ANNUAL RAINFALL (inches)
			Mean Ann.	Range		
Nassau 1874–1920... Bahamas	25°N	13	77.0	11.0	73	51.01
Havana 1899–1927... Cuba	23°N	79	77.0	10.2	76	45.00
Kingston 1908–1927.. Jamaica	18°N	23	79.4	5.3	73	28.90
San Juan 1899–1927 Puerto Rico	17°50′N	98	77.8	5.8	79	61.30
Bottom 1930........ Saba	17°38′N	640	79.0	8.4	71 (St. Martin)	44.50 (25 years)
Basseterre 1899–1927 St. Kitts	17°N	30	79.0	4.8	76	46.60
Bridgetown (10 years) Barbados	13°N	180	78.7	3.9	66	45.90 (28 years)

*Data from the Köppen-Geiger "Handbuch der Klimatologie," Vol. 2, Part 1, 1934.

Geographically the West Indies consist of a long chain of islands from southern Florida in latitude 25° N. to Trinidad in latitude 11° N. (Fig. 29). Most of the islands are of volcanic origin and very fertile. Tables IX and X set out climatic statistics.

Lying in these latitudes, all the islands are in the trade-wind zone and strongly reflect this control. Cuba and Puerto Rico, the two most populous islands, have been occupied by Spanish whites and near-whites for a period of more than 400 years. Saba contains pure-white British and Dutch, who have lived in the tropics for periods of up to 250 years. British whites have also survived in Barbados for more than two cen-

turies, and the same may be true of the British whites in the Cayman
Islands and of the Dutch whites in St. Martin. Two very interesting
groups of pure-white French settlers have lived in St. Bartholomew and
St. Thomas (Virgin Islands) for many years. The German communities
in the country districts of Jamaica have been in the island for nearly a

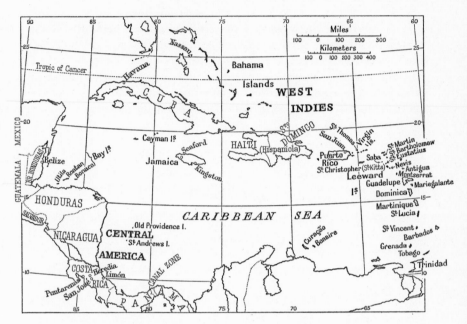

FIG. 29—Location map of the Caribbean region (scale: 1: 27,500,000).

century. In addition to these groups there are small communities of
white peasantry in Grenada, St. Christopher, Old Providence, and probably in other islands.

The present chapter, which is based partly on published accounts and
partly on observations made during a visit to the West Indies in 1933,
deals primarily with settlers of north European stock. Although the
Spanish survivals in Cuba and Puerto Rico are of great interest—the
whites here, in direct contrast to the general trend of events in the
tropics, are absorbing colored races—circumstances did not permit the
writer to carry out detailed field studies in these islands, and our discussion of settlement by Europeans of Mediterranean origin in the West
Indies will be confined to a brief account of the situation in Puerto Rico.

Puerto Rico

Puerto Rico, a trade-wind island in latitudes 17.5° to 18.3° N., has
an area of 3435 square miles. Topographically it may be described as
"a cluster of rugged hills bordered by a narrow coastal plain."[1] The
culminating height is 4400 feet.[2] The climate is moderately tropical.

San Juan, the capital, which faces the trade winds, has an average annual temperature of 76°, and in the mountain regions the average annual temperatures range from 74° to 68° F.[3] and are thus comparable with the 72° of the Costa Rican plateaus.

History

It is said that in 1508, when the Spanish occupation began, the Borinquen Indians "were 'as thick as bees,'" and that the island "blossomed like the rose."[4] It is estimated that the number of the aboriginal population was 80,000 to 100,000. The Spaniards quickly exterminated the Indians by slaughter, ill-treatment, overwork, and disease. As early as 1515 Licenciado Sancho Velasquez wrote to the King of Spain: "Excepting your Highness' Indians and those of the crown officers there are not 4,000 left."[5] The Census of 1531 lists the following population: 57 Spaniards married to whites, 14 Spaniards married to Indians, 298 single Spaniards, and 675 Indian and 1523 negro slaves. By 1582 the Borinquen Indians were extinct. As a result of a century of Spanish rule the population has been destroyed, the island squeezed dry, agriculture ruined, and the inhabitants had become whites, blacks and mestizos, steeped in ignorance.[6]

To replace the vanishing Indians and in a vain effort to save them from complete extinction the Spaniards introduced negro slaves from 1510 onwards, and by 1530 there were 1500 negroes in the island. At the outset the conquistadors brought no Spanish women, and, as many of the Spaniards were adventurers and criminals, the early Spanish-Indian-negro mixture was of a low type. Later there were influxes of Portuguese soldiers, Catalonians, and English and American immigrants, but there was no great progress. Nevertheless "the tropical peasant economy" was not altogether unsatisfactory, and the people, though poor, were independent and happy.[7]

In the nineteenth century good Spanish stock came from the mainland owing to the revolutions, and the people began to increase, as "three-quarters of the population was engaged in agriculture under healthful conditions."[8] In 1815 the "Schedule of Grace" opened the island to world commerce, and immigrants, including practical farmers from Louisiana, came in. In 1845 the island contained 216,183 whites, 175,791 free colored persons and 51,265 slaves. By the time of the Treaty of Paris, 1898, there were 570,187 whites, 239,808 persons of mixed color, and 75,824 negroes.[9] The standard of living was, however, very low, and the vast majority of the people were illiterate.

The gibaros or peasants spread through the country, more particularly through the mountain districts to which, like the "poor whites" of the southern United States, they were driven by slavery. Some mixed with the Indians or negroes, but many kept their white blood pure. The people as a whole became strongly individualistic, owing to the character

of their settlement, the isolation caused by the Spanish policy of pro-
hibiting foreign trade, and the danger from the buccaneers.[10] The statistics of the eighteenth and early nineteenth centuries show that in this
period the importation of negroes stopped and the population steadily
became more white. The percentage of the colored population to the
total fell from 52 in 1802 to 48.5 in 1860 and 27 in 1920. The Census of
1920 classed only 3.8 per cent of the population as negro compared with
23.2 per cent mulattoes and 73 per cent whites. From 1910 to 1920 the
whites had increased 11.4 per cent, whereas the blacks had decreased by
$15\frac{1}{2}$ and the mulattoes by $22\frac{2}{3}$.[11]

Population

The present population of Puerto Rico is more colored on the coast
than in the interior, but, although this may be partly due to the cooler
climate of the highlands, it is mainly the result of economic reasons. As
in the southern United States, the whites settled in the mountains owing
to the plantation system and negro slavery of the lowlands, and today
the negro tends to remain near the coast in the sugar areas and cocoanut
groves. The predominance of whites is very important, and it has even
been stated that this is the main cause of the rapid progress since the
American occupation.[12]

In recent times the population of the little island has "increased appal-
lingly." Numbers rose by 50 per cent between 1899 and 1930. In the
latter year there were 1,543,043 people, and the population was increasing
at an annual rate of $1\frac{1}{2}$ per cent. Mixer gives the birth rate at 39.12 per
1000. The death rate for 1928-1929 was 27.7 per 1000, so that both
births and deaths are inordinately high. The infant mortality for 1926-
1930 was 155 per 1000; the death rate from tuberculosis 255 per 100,000,
and the death rate from malaria 16.3. These rates for tuberculosis and
malaria were, respectively, three times and eight times as high as the
rates in the southern United States, while the death rate in the two
largest cities was five times that of New York. A recent report on child
health states that malaria appears to have existed before the first white
invasions and that hookworm was probably brought in very early by the
whites. It adds: "There is no doubt that these diseases and other pathological conditions have been most important factors in the physical and
mental deterioration and the social and economic poverty of the rural
people." [13]

In spite of disease, the increase of population creates so serious a
problem that in general opinion the island is "heading straight towards
disaster." [14] Medical science is aiding and abetting this increase, yet the
religion of the Puerto Rican prevents him from adopting the scientific
and "absolutely essential" remedy: birth control.

Poverty and Disease

Theodore Roosevelt, Jr., when governor, made known his deep concern at the state of Puerto Rico, particularly the undernourishment of children, and the Committee that reported to President Hoover revealed a most shocking "vicious circle" of poverty and disease. It appears that the island is in the grip of unemployment, starvation, undernourishment, tuberculosis, and hookworm. Although the Americans have done good work in medicine, the services are hopelessly inadequate. Each doctor is attempting to serve 4500 and each nurse 5000 people, as against 250 in the United States. Some eighteen per cent of children are illegitimate, and this, combined with the fact that about fifteen per cent of the marriages are consensual, leads to the wholesale abandonment of children. Above all, "the immense majority of the rural population is living on the verge of starvation." Food is the vital need.[15]

A recent American writer, Jenks, also paints a picture of unalleviated gloom.[16] The Americans, he says, stamped out yellow fever and smallpox, but the population is riddled with hookworm and malaria, and the death rate from tuberculosis is probably the highest in the world. When the Americans occupied the island the principal articles of diet were dry beans, corn, salt fish, and polished rice. These foodstuffs were largely imported and not sufficiently nutritious. Unfortunately, since the American occupation and the growth of the sugar industry, this "tin-can" diet has been intensified and, together with disease, creates the low standard of child development disclosed by the Health Report.

Jenks notes other evils that the American efforts have mitigated but have failed to remedy. Morality and literacy, for example, are still at a low standard, about one-half of the population remaining illiterate. Behind all lie the economic problems that have been created by the increase of the one-crop sugar industry and the inclusion of Puerto Rico in the tariff system of the United States.

Superficially the sugar industry and inclusion within the American tariff appear to have assisted Puerto Rico. Many Puerto Ricans are doubtful, however, of the real value of these alleged blessings, and there is good reason for their doubt. The sugar industry has brought the usual curses of seasonal unemployment, monoculture, corporation relationships and wirepulling, food importations, and the undue influence of absentee capitalism in the affairs of the island. The United States tariff has brought Puerto Rico splendid markets, but, as in the cases of Tasmania and northern Australia, the tariff has exposed the unfortunate people to a coastal shipping monopoly and has forced them to buy food and other supplies at the high prices existing within the tariff wall.[17]

Economic Problems

To what causes can we attribute the misfortunes of the white population of Puerto Rico? Are the problems of these white workers in the tropics due to tropical climate, to diet, to economic disadvantages, to negro competition, or to health? Obviously the climate is not the main factor. It is true that the whites appear to prefer the cooler regions and tend to build their huts on the higher land in the cooling breezes, which drive away "the ever present and often death-laden mosquito." For the worst misfortunes, however, climate is not directly to blame. Nor are the negroes responsible in this instance, for the white Puerto Rican peasantry has clearly shown its ability to withstand the negroes and is breeding them out. Nor can we attribute the chief difficulties to those diseases that result from the tropical environment. By far the worst scourges are tuberculosis and hookworm. Neither is purely tropical in character, and the ravages of both are due in all probability to shocking sanitation and housing, and to an inadequate and non-nutritious diet. The truth is that in Puerto Rico, as in Cuba and possibly in other tropical countries, the principal trouble is economic. It is poverty and the permanent or seasonal unemployment in the island that create the vicious circle of undernourishment and ill-health. The remedy demanded is the creation of a self-supporting community with a more diversified diet and a higher standard of living and comfort, which will reduce the rate of population increase. It is indeed essential that the Puerto Ricans should deal strongly with the growth of their population, for this, abetted by medical science, has indeed become an "almost irremediable problem," and is leading the island straight towards disaster.[18]

The Future

The brightest hopes for the future lie in the Puerto Ricans themselves. The rising generation is not staggered by its paralyzing difficulties. Bred under American rule and trained in American colleges and in their own excellent university at Rio Piedras, the younger people are undertaking rehabilitation as a national task.[19] American writers have, on the whole, a very fair opinion of the capacity of Puerto Ricans for this work. Jenks, for example, writes that "there can be no doubt of the individual competence of Puerto Ricans to supply material for their own government superior to that of most of the American states." [20]

Mixer considers that in the past the gibaro has not been ill treated but neglected. The experiment in training Puerto Rican recruits during the war showed that the gibaro became an efficient member of society when given sufficient nourishing food and proper clothing, educated in simple, fundamental rules of hygiene, and provided with enough education to show him something of the world about him, so that he might unload the burden of superstition and fear that formed so large a part of his thoughts.[21]

The "Inquiry as to the Health of the Children of Puerto Rico" states that the Puerto Rican peasant is in the main "honest, law-abiding, courteous, gentle, humble and hospitable." The people have unusual manual skill and unerring artistic sense. V. S. Clark considers that Puerto Ricans cannot compete with the negro in very rough labor, but that they produce good mechanics, factory operators, and professional people and as field hands compare favorably with Orientals and with persons of Spanish or Portuguese stock in Hawaii.[22]

Whatever may be said against the American sugar barons, the American government has given generous scientific and philanthropic assistance to the island and will continue its good work. In spite of the present gloomy outlook, there are hopes for these Puerto Rican white people.

Puerto Rico provides important evidence on the question of white settlement in the tropics. The pure-white element of Mediterranean origin demonstrates how erroneous is the belief that after three generations the white man cannot breed in the tropics. The mixed element exposes the popular fallacy that sterility overwhelms crossbred stocks. These communities have also shown that the negro cannot always underlive and absorb the whites, but that the Mediterranean white can survive and make progress in the trade-wind tropics.

St. Martin

The little Dutch islands of Saba and St. Martin throw light on our problem, for they are the home of pure-white north Europeans who have lived in the tropics as peasant workers for several hundred years. As such cases are rare and important, I spent some time in 1933 in these islands, which are situated respectively in latitudes 17.37° and 18.3° N.

St. Martin is a small trade-wind island in 18.3° N. It is shared by the Dutch and French. These nations have colonized the island since about 1648, and it has been conquered by the English several times. Hence, although the majority of the population is negro, there are many Europeans of pure-white stock (English, French, and Dutch), and the people speak English in addition to Dutch and Papiamento, the strange negro-European language of Curaçao. We saw some European families that were obviously degenerate through inbreeding and miscegenation. In one case three generations of whites were all cross-eyed, while the third generation included white and mulatto children from the same mother. Many of the whites are of good stamp, nevertheless. We traveled, for instance, with two intelligent St. Martin schoolmasters and with the St. Martin-born wife and child of a third schoolmaster who was of German extraction. This man's family had been in the island for more than a hundred years. In Saba, too, we met a St. Martin-born schoolmistress of good ability and education.

The most important group of whites in St. Martin is the Simson's Bay fishermen. The governor of St. Martin informed us that the origin of this pure-white group of about 160 persons is unknown. They are, however, English-speaking, and some have names like those found on Saba, for example, Pieterson. However, other authorities, including Dutch medical officers, say that these people, like the Chachas of St. Thomas, are largely descended from the French of St. Bartholomew Island. Owing to disease and to the fact that this community lives on a narrow strip of land between the sea and lagoons, the settlement used to be completely isolated from the rest of the island, and the people degenerated almost to animal level. Some three years before our visit, in 1933, the Dutch government built a bridge to connect the village with the island and conducted a hook-worm campaign in the community, which was riddled with disease. The government forced medicine on the people, provided pit privies and a supply of uncontaminated water, and installed a policeman to compel the villagers to wear shoes. As a result of three years' work the people look comparatively strong and healthy. Their cabins are of good type and neat and clean (Figs. 30, 31). Possibly owing to the presence of the governor at the time of our visit, the whole community was wearing shoes. The Simson's Bay settlement thus provides an example of the danger of isolation in the tropics and of the results that can be secured by a health campaign.[23]

SABA [24]

Saba is a young volcanic island [25] some five square miles in area, a tangle of rugged hills that rise by steep slopes or sheer cliffs to a cloud-capped mountain peak 2887 feet above the sea [26] (Fig. 36). The early history of white settlement is obscure, but it is known that the Dutch colonized the neighboring island of St. Eustatius (Statia) in 1636,[27] after an attempt by the French under Du Cusac had failed through lack of water, a lack that the Dutch remedied by building cisterns such as those that form so prominent a feature in Saba and Statia today.

The English captured Saba in 1665 and held it until 1667. They again took the island in 1672 and, although they nominally restored it in 1674, continued to administer it for eight more years. These English occupations and the sea interests of the islanders probably account for the fact that Saba remains English-speaking today. Hamelberg makes it clear that when the English captured Saba in 1665 the island was inhabited by a variety of races and that some of the people were probably planters employing negro slaves. The records state that there were 87 Hollanders and 54 English, Scots, and Irish, with 85 negroes and Indians, and that the English sent the defeated Dutch settlers to the island of St. Martin. It is fairly certain that during the latter half of the seventeenth century the Saban community consisted of small planters and seafarers, the latter engaged in more or less legitimate vocations.

Father Labat, who visited the island in April, 1701, paints a very favorable picture of a prosperous little planting community.[28]

Abbé Raynal gave another happy description of Saba almost a century later.[29] He said that in the island plants grew to an extraordinary size. Fifty European families with some 150 slaves raised garden produce and

Fig. 30—A white fisherman's house, Simson's Bay, St. Martin.
Fig. 31—White fishermen, Simson's Bay.
Fig. 32—The British government's attempt to provide decent housing and sanitation at a cost of $126 per dwelling, St. Christopher.

Fig. 33—Landing a boat, Saba.
Fig. 34—Village of Bottom, Saba. Note path to cliff villages in right background.
Fig. 35—In Windwardside village, Saba. Note grave to right and water cistern beyond.

cotton. Throughout America there was no blood so pure as the Saban;
the women preserved a freshness of complexion not found in any other
island of the Caribbean.

Meager as are the historical records, the important point is that they
include, at a very early date, the names of some of the present white

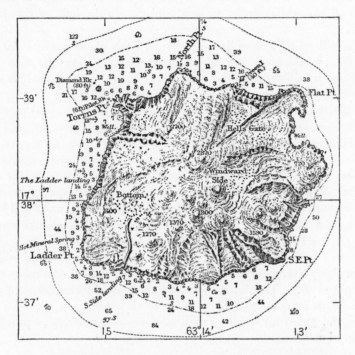

FIG. 36—Map of Saba Island (from U. S. Hydrographic Office Chart
No. 1011, 1914) (scale: 1:71,500). A later figure, West Indies Pilot (4th
edit., 1929), gives the altitude of the culminating peak as 2887 feet.

families. It seems fairly certain that by 1700 most of the leading Saban
families were already residing in the island or in near-by Statia.

Access to the Island and Its Villages

Little that is authentic has been written about Saba, for all communications were by small and uncomfortable schooners until a few years ago,
when the Dutch government subsidized a passenger and cargo service by
a small steamer of the Royal Dutch Netherlands Company. Sensational
writers have done some harm by absurd exaggerations of the difficulties
of access. In point of fact, one or the other of the two regular landings
at Fort Bay in the south and Ladder Bay in the west is so safe in every
wind that only one fatal accident has been recorded in recent times.
From the two main landings excellent stone and concrete paths and
stairways lead to the village of Bottom (Fig. 34).

The ascent to Bottom may be made on foot, by horse, or in a chair borne by negroes. The paths are too steep for wheeled vehicles. Donkeys, a recent importation, are somewhat unpopular, on the ground that they cause unemployment. Porters still handle the heaviest "buns" or parcels. Every plank of building material and every piece of furniture has been lugged up the cliffs by human labor, even such articles as pianos. The whites prefer to let the blacks do the bulk of this heavy work.

The village of Bottom lies in a circular basin about a mile in circumference. It contains 436 inhabitants. Commanding the two chief landings, it still remains the seat of government, although it is overwhelmingly black and is smaller than Windwardside.

Windwardside, the largest village of the island, is situated partly on the eastern slope of the mountain and partly on a neck of land connecting the mountain with Booby Hill, whose flat top furnishes excellent agricultural land. The village contains 511 people, with whites still predominating. Its altitude is about 1400 feet. Hellsgate, a mile or so to the north and 200 feet higher, contains 231 inhabitants, almost all of whom are white. St. John (1200 feet) has 229 people, white and black.

The cliff villages are picturesque, clean, and well kept, like most of those in the Dutch possessions. The pretty little wooden houses are for the most part painted white, with green or brown shutters and red roofs. They average four or five small rooms but often contain as many as eight or nine. The Sabans use very substantial frames of hard wood set in firm foundations. They reinforce their buildings wherever possible, and guard all windows with solid wooden shutters as protection against hurricanes.

The Climate

Despite the rhapsodies of visitors, the climate of Bottom is distinctly tropical, as the elevation is only 900 feet. Conditions are, however, ameliorated by the winds, which blow almost constantly through the Fort Bay and Ladder Bay gaps on the south and west, although neither gap is more than a few hundred feet wide. Also the towering mountain on the east and the hills on the west lessen the hours of tropical sunshine by as many as four hours a day. The government keeps no record of wind or humidity but reads the temperatures in Bottom at 7.45 a.m. and 1.45 and 3 p.m., while the Royal Dutch Meteorological Institute publishes, somewhat irregularly, rainfall figures for Bottom, Windwardside, and St. John.

The figures indicate just such rainfall variations as one would expect. Bottom, 900 feet above the sea and in the southwestern rain shadow, had an annual average of 1047 millimeters in 13 years recorded between 1919 and 1932. St. John, 1200 feet and in the same rain shadow, had 1060 millimeters in 7 recorded years, and Windwardside, 1400 feet, on the northeast, and in the trade winds, had 1126 millimeters in 8 recorded years. There is usually some rain during every month of the year.

We were told by the Receiver that the temperatures in Bottom usually vary from an average of 22° to 27° C. (71.6° to 80.6° F.). These are distinctly temperatures of the tropical coast lands, as may be seen by comparison with figures for Basseterre, St. Kitts, situated some 40 miles from Saba at an elevation of 157 feet.

TABLE X—SABA AND ST. KITTS: MONTHLY TEMPERATURES
(in degrees Fahrenheit)

	J.	F.	M.	A.	M.	J.	J.	A.	S.	O.	N.	D.	YEAR
Bottom Saba, 1930[a]													
7:45 A.M.....	73.9	74.5	75.0	78.0	79.9	80.6	80.2	82.2	82.2	82.2	79.3	78.2	78.9
1:45 P.M.....	82.4	84.2	85.8	87.5	88.0	88.7	89.0	91.4	91.8	92.2	89.9	86.6	88.2
Basseterre St. Kitts													
Mean, 1930[b]	74.1	75.3	76.7	79.2	80.9	81.9	81.2	80.7	80.7	81.1	79.0	78.5	79.1
15-19 year mean[c]	76.5	76.5	76.5	77.9	79.4	80.4	81.0	81.4	81.4	80.9	79.7	77.5	79.0

[a]Unpublished data collected by the author.
[b]From U. S. Weather Bureau, Climatological Data, West Indies Section, 1930.
[c]From the Köppen-Geiger "Handbuch der Klimatologie," Vol. 2, Part 1, 1934.

Profuse perspiration follows any exercise and indicates that the humidity is great. The climate is undoubtedly better in the cliff villages, but even in these the air is hot and the humidity high. We found that it was by no means cold at the summit of the mountain (2887 feet) on a rainy and cloudy day.

Slave-Owning and Sailing-Vessel Days

At first glance Saba seems to provide some splendid data for those who emphasize the influence of climate on white settlement in the tropics. Bottom (900 feet) has become almost entirely black. Windwardside and St. John (1200 to 1400 feet) are partly white and partly colored. Hellsgate (1600 feet) is almost entirely white. Marypoint (about 1000 feet) is white but decadent. Unfortunately, we dare not accept the simple climatic explanation. Even these small settlements illustrate the complex factors influencing white people in the tropics.

The village of Bottom remained the seat of many prosperous white families until some time after the slave-owning and sailing-vessel days. In that era the inhabitants of Bottom considered themselves the élite of the island. Like the Chachas of St. Thomas, they married only in their village or with a few newcomers, such as the children of clergy or doctors.

Throughout the island the whites of that period seem to have maintained a very fair standard of morality and close observance of the color bar.

Extraordinary statements have been made to the effect that all the inhabitants of Bottom are Simmonses and that only Hassells are found in Windwardside. Yet the early records contain at least seven family names, and the list of slave owners compiled for the emancipation of 1863 gives some eighteen different names. The last census (1932) made no color distinctions, as is the Dutch policy, but it seems that there are now some twenty white family names.

Although the paucity of names in Saba has been exaggerated, inbreeding has been considerable, owing particularly to the isolation and local spirit of the villages, a usual feature in mountainous country where difficulties of communication are great. Yet, except in the tiny village of Marypoint, inbreeding does not seem to have destroyed fertility, stamina, or ability. From 1852 to 1861 white births numbered 201 and deaths only 160, and many members of the oldest Saban families who left the island showed capability in the outside world.

Changes After 1860

Between 1860 and 1920 two blows ruined the white settlers of Bottom. The first, which also affected the whole island, was the action of the Dutch government, which in 1863 emancipated 700 Saban slaves.

The second trouble was the change from sailing vessels to steam. About thirty years ago most of the energetic young men of Bottom and many from the cliff villages were attracted by the inducements offered by the headquarters of steamship companies at New York and elsewhere, and emigrated, often taking with them Saban wives. It was then that the inherent qualities of these tropical whites became evident. Large numbers of the islanders secured positions as commanders and officers of important steamers. Others proved capable as harbor masters or pilots. Some made good in university positions and in business, and today quite a number of island men and women can be found in good social positions throughout the Caribbean. The point remains, however, that Bottom lost her slaves, schooners, and vigorous young people. Today the remnants of white population consist largely of aged persons.

White Agriculture

The whites of Windwardside and Hellsgate may be classed as small yeomanry or peasant farmers of a very fair type. As the number of slaves—men, women and children—averaged only seven to a proprietor at the emancipation, most of the whites must have worked beside their slaves. Many of the men of the present generation are away at sea or are engaged in carpentry, wood polishing, and similar industries in the United States, but almost all the remainder are occupied with cultivating

FIG. 37—White youth carrying a load of elephant grass, Saba.
FIG. 38—Negro family, all workers, Saba.
FIG. 39—Children at government school, Windwardside, Saba.
FIG. 40—Children at Roman Catholic school, Bottom, Saba.

FIGS. 41 and 42—Whites of Marypoint village, Saba.
FIG. 43—French whites, village of Carenage, St. Thomas, Virgin Islands.

the mountainsides and small areas of fertile ground on spurs and elevations such as Booby Hill.

Transport difficulties would appall anybody but these hardy Sabans.
Even donkeys cannot climb the terribly steep slopes, yet, over rough
paths and with the aid of hands and knees, the whites "head" heavy
loads from the mountaintop to Windwardside as often as three times a
day (Fig. 37).

Diet and Health

The rich soil would no doubt produce many commodities for export,
but we were informed that the people are intensely conservative and
are unwilling to make experiments or undertake the rotation of crops.
This is undoubtedly a result of isolation. Even with the present variety
of products diet should be better. Sabans who have been in the United
States appreciate the value of milk, fruit, and green vegetables, but the
colored people use them little, while many of the whites suffer from
dyspepsia owing to a diet consisting largely of biscuits, bread, and tea.
In this respect the influx of outside money has been unfortunate, resulting as it does in imports of salt fish and tinned goods. One suspects a
deleterious change of diet since the self-supporting slave days. The
majority of the men look strong and healthy, nevertheless, and they are
capable of working long hours on the hot hillsides and of carrying
unbelievably heavy burdens. They thus give some support to the contention of some Australian tropical doctors that the whites can maintain
their standard in the tropics, if, as a people, they guard health carefully
and engage in strenuous manual work.

The Saban white women support the Australian theory from another
angle. Debarred by the traditions of the slave days from healthy field
labor or even from taking positions as housekeepers, nurses, or domestic
servants, they spend their time, when they cannot migrate, largely
indoors. As a result they appear to be nervous and high-strung, and
they lack the rosy cheeks that previous observers have acclaimed. Some
of the trouble may be due to the fact that the tropical climate is said to
accentuate the usual women's disorders. There is no doubt, however,
that important factors are isolation, sedentary life, poor diet, insufficient
care of teeth, and the long hours spent under oil light at the sedentary
occupation of drawn-thread work. They show great skill in making this
so-called Spanish lace and in the past have earned large sums through
sales in the United States.

Like many isolated people these women are intensely conservative and
do not make sufficient effort to keep pace with the rapid changes of
demand in the centers of fashion. Like those in other tropical communities also, these islanders are helpless victims of the changing economic
and social policies of the great cool-temperate lands. The recent history
of Saba, for example, has been largely colored by events in the United
States. Even this little island has felt the effects of a changed emigration

7

policy, the purchase of St. Thomas, the temporary demand for labor at Panama, and the tariffs, which have now reached a figure of 68 per cent against Saban Spanish lace.

Another factor gravely affecting the women of Saba is the extraordinary disproportion between the number of women and men. The Census of 1932 showed that there were 342 men, 655 women, 233 boys, and 219 girls in the island, the comparative paucity of men being due to the numbers who are earning livings at sea or in the United States.

We were told that the health of the children is satisfactory, as indeed is that of people of all ages in most parts of the island. Many white Sabans live to a great age. There is no malaria and few filarial or other tropical afflictions. The doctor resident on the island in 1933 had discovered no trace of hookworm, although one suspected its presence at Marypoint, where no sanitation existed.

Marypoint: A Degenerate Community

The worst effects of isolation and inbreeding are to be seen in the small village of Marypoint. Here a community of some thirty to forty persons is composed almost entirely of seven families of Sagors, all closely intermarried and interrelated. The land seems fair, the settlement was once quite flourishing and progressive, and a few of the people still possess good physique. Many, however, show evidence of mental and physical degeneration. The whole settlement receives government relief. The diet is miserable, consisting mainly of bananas and sweet potatoes, cassava, and fish. Little effort is made to provide the children with greens or milk on an island where vegetables grow in profusion and goats are numerous. The people have even lost their former knowledge of baking, and they carry bread, biscuit, and condensed milk from Bottom by "head" (Figs. 41, 42). The state of this white settlement seems to offer two lessons. Situated as it is at a height of about 1000 feet and exposed to constant sea breezes, it indicates, when compared with the other cliff villages, that isolation and inbreeding can be as potent influences upon white settlement as is climatic control. The fate of this small community carries a warning to temperate countries against the efforts of company promoters to establish small white communities in isolated tropical regions.

Education

Owing to isolation, the mixing of races, and the time spent in teaching the Dutch language, most of the children in both the government and parochial schools use books of a standard one year lower than that of the corresponding English or American grades. It is significant, however, that in the one almost wholly white school—the government school at Windwardside—the children are capable of working to the corresponding

English grade. As regards the relative ability of white and colored children, most of the teachers supported the evidence secured in Jamaica and the Cayman Islands by the Carnegie Institution and published in "Race Crossing in Jamaica." [30] The whites excel in mathematics and in other subjects requiring judgment, the blacks in music and rhythm; the mulattoes include a few children of high ability, but on the whole their children appear to be inferior to those of either parent race. We were very favorably impressed by the white children and by the standards of the government school at Windwardside, which was conducted by a head mistress of English descent, born on the tropical island of St. Martin and trained in the Netherlands. The children were alert, well-dressed, and clean, although they lacked the rosy cheeks that impressed earlier visitors. Allowance must be made for the fact that we visited the island at a time when diet had been poor for a considerable period owing to a long, dry season preceded by a disastrous hurricane.

Increasing "Negrodation" of Saba

As regards the future, Saba, in spite of its large proportion of whites, is clearly turning colored, as are almost all the islands and borderlands of the Caribbean. No matter how greatly the altitude or the trade winds may mitigate tropical disadvantages in favor of white settlers, the whites cannot compete with the prolific families of the negro, whose men, women, and children all engage in manual work (Fig. 38). The negroes possess greater immunity from tropical diseases, they are prepared to accept a lower standard of life, and scientific medicine is improving their vitality.

The drift in Saba is clearly shown by recent figures. In the three years 1930-1932 there were 32 white births to 78 colored, while white deaths numbered 34 and negro only 42. Exact figures of the total white and colored populations are not obtainable, but it may be estimated that the 1449 people can be roughly divided into equal numbers of colored and white. The schools give evidence of the same process. In the five schools of the island we counted 100 white to 110 colored children, but the proportion of colored was far higher in the younger than in the older grades (Figs. 39, 40). Furthermore, scientific birth control has made its appearance, and this, together with the long absences of the males, must react against the white population.

From many points of view this "negrodation" of Saba is a deplorable thing—the passing of the supremacy of a high-grade, kindly people to a less advanced race. Allowance must be made for the comparatively recent liberation of the negro, but at present his disregard of sanitation, his dirt and carelessness, his miserable cabins, and his neglect of the good "white" houses that he so frequently occupies in Bottom contrast sadly with the standards of the people he will almost certainly supplant.

Conclusions Regarding Saba

Saba offers several lessons to the student of settlement. In the first place, the history of the island indicates the complexity of factors governing white settlement in the tropics. Second, it appears that northern whites can retain a fair standard for generations in the trade-wind tropics if the location is free from the worst forms of tropical disease, if the economic return is adequate, and if the community is prepared to undertake hard, physical work. Third, it seems that even when a north-European working community maintains itself for a long period against a tropical climate, diseases, isolation, and inbreeding, it must inevitably fall before the economic competition of a colored people who are prepared to accept a lower standard of life.

The German Peasants of Jamaica [31]

In certain remote country districts of Jamaica, particularly at Seaford in Westmoreland, Germans, who have survived since 1834-1835, constitute a particularly interesting group among the white communities of the island. In the Seaford area "there are still some fifty or more pure white families, and altogether approximately 500 pure whites of German descent." Unfortunately, I did not obtain, while in Jamaica, climatic statistics for Seaford, but it seems from the general statistics of the island that the mean annual temperature probably exceeds 77° and that the rainfall is heavy (about 80 in.) as throughout the western part of the island. Considering that the Germans were planted in fairly low country with an enervating climate, which allowed of no very intense physical labor, and that they were afflicted by malaria and hookworm, the conditions were very severe.

The Germans settled in Jamaica soon after the abolition of negro slavery in August, 1834. It was the hope of the government to combat the economic losses by bringing in European peasant workers who might introduce new methods and new cultivations (such as the vine), influence the freed negroes favorably, and, although the legislature was tactfully silent on the subject, provide cheap white labor. The first German emigrants were enrolled by one Lemonius, who told the towns of the Hanover and Weser districts wonderful tales of the prosperity and riches of Jamaica. Unfortunately the emigrants whom he secured were artisans and largely unsuitable. The first shipload of Germans reached Kingston in December, 1834, and were terribly disillusioned. Many perished on the journey from Kingston to Cornwall, and after they settled down fevers were rampant, especially among the women. Although Lord Seaford had generously placed the land at their disposal free of charge, it proved to be unhealthful and economically isolated, as there were no "usable communications" with the neighboring towns. The sale of products was impossible, and the peasants were unable to communicate

with their fellow Germans settled in Kingston. In such circumstances
the colonists could make no headway, and, although from 1000 to 1500
Germans came to Jamaica, the number of pure whites declined partly
by absorption in the general negro population and partly through emigration to the United States. Dr. Wahrhold Drascher gives the following
statistics: [31a]

	1836	1838	1839	1840	1841	1930
Ground under cultivation (acres)	...	119	131	140	145	1000
Number of inhabitants	262	132	144	110	107	500
Births	...	4	6	3	3	...
Deaths	...	46	16	10	12	...

Fortunately the German people were more mindful of these tropical
exiles than were the British or Jamaican governments. In 1879 Father
Sauer, a Tyrolese, came to the district, converted the majority of settlers
to Roman Catholicism, reported their distressed condition, and, when
the region was visited by violent hurricanes and earthquakes, obtained
help from Germany. Later there came a decided improvement with the
growth of the banana industry and the construction of a network of
good roads.

Descriptions of the German community as it is today are not unfavorable. Davenport and Steggerda state that most of the existing German
planters of Seaford own their own land and are in the main thrifty and
prosperous. They have completely lost their language. Very little race
mixture is practiced, but, owing to the scarcity of whites, there is much
consanguineous marriage.[32] "It is said that 'all could join hands in relation some way.' The majority of the Seaford people are dominated by
great caution. The families seem contented and quite self-centered. . . .
The peasants all work hard at agriculture. . . . No one seems to have
any definite idea of time. . . . One teacher has taught in the community
for 26 years, and states that the White children have a very bad temper
when compared with the Blacks. It is his experience that the White
children seem to learn more easily than the colored ones."[33] A number
of these points are typical of an extremely isolated community, and there
is no indication that the tropical climate is to blame.

A Jamaican doctor who knows the German communities well states
that even today the settlements are very isolated and have no national
spirit. The British government gives these whites no special medical or
educational facilities, even though hookworm and typhoid are very
severe. Malaria is not a menace, however, as the settlements are at an
elevation of about 1000 feet. The people of Cave Valley hold more land
and are of a better type than the other settlers. In spite of living from
hand to mouth and of contact with a generally inferior population, the
Germans are more reliable, more industrious, better housed, and on a
higher economic level than their negro neighbors.

It is also interesting to note that, although the Carnegie publication
"Race Crossing in Jamaica" gives no detailed figures for the German

community at Seaford, it reaches the general conclusion that in spite of residence in the tropics the whites of Jamaica and the Cayman Islands have greater mental capacities than the blacks, while the mulattoes and other persons of mixed blood are, with some outstanding exceptions, below the standard of either race.

On the whole we may say that, although the German communities in the Seaford region have deteriorated as a result of negro competition and will inevitably be absorbed by the negro population, they have survived almost overwhelming geographical and economic difficulties for more than a hundred years. All questions of climate aside, and though isolation, disease, and negro competition might well have destroyed these white settlements almost immediately, several of the communities still exist. We can agree with Dr. Drascher that "even in circumstances of great difficulty of climate and otherwise, within the tropical zone the German is able to persist for at least a number of generations." [34] This seems a moderate claim, yet it flatly contradicts popular beliefs as to the possibility of survival of the northern white in the tropics.

THE FRENCH PEASANTS OF ST. THOMAS, AMERICAN VIRGIN ISLANDS [35]

About 900 peasants of French descent in the island of St. Thomas deserve examination, partly because they comprise two communities that show important differences in type and partly because they have been in the tropics for many years.

St. Thomas is a small island, volcanic and mountainous, situated some forty miles east of Puerto Rico, in latitude 18.20° N. The climate is typical of the trade-wind zone. The annual temperature of the capital, Charlotte Amalie, which is situated on the lee side of the island, is about 81° and the rainfall 38 inches. The north coast, although only a couple of miles across the range, enjoys a heavier rainfall and the cooling effects of the trades.

St. Thomas contains two French settlements. Their origin is clouded in mystery, but it is believed from their language and customs that both groups are of Norman origin. Possibly their ancestors came from France to the French island of St. Bartholomew some time after 1685 and colonized two areas, Gustavia in the west and Lorient in the east of that island. Here they seem to have developed different occupations and characteristics, the Gustavians becoming fishermen and leading a village life, while the people of Lorient formed a farming class. Both groups speak a French patois together with some English. Both are devout Catholics with a great love of France.

The French always neglected St. Bartholomew, and the island remained in a chaotic state owing to the misrule of civil and religious officials. Emigration to the then Danish island of St. Thomas began about 1860, and it appears that the sufferings caused by the Franco-Prussian War led to a large exodus about 1870. It is certain that the two

French groups have lived in St. Thomas for some sixty years, and their ancestors probably inhabited the tropical island of St. Bartholomew for generations.

The first interesting point one notices in St. Thomas is that the French settlers are almost all pure white and that there has been very little miscegenation. The second important feature is the difference between the two settlements. The "northsiders" engage in agriculture on the steep and stony trade-wind slopes. In spite of negro competition they form the "largest single farming class" in the island and produce many of the bananas, pineapples, and vegetables sold in the market. The second group consists of village fisherfolk. They number some 550 and inhabit a village known as Carenage on the outskirts of Charlotte Amalie (Figs. 44, 45). To their vocation these people owe the general and much disliked nickname of Chacha, which comes from a small and insignificant fish.

As a whole the Chachas look very poor, anemic, and unhealthy (Figs. 43, 46); the northsiders are taller, heavier, and less poor and sickly than the Carenage people, with whom they seldom mix. A close study of the settlements, in order to decide whether the differences are due to race, inbreeding, occupation, diet, or the trade winds, might yield valuable results. Both groups look as if they suffer from hookworm, owing to careless sanitary habits and the failure to wear shoes. Both suffer from the vice of hoarding money and live in the most miserable cabins in order to avoid taxation. In both inbreeding has undoubtedly had bad effects. The northside community has, however, reached the higher standard. Lubin Pickwood notes that the height of the northsiders averages some 5 feet, 10 inches, and their weight 170 pounds, as compared with the 5 feet, 5 inches, and 150 pounds averaged by the people of Carenage. He continues: "Because the Northsiders are farmers and have fresh vegetables around them, they are able to have a more balanced diet." They are also able to catch enough fish for sale and for their own consumption. "Thus they are robust and healthy, and, since they do not specialise in loud colors to quite the same extent as the Gustavians, they never seem so queer" [36] (Fig. 47). They buy land, and some own "great tracts"—indeed, to such an extent that they parcel out land to various members of the group.

Recent developments of considerable importance are, first, the rise of a racial feeling against the negro, which is shown particularly by the Carenage fishermen, and second, the wealth acquired by some of the Chachas under prohibition. Local feeling is rising against this section of an American community that openly boasts of its affection for France, keeps aloof from the rest of the populace, and pays practically no taxes, notwithstanding the fact that it has secured considerable poor relief, a health clinic, and substantial sums from the liquor trade. On the whole we can sympathize with the negro population of St. Thomas, for the anemic, sickly-looking Chachas, particularly those of the miserable village of Carenage, are not an alluring folk. Nevertheless, several observers have written favorably of the northsiders, and we must give considerable weight to what the Chachas of St. Thomas have achieved. It is no mean feat for them to have kept their blood white and to have held their own in open competition with the negroes under a peasant economy that has given the whites no advantage.

Shaw closes his account of these people by the following favorable summary: "In spite of an environment endowed with few economic opportunities, the industry, patience and thrift of the Chachas enable them to make a modest living." This is so even in the harsh farming environment of the windward mountain sides where they have had to build terraces.

If all the people of St. Thomas were as industrious as the French, the island resources would yield to a maximum; if the colored people were as thrifty as the Chachas, fewer favors would be asked of a paternal government; if the sex morality of the Negroes were as strict as that of the French, there would be less illegitimacy and a smaller percentage of mixed population. In short, the Chachas afford a constructive example to both natives and outsiders. They have made a living in a hard environment by means of pluck and hard work and with little help from outside; and they have maintained rigid sex standards and racial purity in the tropics—a task some believe impossible.[37]

SOME GROUPS OF BRITISH DESCENT

The whites of St. Martin, Saba, St. Thomas, and Jamaica were so interesting that I was sorry that lack of time prevented an examination of other Caribbean survivals. It would have been helpful to have seen the French communities in St. Bartholomew and the white groups in the Bahamas, Cayman Islands, Old Providence, Utila, Grenada, and Barbados, all of which are said to be of British descent. Some days were spent, however, in St. Kitts, which still contains a few white peasants and some upper-class families with an experience of several generations of tropical settlement. A visit was also paid to Curaçao and Bonaire in the southern Caribbean, where Portuguese and Dutch whites have been settled for many years. Throughout the journey we encountered administrators, doctors, and well-educated and informed whites from many of the most important islands.

It is a reflection on the British authorities and rule in the West Indies that they claim to possess very little information on the white settlers. There is little doubt, however, that the British home and local governments, and even the old white families, are abandoning the hopeless struggle against a negroid population whose numbers become more overwhelming each year. In almost every island the blacks are rising to the leading positions in all walks of life. They are beginning to command majorities in legislatures such as that of Jamaica, and the governors sent from England tend more and more to be negrophiles. In such circumstances it is small wonder that the British, who in the past either neglected their white peasantry, as in Jamaica, or maltreated them, as

FIG. 44—Village of Carenage, inhabited by French whites, St. Thomas, Virgin Islands. (U. S. government photograph.)

FIG. 45—House in Carenage. (U. S. government photograph.)

FIG. 46—French whites, village of Carenage, St. Thomas, Virgin Islands. (U. S. government photograph.)

FIG. 47—Typical French family, "Northside," St. Thomas. (U. S. government photograph.)

in Barbados, should today place the survivors on precisely the same basis as the negro and afford them no special attention in such matters as education, sanitation, and health. We found that the authorities in St. Kitts had no information on the small body of white peasantry remaining. In reply to inquiries the administrator of Grenada wrote that "there are no reports or publications dealing with white settlement." [38] The government of Barbados answered that it had access to some historical information but no details of the present state of descendants of the so-called "Red Legs." [39]

How different is the scientific outlook of the Americans! The Chacha settlements in St. Thomas are no advertisement for the United States, yet the administrator, who was absent from the island at the time of our visit, forwarded Lubin Pickwood's valuable account of the French settlers, illustrated by excellent photographs. Thus we must rely primarily on American researches in the Caribbean for the little information procurable.[40]

Grand Cayman Island

One of the best studies of a white group in the British West Indies is Davenport and Steggerda's account of Grand Cayman Islands, a work that we supplemented by a number of interviews with Cayman Island officials and Cayman islanders in Jamaica. The islands form a small dependency of Jamaica and lie some 300 miles northwest of that island in latitude 19.44° N. Davenport states that the population numbers about 5000, 2000 of whom are white, 2000 brown, and 1000 black. The blacks are the result of the slave days; the whites are descendants of shipwrecked mariners and possibly of the old buccaneers. The islands were never occupied by Spain, being settled by British from Jamaica. We were told that this colonization took place under land inducements about 200 years ago. Whatever may be the history of the people, the fine Cayman islanders whom we interviewed in Jamaica came from families who had been resident in the tropics for several generations.

Davenport states [41] that the whites are chiefly mariners and shipbuilders. They do not take advantage of the good agricultural possibilities but work in the Gulf ports of the United States, sail on deep-sea voyages, or act as woodcutters, farm hands, and clerks in Nicaragua and Honduras. The women do not labor in the fields, although they undertake housework. The diet consists mainly of the starchy breadfruit and yams and plantains—periodical hurricanes have a devastating effect on the supply—and of turtle meat and fresh fish. Vegetables are chiefly canned and are imported from America. "Naseberries and the wild mango and plums grow very luxuriantly. These fruits form a great part of the diet of the natives." [42] The main drink is cocoa. There is only one liquor shop on Grand Cayman Island, and there is very little alcoholic excess. In their attitude toward the sanctity of marriage, the long absences of the husbands at sea, and the inbreeding in the various villages, the Grand Cayman people seem to resemble Sabans. Davenport, however, considers that "the effects of inbreeding are not markedly injurious, though cases of feeble-mindedness and insanity occur." He writes of the white Cayman islanders: "Their physique is of the best. They are tall and well built . . . in the main very healthy." [43] So high, indeed, is the physical standard of these whites that the Carnegie survey especially noted that it raised the general standard of the Jamaican whites. The birth rate, 30.4 per cent (1917-26), and the death rate, 9.7 per cent (1917-26), seem very favorable. Yet, except for the fact that the trade winds sweep across the low-lying island, one cannot find any climatic conditions that might account for the superiority of these tropical islanders. The annual temperature is about 80° (with a range of some 20°), which makes the conditions definitely tropical, and the annual rainfall is about 60 inches. The islanders suffer an annual plague of mosquitoes, which teem from May until October, but there is little malaria fortunately. The houses are large, well-painted, and built on poles so as to let the air circulate beneath. They are well kept and screened against mosquitoes, although the poorer people have to resort to the burning of smoke pots outside the doors.

We were informed by educationists in Jamaica that the Cayman islanders possess both good physique and good intelligence. A primary school system was not established until 1928, but by 1933 the standard was only a year behind that of the best Jamaican schools. One Cayman islander came fourth amongst 1600 Cayman and Jamaican children in a general examination set on the Jamaican syllabus. Another Cayman Island white of the third generation in the tropics recently won a Rhodes Scholarship from Jamaica and, after obtaining his degree in Oxford, secured a place in the British Civil Service in Burma.

On the whole, one is inclined to attribute the high quality of the Cayman islanders to factors of health and diet, which should certainly be analyzed, and to their satisfactory standards and energetic mode of life. As in Saba, sea industries have produced reasonable prosperity and have maintained the whites above the negro basis. [44]

The Red Legs of Barbados

In Chapter III we traced the appalling history of the white British peasantry of Barbados and other islands. In spite of this disgraceful chronicle some groups in St. Kitts, Barbados, and Grenada still survive. The only fair-sized community is that in Barbados, where scientific information is obtainable as the International Health Board of the Rockefeller Foundation has done some work there.

Barbados is situated in latitude 13° N., but the tropical climate is modified by the fact that the island lies in the open ocean to the northeast of the chain of the West Indies and is so low-lying that it is swept throughout its area by the trade winds, which have an average velocity of about ten miles per hour.

Chapter III indicated that the population of Barbados, which consisted of 37,200 whites and 6000 blacks in 1643, had changed by 1916 to 13,500 whites and 167,016 blacks and browns. We also saw how war, disease, ill-treatment, the exhaustion of the soil, the plantation system, a one-crop industry, and the introduction of the negro ruined a well-established white yeomanry. The survivors of this population of small white farmers were riddled by the hookworm, which the negro introduced,[45] and fell into the usual vicious circle of poverty and disease. Instead of advocating assistance for their unfortunate fellow whites and fellow Britishers, English visitors to the West Indies seem to have vied with one another in hurling abuse at them. The following bitter account, attributed to H. N. Coleridge (1825), is typical:

In consequence of the large white population in Barbados there exists a class of people which I did not meet with in any other of the islands. By the laws of the colony every estate is obliged to maintain a certain number of whites in proportion to its extent. These men are called the Tenantry, and have an indefeasible interest for their lives in a house and garden upon the respective plantations. They owe no fealty to the landlord, make him no acknowledgment, and entertain no kind of gratitude towards him. The militia is principally composed of these persons, and with the exception of that service, the greatest part of them live in a state of complete idleness, and are usually ignorant and debauched to the last degree. They will often walk half over the island to demand alms, and if you question them about their mode of life and habits of daily labor, they stare in your face as if they were actually unable to comprehend the meaning of your discourse. The women who will work at all, find employment in washing and mending the clothes of the negros, and it is notorious, that in many cases whole families of these free whites depend for their subsistence on the charity of slaves. Yet they are as proud as Lucifer himself, and in virtue of their freckled ditchwater faces consider themselves on a level with every gentleman in the island.[46]

A century later G. P. Paul explained this condemnation in terms of modern science.[47] Paul traces the way in which the negroes replaced the early and energetic white farmers and describes the climate, under which, owing to the sea breezes, "white people can live for years, even for a lifetime . . . without feeling the ill-effects of the tropics."[48] At the time when Paul wrote there was no malaria, since there were no anopheles because of the little permanent water, the extensive cultivation of the soil, and a larvae-eating fish. He showed, however, that an enormous percentage of the population was riddled with hookworm and that the whites, particularly the white peasants of the Scotland area, were bearing the brunt of the disease. Of 4240 houses visited 2132 had no sanitary conveniences. Some of the schools had no privies, and many people were using water from polluted wells. As might be expected, the death rate, 19.2, and the infant mortality rate, 19.3, were still high, although the British government had improved the situation in this regard. The incidence of hookworm remained very high and indicated that the whites suffered particularly. From the racial standpoint the figures showed that 65 per cent of the whites were affected, as against 36 per cent of the blacks and 33 per cent of the browns. Conditions were particularly serious in the parishes of St. Andrew, St. Joseph, St. Thomas, and St. John (the Scotland area) where soil conditions favored the hookworm. In this region some 25,000 persons were affected, the incidence in St. Thomas reaching 69.1 per cent. Paul states that the effects of the disease were clearly seen in profound anemia, emaciation, and faulty growth. He writes that all ages and sexes were diseased, and "the negro, although not showing the effects, constitutes a menace." [49] Paul's account of the results of the disease explains the prescientific visitors' accounts of the poor-white peasantry. "All these poor whites presented signs of marked anaemia by the skin, lips, tongue and conjunctival shortness of breath, palpitation of the heart, giddiness and pain in the pit of the stomach. Pot belly and dwarfism were common symptoms. It may be truly stated that this class of the population is sorely affected by the ravages of the hookworm disease." [50]

It would be interesting to know how far the British administration in Barbados has acted on this report. Certainly, it does not appear from the Colonial Secretary's letter of January 17, 1935, that anything special has been done for the poor whites, who are deserving of commendation rather than blame. Driven into a corner of a tropical island by the low living standards and the diseases of the negro and riddled with his ailments, some thousands of them have nevertheless managed to keep their white blood pure and to make a living in spite of the vicious circle of poverty and disease. The Dutch health work in St. Martin indicates to what an extent these poor-white peasants can be raised, and it is a grave reflection on the Empire if the British are not providing scientific aid.

The Bay Islands and Old Providence Island

During 1933 information was received on two little-known but interesting white groups. Dr. T. Molloy, a Rockefeller physician stationed in Central America, gave details of a white settlement in Utila, one of the Bay Islands owned by the Republic of Honduras. Though they are citizens of the republic, these people are English-speaking and largely descended from old British families—Hendersons, Woodwards, and Warrens. They appear to resemble the sea groups in the Caymans and Saba, as they are sturdy and hard-working, possess fine physiques, and do not suffer severely from malaria and hookworm. One of their main occupations is shipbuilding. Their mentality is fair considering the isolation, and they do not seem to have degenerated through inbreeding.

A further and important account of this community was given by Peter Keenagh in the London *Times* (Jan. 16, 1937).[51] Keenagh states that the Bay Islands are situated some forty miles off the tropical north coast of Spanish Honduras. The people are of British ancestry, the descendants of British pirates and mutineers who took refuge among the islands in the seventeenth and eighteenth centuries. The islands were ceded to Honduras in 1859, but English is still the only language spoken fluently. The population numbers about 4000, mainly centered in the three principal islands of Roatan, Guanaja (or Bonacca), and Utila. About 50 per cent are whites, and the names Kirkconnell, Cooper, Eden, McNab, Bodden, and Warren cover most of the island families. The islanders are proud and very strict in their racial prejudices. There is practically no intermarriage, and the people look down upon the mixed stock of the main. The large islands are low and very fertile, and the communities are self-sufficing and well arranged. The men are magnificent seamen and build their own schooners, most of which are communal possessions. They voyage to Tampa and New Orleans selling bananas and copra. On the islands agriculture is the main industry, the proceeds including pineapples, cocoanuts, and guavas. The islanders have done much gun-running for the revolutions in Central America. The relations with the Honduran government are not cordial, and Honduras has made great efforts to destroy the British tradition. The island people are well built and of handsome appearance, although they admit that they are becoming inbred through lack of new blood. There is very little to distinguish the modern generation of islanders from their British counterparts, and almost any of them would pass unnoticed in England. The women have brought in some Spanish blood, but many are of British origin from Belize. As in Saba, the speech is singsong, slurred, and high pitched, with a pronunciation influenced by negro contacts. The singing is very high and sounds almost falsetto.

Dr. Thomas Barbour, Director of the University Museum, Harvard, visited in 1932-1933 the almost unknown communities of Old Providence and St. Andrews Islands in the Caribbean. These islands are now administered by the Republic of Colombia. Dr. Barbour stated that Old Providence contained a population of several thousands who speak English and are very largely white. Many possess the family name of Morgan, from the famous buccaneer who used Old Providence when outfitting the expedition that sacked Panama city in 1671. Dr. Barbour considered that this community of sea-whites was of good type in spite of infection by malaria. The group appears to deserve further investigation.

The Bahamas

In "Civilization and Climate" Professor Ellsworth Huntington gives a gloomy picture of white degeneracy in the Bahama Islands, which he has visited.[52] This he attributes almost wholly to the hot climate. Although the islands have "wonderfully fertile" soil and little malaria or hookworm, the descendants of the American loyalists have declined in physique and in mental activity. Huntington denies that this is due to inbreeding or to diet, although he admits that the monotonous diet may be a factor. The fundamental cause is, in the opinion of the people themselves, a decline in energy due to the climate.

I could not visit the Bahamas and cannot speak with authority. Criticisms have, however, been leveled at Huntington's conclusions, and other observers have attributed the degeneracy to poor or exhausted soils, isolation (which has led to inbreeding and hereditary diseases in small isolated communities), the presence of colored peoples, and monotonous diet. From observations in other West Indian islands it may be concluded that all these factors are important but that hot climate has also contributed to the decline.[53]

Some Conclusions

In this chapter we have examined a considerable number of communities of northern and Mediterranean whites who have lived for generations in the moderate tropics of the Caribbean. The study has made it clear that most white races of European ancestry can survive for centuries against appalling difficulties in regions where the annual temperature is from 75° to 80° and where the rainfall is sufficient without being of the heavy equatorial type. It further appears that the whites do best in, and deliberately seek, regions of steady air movements, such as the trades. The tropical climate per se may be deleterious, but it is evident that many European races and communities can acclimatize, at any rate to an extent that enables them to survive its effects. Other controls that have been noted are disease, isolation, the standard of living or comfort, and the influence of colored races of a lower economic or social status. Practically all the communities discussed have survived isolation, inbreeding, and decimating diseases, but, with the exception of the Spanish populations of Cuba and Puerto Rico, they cannot stand against the diseases and economic standards of the negro and are being gradually absorbed. In some instances governmental action might break the vicious circle of disease and poverty and elevate the whites, as the Dutch have done in St. Martin, but it seems that nothing can ultimately prevent the complete absorption of these numerically inferior groups. This being so, no white government should direct emigration to the Caribbean, which is clearly destined to become a negro region. The conditions of these people will, no doubt, continue to improve, but for generations they will suffer from disease and from comparatively low standards of life.

CHAPTER VIII

THE ARID AND WET-DRY TROPICS: I. TROPICAL AUSTRALIA

White settlers, as we have seen (Chapter VI), have made remarkable progress in a favorable part of the Queensland tropics. The present chapter will discuss the potentialities of the rest of tropical Australia, which comprises arid or wet-dry monsoonal regions.[1] There is little European settlement in similar parts of the other continents, and an analysis of the problems faced by white Australians will explain many of the difficulties confronting white races in similar tropical lands.

THE ARID REGIONS

The arid regions of tropical Australia are shown in Figure 5. Taylor estimates that they embrace as much as 600,000 square miles, but we can at once dismiss this zone as holding little prospect for close white settlement. Throughout most of the division the rainfall (10 to 20 in.) is low and unreliable and the evaporation is immense (Figs. 5, 6, and 7). Boulia in southwestern Queensland has an evaporation of 124 inches, and everywhere the evaporation probably exceeds 100 inches.[2] Professor J. A. Prescott's map (Fig. 16) gives an excellent idea of the surface conditions, which consist very largely of sandhills and desert steppe. Taylor describes the Great Sandy Desert of Western Australia as a land of fixed dunes, extending for the most part east and west, 30 to 50 feet in height and numbering 3 or 4 to the mile. These dunes "are fixed by a sparse growth of gums, mulgas, and above all by the so-called 'Spinifex' (*Triodia irritans*) which is a sparse tussock grass growing in clumps up to 10 feet across and several feet high." [3] Thick belts of mulga occur in places, and ground water can often be found at depths of about 50 feet. Intermingled with the true desert are areas of semi-desert of some pastoral value, particularly where the arid country merges into savana and Mitchell-grass lands in the northeast, north, and west (Fig. 16).

The semiarid regions carry an acacia association (mulga, myall, gidgee) and shrub steppe (salt bush and blue bush) and can support stock in good years, although the droughts are so severe that the cattle herds rarely increase. There is practically no hope of any close white settlement of a permanent nature, except by developing the Mitchell-grass areas, like the Barkly Tableland, under seasonal crops such as millet. Mining may produce temporary settlements in a few places, but mining is a "robber industry," and mining towns in arid country do not maintain permanent close settlement after the exhaustion of the mines.

In crossing this arid region from south to north and back in 1932 I was strongly impressed by the reactions of the white settlers to a hard and isolated tropical environment. In most cases the housing was utterly unsuited to the fierce summer temperatures, and only the most hardy of white women could survive. The deteriorating influence of the semicivilized aborigine, and more particularly that of his lubra, was greatly in evidence.

Strenuous efforts have been made to develop this region for more than seventy years. Explorers and pastoralists penetrated it in the sixties. The overland telegraph from Adelaide to Darwin crossed it in 1872. Several stock routes, equipped with wells, have been forced through. Railways touch its northern, eastern, southern, and western boundaries at Birdum, Cloncurry, Alice Springs, and Marble Bar. No people could have made more heroic efforts at development than the Australian explorers and pastoralists. Miss Bessie Threadgill has summed up the story in a charming and scientific study:

Australia . . . lost its mystery, but never its caprice. Trigonometrical stations might take the place of the explorer's solitary cairn of stones; the survey camp, his marked tree. Cattle might pasture on the downs and grass land he had so hardly rescued from a scrubby wilderness; telegraph and railroad track might span his creek bed or rotten alluvial plain, but Australia's whimsical changefulness remained. The history . . . is a record of misinterpretations, due to seasonal differences of temperature and rainfall; and to each newcomer the interior will show a different face, scorching the lives of some in angry sacrifice to its implacability, beckoning others smilingly through its most favoured glens and pastures to an eternal Wingilpin.[4]

Translated into the hard terms of scientific geography the eternal truth is this: the arid country of the Australian tropics is totally unsuited to the intensive settlement of any human race.

The Wet-Dry Regions or Regions of Winter Drought

The struggle to develop the north Australian monsoonal regions of winter drought is one of the most stirring epics in the history of efforts by white races to develop the tropics. More than this, the story teaches Australia and the outside world many highly important lessons and, not least, the folly of attempting to occupy an unknown country without previously making a scientific survey.

History

There is no room to trace in detail the romantic history of the exploration and prescientific invasion of the north Australian tropics, but we may outline the main events. The first four decades of the nineteenth century saw the examination of the coast line and the discovery of the northern harbors and rivers by Flinders, King, and Wykeham, whose discoveries led to the establishment of British "holding stations" at Melville Island, Raffles Bay, and Port Essington (1824-

Fig. 48—Road with wire netting which makes it possible to drive cattle over sandy country, near Shark Bay, Western Australia.

Fig. 49—Mule team bringing wool into Broome, Western Australia.

Fig. 50—Camel team from a station 150 miles in the interior delivering a load of wool at Carnarvon, Western Australia.

These figures were furnished by courtesy of Mr. Malcolm Uren, Western Australia Newspapers, Ltd.

Figs. 51 and 52—Homesteads in North West Division, Western Australia. (Courtesy of Western Australian Government Printing Office, Mr. F. W. Simpson, Government Printer.)
Fig. 53—A pearler's house, Broome, Western Australia. (Courtesy of Mr. Malcolm Uren, Western Australian Newspapers, Ltd.)

1849). The four decades 1830 to 1870 saw the exploration of the coast lands and interior by such men as Sir George Grey, Alexander Forrest, and above all John McDouall Stuart, who pioneered the first practical route from the south coast of the continent to the Northern Territory.[5] The work of these explorers was more than a picture of "impossibly hairy men climbing impossibly purple boulders." It was, in many cases, a record of careful scientific examination conducted under circumstances of great peril and difficulty. Yet, over and over again, the accounts of the explorers were colored by the time of year and by good or bad seasons. Stuart, for example, stated that the Northern Territory would become "one of the finest colonies under the Crown suitable for the growth of any and everything." [6] Report after report reflected northern Australia's "whimsical changefulness."

After the explorers, and sometimes before them, came the cattle-men. The squatting invasion of tropical Australia rolled forward in three great streams. The first occupied northwestern Queensland in the sixties and threatened to penetrate the north-central regions, now known as the Northern Territory. The pressure of these Queensland squatters was so severe that as early as 1861 the British government extended the northwestern boundary of Queensland to the 138th meridian. Queensland could then have gained the whole Northern Territory, but she wisely pointed out that Brisbane could not ad-minister so distant a dependency.

The second invasion came from South Australia. Here the squatters were suffering from land hunger and demanded the Northern Terri-tory as a reward for Stuart's work and on the supposition that the huge region could be developed by a northerly penetration along Stuart's route. Heedless of the failure of the early British stations, South Australian fools rushed in where Queensland angels feared to tread. In 1863 the British government, which was anxious to avoid the expense of managing another rush of squatters or a new tropical dependency, gave the weak but ambitious colony the whole of the Northern Terri-tory—an area of 523,000 square miles.

A third stream from the south developed the northern part of Western Australia at a slightly later date. From 1858 to 1861 the explorer F. T. Gregory reported good pastoral country on the Gascoyne, Fortescue, and Ashburton rivers, and pastoralists opened up the region near the tropics. Attempts to occupy the more northerly monsoonal country were not successful until the late seventies and early eighties, when Alexander and John Forrest discovered fine pastoral land and the Kimberley district was proclaimed. The new district attracted settlers from all parts of Australia. Pastoralists spread rapidly, and by 1883 millions of acres had been leased.[7]

Of the three regions thus placed under colonial governments north-western Queensland with its comparatively low rainfall (Figs. 7 and

8

15) offers little hope of close settlement, although there is some good cattle country. Brigden and Wynne Williams estimate that tropical Queensland contains 6,350,906 sheep and 2,297,177 cattle. The Barkly Tableland is a promising pastoral region. The Queensland section is said to contain the best cattle-carrying country of the whole northern littoral, and much of the region between the Great Artesian Basin and the Queensland highlands is fine country for merino sheep. Pastoral pursuits, however, cannot produce close settlement and from this aspect the potentialities of tropical Western Australia and the Northern Territory only deserve close consideration.

Western Australia

Tropical Western Australia contains 364,000 square miles (Fig. 15). The summer rains influence the whole region, but a very large part must be classed with the arid lands. "The topographical features of Western Australia have been classified as (1) the Coastal Plain; (2) the Hill Ranges, and (3) the Interior Plateau."[8] In general, the plateau lies at an altitude of 1000 to 1500 feet. Mount Hann in the north is 2800 feet in elevation, and the country to the south of the Fortescue River reaches 4000 feet. The altitude, however, has little influence on the rainfall. Precipitation declines steadily southwards, and, whereas the Kimberley highlands receive some 30 inches, Mount Brine near the tropics receives only 10 inches, in spite of an altitude of 4000 feet. Andrews' map (Fig. 7) illustrates the high variability of the rainfall, and the region is also one of high evaporation.[9] Statistics for Wyndham and Roebourne (Table VII) show that the whole region suffers from winter droughts. Despeissis gives a favorable account of the northern soils, which he supports with a number of analyses.[10] The surface comprises a succession of prairie lands intersected at distances by the beds of rivers and watercourses, a number of which run for only a few months of the year. Immense plains extend between the seaboard and ranges that rise about 60 to 100 miles from the coast. The soil on the whole consists of deep alluvial deposits, and Despeissis considers that it is physically and chemically suitable for the raising of some tropical crops. The vegetation consists of a small area of sclerophyll forest in the north. This merges into savana woodland, which passes through savana and Mitchell-grass downs into desert. West of the desert another region of Mitchell-grass downs with some arid vegetation runs inland from the coast (Fig. 16).

The existing industries are the pasturing of cattle and sheep (Figs. 9 and 10). Sheep are comparatively few and are confined by climate to the south. There is a little mining, but sea industries hold possibilities. Pearling is important at such centers as Broome.

Potentialities of the Region

Despeissis had not seen the northern Kimberleys but believed from conversations with explorers that the elevated hinterland offered in the tropics a salubrious home for whites. He considered that white men could engage in most agricultural work as far as the latitude of Broome (18.5°), but from Broome northward malaria and summer climate would prove embarrassing.[11] Although Despeissis refrained from advocating colored labor, he obviously favored the introduction of a plantation system with Mediterranean or colored workers. W. R. Easton, who commanded the Kimberley expedition of 1921, also formed a favorable opinion of the northwest. He stated:

The North Kimberley District is pre-eminently a cattle country, and can best be developed by settlement on those lines. The successful agricultural development of this country rests entirely with capital and labour, and it is not a question as to its suitability for the white race. The climate is not too trying, but until the cost of labour is such as will enable us to grow tropical produce at a price at which we can hope to enter into competition with other countries in the world's markets, there is little hope for success in this line.[12]

Population

Despeissis, writing in 1921 and basing his population figures on the Census of 1911, calculated that the northwest contained some 7000 whites, including about 1000 women. This figure seems excessive, as the Commonwealth Statistician gave the European population as 3122 in 1923 and 3324 in 1933. Despeissis's conclusions on white settlement were not cheerful. He writes:

It is hopeless to expect that the North will be populated by the residents there, and until the South-West produces an overflow of population that province, under present conditions of land settlement, must remain an empty territory, and the longer this state of affairs is allowed to continue the more serious will the situation grow. Unfortunately it is unpleasant to record that a long sojourn in Kimberley tells on the women-folk, and unless they are fortunately enough circumstanced to be able to recuperate pretty frequently in the southern portion of the continent, their health often remains severely affected. The men on the whole stand the climate better, but under the present hard conditions of living there they also require periodical changes to cooler climates. In fairness to the more temperate North-West, it must be recognised that the conditions are not so severe there to the white population, particularly on the higher tableland away from the coast.[13]

The Census of 1933 (Table VIII) supports this opinion. The birth rate (1929-33) is considerably lower than the Australian average. The death rate and the infant mortality rate are far more severe.[14]

One can conclude from the foregoing studies of tropical Western Australia that the region is one of considerable pioneering difficulty and possesses a rainfall that seems suitable only for pastoral settlement. North of the tropic there are comparatively few sheep, but the savana country—particularly in the Fitzroy Valley—is one of the most important cattle regions of the continent. In 1927 Western Australia contained 846,735 cattle. Of these 630,281 were in the north and north-west, East Kimberley containing 319,337 and West Kimberley 245,175. Government meat works have operated for many years at Wyndham.

In spite of the value of the Western Australian tropics as a cattle region, the difficulties of the industry, as set out by the Royal Commission of 1928,[15] are very great, and later years have increased the disadvantages. The number of cattle is showing a decline. The stock is deteriorating, and there are grave troubles arising from droughts, isolation, pests, the development of beef chilling, and the lack of markets. Nor do the policies of the Australian nation help the struggling pioneer, who is loaded with tariffs and high costs of wharfage, handling, transport, and freight. A most scandalous instance of government-made difficulties occurred in 1927, when the two Western Australian state ships broke down and an overseas steamer was actually prohibited from helping the isolated people of Wyndham, owing to the Navigation Acts.

The Northern Territory

The tremendous efforts made to develop the Northern Territory make that region the most interesting of the north Australian winter-drought lands to any student of tropical settlement.

The whole region, both arid and monsoonal, covers an area of 523,620 square miles (Fig. 54) of which about 190,000 square miles have more than 20 inches of rain. Figures 6, 7, 15, and 55-57 illustrate the high temperatures and the fundamental control of rainfall. They clearly indicate the variability and winter drought, which with high evaporation have created such grave difficulties for white settlement. Most of the Territory consists of low plateaus that rise to about 1500 feet in Arnhem Land, but the slight elevation has little effect on precipitation. Some of the rivers—the Victoria, Roper, Adelaide, and Daly—are navigable for distances of as much as 100 miles by shadow-draught vessels, but the importance of these streams is greatly diminished by summer floods and winter droughts. Much of the soil has been formed from the breaking down of desert sandstone and has been leached by the heavy seasonal rains (Fig. 58). Tate, H. Y. L. Brown, and other scientists have given very unfavorable opinions of the soils, which have been supported by the failure of many agricultural undertakings conducted with both white and colored labor.[16] In Professor Taylor's words:

In spite of the heavy rainfall, large portions of "Darwinia" are of a somewhat sterile character. This is largely due to two factors. The region is lacking in basic and other rocks which weather to form good soils, and secondly, the long dry hot periods have led to surface formations which are not favorable to luxuriant vegetation. By a process of "sweating" the soluble magnesia, iron and siliceous salts have been transferred to the surface and deposited as magnesite, laterite, and flint (or quartzite) respectively.[17]

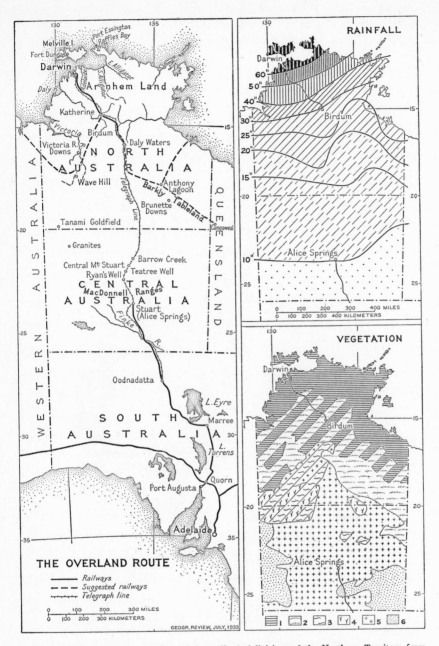

FIG. 54—Maps of North and Central Australia (subdivisions of the Northern Territory from 1926 to 1931). The left-hand map (scale 1: 20,000,000) shows the existing overland route. The upper right-hand map (1: 24,000,000) shows the mean annual rainfall. The lower right-hand map shows the vegetation after Prescott (see Fig. 16 in the present volume). Key: 1, savana wood-land; 2, savana and Mitchell grass; 3, mallee and sclerophyll woodland; 4, heath and sclerophyll scrub; 5 acacia semidesert and shrub steppe; 6, sand hills with desert grass.

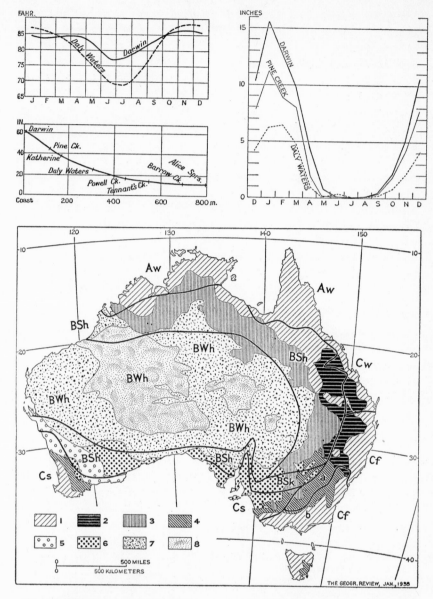

FIG. 55—Temperatures at two stations in the Northern Territory, Australia (after Griffith Taylor, The Australian Environment, p. 73).

FIG. 56—Relation of rainfall in the Northern Territory to distance from the coast (after Taylor, op. cit., p. 69).

FIG. 57—The monthly distribution of rainfall at three localities in the Northern Territory (after Taylor, op. cit., p. 71).

FIG. 58—The major soil divisions of Australia, after Prescott (scale: 1:40,000,000). Key: 1, podsol; 2, black earth; 3, gray earth; 4, chestnut earth; 5, very lateritic; 6, mallee; 7, desert-steppe; 8, dune. Laterites are widespread north of 20° S. latitude. Climatic regions, after Köppen (see Köppen-Geiger: Handbuch der Klimatologie, Band IV, Teil S, p. S 76), are added for comparison.

The great coastal flood plains of the Adelaide and the Alligator Rivers appear to contain fine black soil, but even this soil is shown by analysis to lack potash, while the necessity of drainage in summer and irrigation in winter would make agricultural settlement expensive and difficult.[18] Vegetation is controlled by the winter drought of five to seven months a year. There is no tropical rain forest (Fig. 16) except in the beds of creeks. The semidesert vegetation passes northwards through savana and Mitchell-grass downs to a savana woodland, where in most places the tree growth is sparse.

At the time of the Census of 1933 the population numbered 4870, exclusive of some 19,500 aborigines. Many of the non-aboriginals were Chinese and of other colored races. The pure-white population dwindled from a maximum of 3767 in 1919 to only 2800 in 1931. Questions of white health and energy in this region have been discussed in the chapter on Queensland (Chapter VI). The chief industries are the pasturing of cattle on the interior grasslands and a little mining, pearl shelling, and buffalo shooting.

History

The history of the efforts at white settlement in the Northern Territory is worth consideration. There were three eras of experimental settlement in the dependency, those of the British military stations, the South Australian administration, and the Commonwealth rule. Each provided a different type of settler—the soldier, the Chinese coolie, and the white industrialist. The first two may be classed as relics of the old prescientific invasion of the tropics. The third falls into the scientific regime.

The British coastal stations of 1824-1849 proved that the Territory was remote from the trade routes, that the soil was "sterile and ungrateful," and that the Asiatic, in his wisdom, was unwilling to come in. The failures also created the impression that the climate was "malignant and unhealthful" and that the seaboard was "unfit for the residence of civilized man."

The South Australian Administration

In the sixties the tide of squatters approached the Territory, and, as Queensland wisely refused to superintend a latitudinal penetration, the British government accepted the offer of South Australia to conduct an inexpensive longitudinal occupation northwards along the line of J. M. Stuart's route. On obtaining the dependency, South Australia perpetrated a virtual breach of faith and attempted to develop the country through the coast lands rather than the healthful tablelands— by the seaways rather than the landways—a proceeding that could have been conducted better from India or Singapore. Under the old

conditions of tropical colonization South Australians died like flies
on the coastal gold reefs, and the colonists concluded that English
farmers would be useless in "the most barren country God ever made."
The government then turned to colored labor, and, although in 1876-
1877 the Japanese government refused the offer of free immigration and
free passages, the administration poured in Chinese coolies from Singapore. Thus the Northern Territory became the keystone of Chinese
settlement in Australia and the last stronghold in the continent of the
Chinese race. Nevertheless, South Australia failed to develop the country
with coolie labor, for owing to poor soils, pests, and variable and deficient rainfall agricultural plantations proved a dismal failure. Also,
although the Chinese won large quantities of gold, they were little
controlled and despoiled the best mines. Yet the South Australian administration possessed redeeming features. The settlers proved the
climate fairly healthful, and the whites lived in comfort with a substratum of colored labor. There were no political disturbances. Mining
and pearling advanced, and cattle, despite the terrible red-water scourge,
made some headway. The dependency remained poor but economical.
In forty-eight years it contracted a debt of only six million pounds,
which included the cost of the northern and southern sections of the
proposed transcontinental railway.

The Commonwealth Administration

From 1911 onwards the federal government took over the Northern
Territory and attempted an invasion on modern scientific lines. The
chapter opened with the high ideals of the "White Australia" policy,
the lavish spending of borrowed money, and a course of development
based on insufficient scientific data. Once again, however, the effort
was wasted in the tropical coast lands and in a longitudinal penetration,
and the resulting disaster was more extensive and tragic than any in
previous days. Urged by South Australia, the Commonwealth spent
many millions on an undertaking still unfinished, the building of the
transcontinental railway, which, even when completed, is unlikely
to prove of great economic importance. Federal governments wasted
huge sums in unsuccessful experiments on agriculture and mining in the
coast lands, but they made some excellent improvements on the stock
routes to the east and west. Unfortunately the hopes for the cattle
industry proved illusive, and Australia witnessed a serio-comic farce
when the Vesteys introduced industrialism into the Territory in an
effort to establish a vast meat enterprise at Darwin—the old, deceptive
northern gate. Thus Australian socialism, bureaucracy, and industrialism entered the dependency to play their tragic comedy in raiments
of borrowed gold. Official and extremist fought for supremacy, while
the weak administration of the young Commonwealth watched with
indifference the failure of its experiment and made little effort to up-

hold its prestige and honor when its representatives were assaulted or expelled by labor extremists. By 1920 the battle was over, and the left wing of the white industrialists had gained a triumph, which itself showed the utter inadequacy of the victors as tropical pioneers. Industrial arbitration had forced wages to a figure rendering agriculture, mining, and transport utterly prohibitive. The Vesteys had closed with a staggering loss. The only economic industries, pearl shell and cattle, depended upon the colored labor of Asiatics and aborigines. Yet the federal government had no perception of its weakness or its failure. From 1926 to 1931 it divided the Territory into North and Central Australia and proposed that the Commonwealth should add the remaining parts of the tropics to the huge region in which it had so lamentably failed.[19] In view of the federal record, however, it is little wonder that Queensland and Western Australia refused to trust the national administration in a wider enterprise.

Agricultural Possibilities

Australians may well ask themselves whether they are facing insuperable natural difficulties in the Territory and why it should remain a region of tragic disillusionment, uninfluenced by Queensland's success. History and science provide the answer, and it is one that all who would advertise "the vast and undeveloped potentialities" of the continent should read and understand.

Scientific analysis has shown the poverty of a soil leached by the short and heavy summer rains. The rainfall is low and unreliable for a tropical region and its seasonal distribution is poor. In the opinion of Dr. James Davidson the small number of months having an effective rainfall, the evaporation, and the poor soils damn the area for anything but sparse settlement.

An authority of great experience, W. Wynne Williams, comments as follows on the rainfall: "Darwin's dry season rainfall is 3 inches with $32\frac{1}{2}$ per cent of dry months. . . . . The dry season rainfall does not increase to any appreciable extent as we go inland and the percentage of dry months becomes greater." These conditions prevail in the whole of tropical Australia, except for parts of eastern Queensland and the tip of Cape York. "How then," asks Williams, "is it possible to hope for settlement of the Australian tropics, when agriculture and even dairying have ceased to exist, . . . under favourable conditions of soil and market, when the dry season rainfall becomes as low as 10 inches and the dry months as great as 10 per cent of the total" (Fig. 15).

The same authority continues:

When we inspect the map of the northern coast of Australia, particularly the watershed of the Gulf of Carpentaria, it may seem almost incredible that agricultural settlement could not be established somewhere in that vast area at least with the aid of irrigation; but from the tip of the Cape York Peninsula to the western confine of the

Gulf of Carpentaria the so-called rivers are mere sandy flood channels, with the exception of a few insignificant streams and the Gregory and Roper Rivers. During the torrential summer rains they become swollen torrents flooding their narrow alluvial frontages. Then for some months of the year they are empty sandy beds with random pools and lagoons . . . In these ultra-tropical latitudes we are faced with a further difficulty in the wilting effect of the great heat upon our temperate crops which confines such activity to the cooler months of the year . . . Agricultural settlement is possible to this extent, i.e., if a mining population arose in proximity to any of these large watercourses, patches of land would be cultivated here and there. Semi-tropical crops such as ground-nuts, cowpea, and maize might be grown during the wet season for some milking cows, and temperate crops would be grown during the winter months with the aid of hand irrigation. The high prices received for this produce from such a community would warrant a limited amount of such agriculture; nevertheless, not one of all large mining centres of the tropics has left an agricultural settlement behind it.[20]

Strong as these arguments are, we must consider contrary opinions. Some authorities believe that the Adelaide-Alligator coast lands would produce rice under such properly controlled irrigation as is practiced by certain colored races. Mr. C. W. D. Conacher, who possesses great knowledge of the Northern Territory, wrote me, Mar. 11, 1937:

There seems no doubt that in many places between Darwin and Birdum, cotton could be successfully grown if a market could be found for it but at present the cost is too high; also a number of natural pests have to be overcome. No doubt tobacco could also be grown. The point is that with regard to these and other commodities, they can at present be grown to more advantage in other parts of Australia.

On the same question of agricultural possibilities the Director of Agriculture at Ibadan, Nigeria, notes:

I imagine that it should be possible to work out a system of intensive mixed farming suitable for your conditions, based on the same principles as ours, i.e. the stall feeding of Zebu cattle and possibly some small stock such as pigs or goats, and the use of Zebu cattle as draught animals. With more capital than our farmers have, I imagine it might be possible eventually, with such a system, to work up a gross return of at least £2 per acre of cultivated land. It might even be possible to reach £3 per acre; but I should think that it would be very difficult to pass that figure. I should imagine that a white, small-holder, working long hours during the cropping season, with his wife helping him in care of stock and with light work on the land, could manage a farm of 50-60 acres, of which 30-40 would be cultivated, and the remainder in grass . . . (This allows that the white has more stock and implements than the coloured peasant.) To work out such a system would need some 10 years' work at an experimental farm devoted solely to this purpose.[21]

Similarly the Director of Agriculture, Bombay Presidency, India, writes:

I should say that the conditions in the Ahmednagar, Sholapur and Bijapur districts are not dissimilar. We have there average rainfalls per taluka ranging from about 17 to about 27 inches and with six months of the year having very little rain. Yet these areas support a large population dependent on agriculture. In Ahmednagar and Sholapur districts there are of course certain areas commanded by canals, but the great bulk of the three districts has got no irrigation. Both *kharif* and *rabi* crops are grown. . . . I cannot see therefore that Mr. Williams is justified in the very sweeping statement. . . .[22]

These opinions cannot be disregarded, although the Payne Commission has just reported that "it is difficult to visualize much development in the way of closer settlement, mixed farming, or agriculture in the lands of the Northern Territory." [23] It is possible that a colored population, content with a very low standard of living, could settle parts of northern Australia as mixed farmers, cultivating seasonal crops and keeping Indian buffaloes or Zebu cattle. It seems unlikely, however, that any white race could secure an adequate living standard in such regions, and it is improbable that any people, white or colored, would settle these tropics if they could secure a footing in the more pleasant, more fertile, and more temperate parts of the continent, at present only sparsely settled by Australians.

The Cattle Industry

A question of first importance is that of the cattle industry, which has met with some success in the Northern Territory, where cattle numbered some 900,000 in 1935. Here again we quote W. Wynne Williams:

The safest and heaviest carrying cattle pasture [in the Australian tropics] is situated on the eastern littoral, reaching 200 miles inland on the Tropic of Capricorn, and narrowing to the northward till it becomes reduced to nothing at the back of Cairns. Its dry season rainfall varies from 5 to 7 inches. From a pastoral point of view this area is well developed with holdings varying in size from 20,000 acres upwards. Only under greatly increased prices for meat can this area be expected to carry a much larger population. It is, in the main, a region of wooded hills and valleys containing no outstanding qualities in the way of rich soils, and it is incapable of supplying anything greater than a small percentage of its stock in a fat condition during the dry months of the year. To the westward of this area merino sheep have ousted the cattle from the rolling prairie and park-like lands of the interior and have spread to the westward until the rainfall has become too low and artificial water too costly to provide for them. Here the cattle remain in occupation of vast areas, walking long distances to water. Apart from this limited area of sheep land, cattle-raising is the only industry of the Australian tropics other than mining. The coastal summer rainfalls are exceedingly heavy but the dry season rainfalls seldom exceed 2 inches. The carrying capacity of a good cattle holding throughout the tropic coast is 30 acres to a beast, and it is in this tropic cattle-breeding area that hopes have been entertained for expanding the industry in the direction of the chilled meat export trade. In order to make the situation clear a short description of the routine of the lives of the cattle on a large holding might not be out of place.

The cattle fatten rapidly on the commencement of the summer rains, which arrive usually in December or January and continue in the form of intermittent deluges, till March and sometimes into April. By June or July the green grass has lost its bloom and the cattle lose their condition steadily as the grass becomes dry. Relief arrives occasionally in the form of early thunderstorms during September, October and November, failing which the cattle become very weak. If the opening of the wet season is protracted till January the mortality in the herd is heavy; therefore the large herds do not increase.

Under these conditions cattle cannot be confined in small areas without serious loss. Subjected as these cattle are during every year to a period of stress and starvation they are consequently slow of growth, reaching marketable weights long after the age of maturity desired for the chilled meat trade, and it is quite impossible to market anything but a small minority during the latter six months of the year. This does not suggest that our tropic pastures are unable to supply chilled meat for the export trade, but they cannot supply young meat and will never be able to maintain a continuity of supply throughout the year without the aid of fattening pastures.

This gloomy picture is relieved somewhat by our experience of the swamp buffalo and the Zebu or Brahma beast, which goes to show that certain animals, unaffected by tick-transmitted disease, can multiply exceedingly with no attention whatever. European cattle seem to have thrived remarkably well before the advent of the cattle tick, which has inoculated them with an enervating disease which lowers their natural resistance to the dry and difficult period of the year. Only a small number of buffalo was imported into one of the early settlements on the Northern Territory coast. During the past twenty years from three to six buffalo shooters have been actively engaged in providing buffalo hides for export. Last year I assisted one of these buffalo shooters to calculate approximately the number of hides he had sold during his career; the number was in the region of 30,000. Unfortunately, the buffalo is of no commercial value to us apart from his hide, and, being very wild, he can be captured only with a rifle. A small herd of Zebu cattle was brought to Darwin many years ago, but apparently very little attempt was made to control them. They found a pasture near the mouth of the Adelaide River, a little to the eastward of Darwin, where they exist to this day—a wild, furtive mob, estimated roughly at about 1,500 head. A herd of a similar number of European and Zebu cross existed beside them. A strenuous attempt has been made to wipe out the Zebu strain and to prevent further crossing with the wild mob, because even the half-breeds are very wild and often unmanageable on open range. This Zebu beast will thrive and multiply on the poor coastal tropic land and will retain his condition much better than the European beast during the dry months of the year; nevertheless he is a wild beast on open range, and a wild beast is a bad beast and cannot be tolerated.

I have no hesitation in saying that if we were to replace our European cattle with the Zebu on our northern tropic coastal lands, our herds would be doubled in numbers in an incredibly short time; but on the other hand our cattle industry might be completely ruined and the rifle would have to be used as it is with buffalo and wild horses to-day.

If the experiments being conducted in northern Queensland by the Council for Scientific and Industrial Research lead to the creation of a beef cattle beast maintaining the beef quality and docility of the European strain, with just sufficient of the Zebu blood to ensure immunity from tick fever, then something of great value will be achieved, because the eradication of the cattle tick from our thinly-stocked pastures seems too remote to contemplate.[24]

This is perhaps too emphatic a statement; but Mr. C. W. D. Conacher holds out a like hope. He writes (Mar. 11, 1937): "The experiments now being conducted in Queensland with a view to developing a special breed with a percentage of Zebu blood is, I think, full of hope for our tropical North. It has been proved elsewhere that the hindquarters of such crossbreds are particularly suitable for chilling." [25]

Similarly the letters from Nigeria and India quoted on page 114 indicate that the authorities in these regions believe that the Indian buffalo and Zebu cattle would prove satisfactory for mixed farming settlement. The Director of Agriculture writes from Ibadan, Nigeria, as follows: "When kept as a domestic animal, or in controlled herds, by either Africans or Indians, the Zebu cows are commonly as docile as

European cows, and the bulls generally more docile than the cows."
The Director of Agriculture, Bombay Presidency, considers that Indian
buffaloes or cows might well prove satisfactory, the milk of the former
in particular giving a high percentage of butter fat. Something may
be done on these lines in the future, and the ever-hopeful Commonwealth secured in December 1937 an able and practical report from an
experienced Commission under the Chairmanship of Mr. W. L. Payne.
This report breaks away from the old overoptimistic delusions. It
recommends two short cattle railways, the one into the cattle country
southeast of Wyndham and the other to serve from Queensland the
potential pasturing country of the Barkly Tableland. The Commission
recommends other assistance of an administrative, financial, and economic nature, including freedom from taxation and customs through
Darwin. It is very interesting to note that in spite of the "White
Australia" policy the report states that Chinese gardeners and colored
domestic servants on indenture should be admitted on a limited scale.
If its recommendations are adopted the Commission makes the moderate
claim that in twenty-five years the Northern Territory should have an
annual production worth £4,000,000; the Barkly Tableland should employ 2000 additional persons through the sheep industry, and the total
white population of the Territory should increase to 15,000 in a decade
and 40,000 in twenty-five years.[26] The wisdom of this moderate report
is obvious.

One can see from the geographical controls and the history of the
region little hope to mitigate the following gloomy conclusion of Wynne
Williams:

There are many thousands of square miles of tropic coastlands yet to be stocked
with cattle, but as frozen meat appears to be a drug on the export market and as our
aged chilled meat is not competitive with the early chilled meat from other parts of
the world, there is little prospect of expansion of the cattle industry in view. We
know of no other industry than cattle-raising to suit this vast tropic coastal area
of heavily-timbered stony hills, poor sandy stretches, sandy flood channels and low-
lying seaboards with its torrential summer rainfall and months of drought. We
have explored it through and through and have utilized it wherever it has been economically possible to do so.[27]

Transport

There remain the problems of transport, of the aborigines, and of
white energy and health. As regards sea transport, Australian national
ideals express themselves in the Navigation Acts, which maintain a high
standard of living for white seamen. The resulting costs, however, are
very high, and it is ridiculous that the policy is applied to the pioneering
and isolated parts of the Australian tropics. As regards rail transport,
the northern and southern portions of the future transcontinental railway have cost a total of seven and a half million pounds. In 1930 the
excess of working costs over revenue in the two sections were 170 per

cent and 196 per cent. Yet, in 1932, the freightage from Adelaide to Alice Springs was £25 a ton. In these circumstances cattle are driven on the hoof, and the motor and airplane take the cream of the passenger traffic. Thus it seems absurd for the federal government to complete the transcontinental railway as promised to South Australia, and heavy motor transport is being tried as a means of connecting the northern and southern railheads. The main need of north Australia is not railways but better motor tracks and more stock routes adequately equipped with wells.[28] Nevertheless, the federal government could assist the cattle industry by building two or three short railways. Mr. C. W. D. Conacher notes (Mar. 11, 1937):

> Although I am against the construction of any further long lines of railway for general purposes of development, I still think there is room for one or two short lines in certain key positions to overcome rough country which at present seriously depreciates the cattle travelling over it—for example, a line 200 miles southeast from Wyndham would ensure fat cattle being delivered to the Wyndham meat works in very much better condition than at present. Another short line from the Barkly Tableland connecting with Mt. Isa or Dajarra would serve a useful purpose in getting cattle from that district to Queensland in much better condition than at present.

As previously mentioned, the Payne Commission adopted Mr. Conacher's views in their recommendations regarding railways.

In the future the airplane may possibly ameliorate the evil effects of isolation, which is undoubtedly deleterious to the health of many women. Medical air services are already proving the greatest boon.

The Aborigines

The Australian natives are continuing "the natural progress of the aboriginal race towards extinction," [29] but there remain some 54,000, most of whom are in northern Australia, and half-castes are increasing at the rate of nearly 1000 a year mainly by breeding between themselves (Fig. 59).[30]

It is an interesting comment on the "White Australia" policy that Australia's chief industry is largely dependent on the support of this primitive and formerly despised race. If white labor unions force socialistic governments to apply white wages and conditions to aboriginal and half-caste employees, the stock owners must abandon their lands.

Australian scientists are urging the governments to save the wild tribes by reserving and adequately patrolling large unoccupied areas of generally unprofitable country. To its credit the federal government has already reserved Arnhem Land and a large central region on the South Australian, Western Australian, and Northern Territory boundary. These districts are not patrolled satisfactorily, however, and the unfortunate aboriginal woman is protected neither from the white Australian nor the Japanese pearl fisher. Compared with American

efforts to help the Indians, the amount spent per native by the federal
government in caring for the natives is a national disgrace.

In the settled areas the stations have destroyed the delicately balanced hunting civilization of the aboriginals. Here the whites collect
the tribes and feed them all in return for the work of the men. This

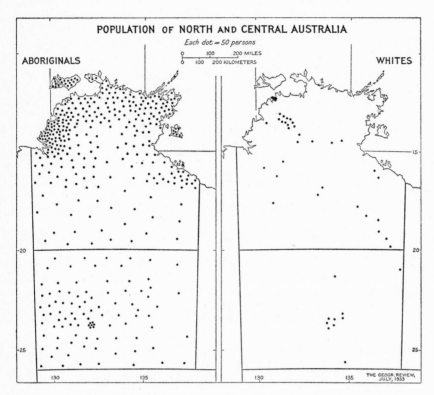

FIG. 59—North and Central Australia (now the Northern Territory), showing the distribution
of white and aboriginal population (scale: 1 : 22,000,000). Distribution of aboriginals (including
half-castes) is after the map in the Official Year Book of the Commonwealth of Australia, No. 24,
1931, p. 671. Figures for the map of white population are from the census of 1921.

on the whole is a satisfactory policy. The cattlemen should provide their
stock "boys" with better quarters, however, and the federal authorities
should increase the present miserable allotment to the old and sick
for blankets and medical stores. Miscegenation is a grave problem,
although the number of aborigines is too small for the evolution of an
important mixed race (Fig. 60). The federal authorities are adopting
a far-sighted policy in regard to the half-castes under their control.
They are training the boys and girls in homes in Pine Creek and Darwin,
inducing them to marry among themselves and finding them suitable
occupations with the hope of raising them to the white level and of
saving them from falling back to native life. Few Australians realize
how strong is the "black control" in the Northern Territory. The ab-

original, and even more his lubra, colors every phase of life in this vast region of sparse white settlement. Despite the "White Australia" policy a great part of the continent is black Australia still.[31]

White Energy and Health

In the wet-dry country of the Northern Territory the position as regards white health and energy is somewhat obscure. As in the northern part of Western Australia, the birth rate is low, and the death rate and infant mortality rate are the highest in the continent (Table VIII). The statistics of suicide, serious crime, drunkenness, and illegitimacy are appalling. But before we blame the climate we must make allowance for pioneering conditions, for isolation, and for a highly mixed population, which includes many persons of low economic and cultural development. People with knowledge of the Northern Territory consider that the statistics presented in Table VIII indicate primarily the lack of control by the local administration, the long economic depression, the absence of permanent industry, the high percentage of unmarried males, and the unsatisfactory character of the population that so often drifts to and stays in the north.

White labor has a miserable record in the Northern Territory, though this may be largely due to isolation and the influence of workers of a poor stamp. It appeared to me, on visiting the Northern Territory in 1932, that some white women had degenerated but that many others, including some of the second generation, were of excellent type. Evidence varies as regards the children. Some residents believe that children should be sent south at about the age of ten, as they develop rapidly and suffer from contact with aboriginal servants. On the other hand, one meets many children who were born in the north, who have lived all their lives there, and who appear to be healthy and energetic. A report on a medical inspection of school children in the Northern Territory indicates the general trend in tropical Australia. At practically all ages children in the Northern Territory are taller than the British standard but do not show a corresponding increase in weight. The girls develop more rapidly than British girls.[32] It is interesting to note that "coloured races, though derived from stock whose physical standard outwardly is inferior to the British standard, are found in North Australia, at any selected age, to approach or even excel the British standard." The health of the children is fair, but 31 per cent suffer from dental caries, and affected eyes are very prevalent [33] (Figs. 62, 63, 65).

Conclusion

What light have Australian efforts in the Northern Territory thrown on the problem of tropical settlement? On the one hand, it is argued that the Commonwealth has never given the Northern Territory a

Fig. 60—An aboriginal family, Central Australia (now Northern Territory).

Fig. 61—Aboriginal girl, age 12, rescued by police living with and being maltreated by a white man, Central Australia.

Fig. 62—Commonwealth government school, Alice Springs, Central Australia. (Courtesy of Hon. T. Patterson, Minister of the Interior, Commonwealth of Australia).

FIG. 63—Roman Catholic church and mission building, the latter well adapted to the climate. Stuart, Central Australia (now Northern Territory).

FIG. 64—"Teatree Well" post office and station, Central Australia. The building is a typical pioneer structure-hut of poles and iron with a stone chimney.

FIG. 65—Commonwealth government school, Alice Springs, Central Australia. Note white, aboriginal, and Afghan children. (Courtesy of Dept. of Interior, Commonwealth of Australia.)

fair chance. Dr. Gilruth, the first permanent Administrator (1912-1919), was forced to operate an impossible policy, and after he left in 1919 the Territory was practically run from Melbourne or Canberra by a governmental department headed by some fifteen successive ministers who had little expert knowledge or expert advice. Those who hold these opinions consider that a strong, well-informed, and expert control would entirely change the outlook of the Northern Territory in from five to ten years. Moreover, a century of experiment has proved that northern white males can survive in these wet-dry or arid tropics and maintain fair standards in the face of isolation and other difficulties, provided they abstain from alcoholic excesses and engage in hard manual work. The position is more doubtful as regards women and children, but undoubtedly some individuals maintain excellent health and high energy in the arid and monsoonal regions, and it may be possible in the future to preselect such individuals by scientific research. On the other hand, history and science have clearly shown that the wet-dry or arid climates of northern Australia present the greatest difficulties to close settlement by any people, white or colored, who seek a reasonable standard of life. In these circumstances Australians would in all probability be wise to cease boasting about the "vast undeveloped potentialities" of tropical Australia. They should place before the world the picture of these regions as painted by scientific knowledge. They should treat them as pastoral and mining areas and avoid further misdirected and expensive experiments that may handicap the legitimate development of the more hopeful parts of the Commonwealth.

9

CHAPTER IX

TROPICAL PLATEAUS: I. COSTA RICA AND SOUTH AMERICA

Costa Rica

The Spanish-American population of Costa Rica falls somewhat outside the scope of an inquiry primarily concerned with the tropical settlement of northern whites, but the history of Costa Rica has been so unusual and the controls are so clearly marked as to warrant inclusion. Moreover, it is a striking fact that the progress, civilization, and culture of the five Central American republics, Costa Rica, El Salvador, Guatemala, Honduras, and Nicaragua, appear to vary in proportion to the percentage of white blood. Costa Rica and El Salvador possess the smallest areas and the poorest natural resources. Yet they contain the highest percentage of white population and they are far in advance of the three larger republics inhabited by a blend in which the Indian element predominates. Some students of the Caribbean have attempted to minimize the importance of race in tropical problems and assume that, given the social solvents of time and intermarriage, no one race is apt to contribute more than another. Those who have seen the Caribbean conditions at close hand seldom share such beliefs. This chapter studies Costa Rica,[1] which is said to possess the most predominantly white population between the Rio Grande and Uruguay.

Natural Features

In natural features and industry Costa Rica falls into three divisions. The Atlantic coastal area consists of low, heavily watered regions of tropical forest. This forms a *tierra caliente* or torrid zone, which extends to a height of about 2000 feet. In this Atlantic zone the temperature varies from 75° to 82° F. and the rainfall from 100 to 250 inches. The precipitation is well distributed, and the climate is humid throughout the entire year.

Above the plains the country rises to plateaus of an elevation of 3000 feet or more, from which tower the central Cordillera. These ranges include four active volcanoes and several peaks more than 10,000 feet in height. The highlands form the *tierra templada,* or so-called temperate zone, although the temperatures vary from about 65° to more than 70° F. for the year. The capital, San José, situated at an elevation of 3700 feet, has a mean annual temperature of 67.5°, which is about the same as the southern tropics of eastern Queensland or the central agricultural regions of peninsular Florida. The rainfall is some 76 inches, and there are wet and dry seasons. In 1929 the rainfall of

San José was 90 inches with 5.4 inches for the five months December–April, the dry period. The predominant soil is a soft red clayey loam of great fertility.

The third division, the Pacific slope, is very steep. Here the climate is again very hot, and the rainfall (some 70 in.) is seasonal. The soil is a black volcanic sand—a rich porous sponge.

On the Atlantic plains a population, almost wholly negro in type, is engaged in the banana industry, which also threatens to invade the Pacific lowlands. The central plateau is inhabited by a white or near-white population engaged in coffee raising, cattle ranching, and similar pursuits. The steep Pacific slope is small in area. In the northwest there is much wild country with a scattered pastoral population. Conditions of the same type prevail in the rugged south, which borders Panama. As regards the pastoral industry, one understands that the importation of grasses, such as the guinea and elephant grass, has proved the salvation of Central America. These grasses are cut, shredded, and fed to stalled beasts. Zebu cattle are proving strong and satisfactory, and the mixed breeds are less fierce than the pure Mysore.

History and Population [2]

The outstanding influence in the white invasion of Costa Rica was the comparatively small number of Indians in a land still largely covered with virgin forest. An estimate of the year 1522 gives the Indian population as only 27,000, and these the whites rapidly absorbed or deported to Peru or Panama; today the republic contains only some 4000 pure Indians. This fact had a profound effect on the Spanish conquistadors, who, unlike their fellows in Mexico, Peru, and other parts of tropical America, were unable to capitalize labor, and were too poor to purchase negroes. They were thus forced to undertake a large part of the farm work themselves. Following this the great estates of the conquest were split up among the children, with the result that the plateaus of the republic now possess a population consisting almost entirely of white peasant agriculturists. Of 58,976 real estate holdings Costa Ricans hold legal titles to 47,000. Hence the republic possesses two of the essential factors for permanent white settlement in the tropics: the population largely consists of free white land-owners, and these whites themselves engage in hard manual work. A third factor influencing the settlement was the comparative coolness, healthful character, satisfactory rainfall, and fertile volcanic soil of the high plateaus, which the whites quickly sought. Both the conquistadors and the indigenous Indians disliked the humid heat of the lowlands, and their objections were strengthened by the fear of tropical diseases, such as yellow fever and malaria. Whether these diseases were indigenous or exotic is immaterial. The essential point is that after the conquest the Atlantic coast became one of the most unhealthful regions in the world. This area in the old days was largely an immense swamp where yellow fever and malaria annually destroyed hundreds of people and made agricultural enterprises and public works impossible. There is no doubt that the conquistadors suffered heavily in effecting their pre-scientific invasion and that, even when the era of railway construction opened, the line that connected the plateau capital, San José, with its Atlantic port of Limon was literally strewn with corpses.[3]

A fourth factor that greatly influenced the white invasion was isolation, although strangely enough this factor had beneficial effects as well as bad ones. In the early days it was very difficult to cross the rugged country to Panama or Nicaragua, and communication was almost impossible between the plateaus and the Atlantic coast. The most practicable route lay down the steep Pacific slope to Puntarenas, and even here transport by horse or oxcart was difficult and dangerous. Although this isolation made the progress of Costa Rica slow and painful, it protected the plateau population from the Indians and especially from the danger of absorption by imported negro slaves.

Another important factor in the old prescientific invasion was the character of the Spanish conquistadors. The invaders appear to have been Castilians, Andalusians, Catalonians, and Galicians of good type, and, although there was miscegenation with the Indians, the whites brought in Spanish women at an early date. Contemporary documents give interesting descriptions of the white immigrants—for example, a group of 300 introduced by Diego de Artieda about 1574. The accounts leave detailed pictures of individual pioneer women, who were "well built," or "of florid complexion . . . with freckles . . . fair and white . . . possessing dimples."[4]

Columbus discovered the Atlantic coast line of Costa Rica in September, 1502, but early attempts at colonization proved abortive until Herman Sanchez de Badajoz founded Badajoz in 1540 and Juan Vasquez de Coronado, assisted by Bartolomé de las Casas, the famous friend of the Indians, subdued the whole country. When the Captain-Generalcy of Guatemala was established Costa Rica was incorporated with it, and the region later formed part of the viceroyalty of New Spain, until, with Guatemala, it attained independence in 1821.

Throughout the colonial period progress was very slow. In 1569 there was only a handful of Spaniards with no money, no export crops, and no transport, isolated on the high plateaus between the two oceans. In 1620 there were only fifty white Spanish families, hemmed in by pirates and Indians and cultivating a little maize and wheat. In 1719 the governor reported that Costa Rica was the most miserable colony in all America. There was not a single piece of silver money in all the country, and the governor had to do his own sowing and reaping or he would have starved. Matters seemed to have improved after this, and the San José and Heredia districts began to develop. In 1751 the valley of San José contained 399 families of 2330 people, "not counting Indians, there being none." By 1763 the Heredia district had more than 100 sugar mills and was shipping produce by the Pacific. In 1783 San José had a population of 4869 Spaniards, mestizos, and mulattoes. By the Census of 1809 there were 50,000-60,000 people and the Indians of the plateau were almost completely absorbed. Nevertheless, until the end of the colonial period and for some time later the country population lived in a state of appalling squalor and ignorance.

After the winning of independence the population of Costa Rica increased rapidly. Between 1844 and 1864 it increased 50 per cent in spite of war, cholera, measles, and whooping cough, and reached a total of 120,499. By 1892 the population had more than doubled and numbered 243,205. By 1927-1929 the banana industry and the Rockefeller Foundation's health campaigns had assisted it to double again and reach a total of 503,858 souls.

The expansion was also due in some measure to improved communications. The Americans, Meiggs and Keith, carried out fine work in constructing railways on the plateaus and connecting them with Port Limon on the Atlantic coast (1890), while the government slowly finished a railway to Puntarenas on the Pacific Ocean.

Much of recent Costa Rican history is wrapped around foreign loans. The story is typical of the disgraceful exploitation of weak tropical peoples by civilized nations and is almost too scandalous and fantastic for belief. Sharks exacted ruinous terms for railway loans. Brokers worked in collusion to secure huge commissions, and the bankers, who handled the business, acted in a manner roundly condemned by a British Parliamentary Commission of 1879. In 1870 Costa Rica possessed a population of 145,983 people and a total income of £183,000. Yet the first annual payment on her loans was to be £84,000 and her second £192,000. In Costa Rica, as in many other tropical lands, we see a tragic dependence upon the selfish and nationalistic countries of the cool-temperate zone. In the words of President Cleto Gonzáles Víquez, "Prosperity or hard times for Costa Rica is forged in London. Depending on a sole crop (coffee) will bring us ruinous experiences." [5] It is a tragedy that this truth has not been grasped and acted on wherever possible by rulers of independent tropical lands, for the trend of world events demands that they should be as self-supporting as possible.

Costa Rica now contains a fairly advanced, fairly well-educated, and democratic people. The Census of 1927 classed 80 per cent of the population as white, and it is claimed that Heredia Province is as white as New York City, while the three most populous provinces run from 87 to 94 per cent white—about the percentage of West Virginia.

The little republic has gradually passed from the rule of dictators to a popular government on the lines of the United States. During the last few years it has made very creditable progress in politics, constitutional standards, free speech, free assembly, and the sanctity of private property. In these respects it now ranks high among Latin American republics.

The republic is peculiarly and justly proud of its educational system, which has reduced the percentage of illiterates to 23.6. This is much lower than the figures of other Latin American countries and compares excellently with Italy (27 per cent in 1921) and Spain (45.8 per cent in 1920). Such advance is a fine achievement for a small and poor people who possess a land where communication is still difficult. It is particularly satisfactory in view of the fact that when independence was secured almost the whole population was illiterate. Costa Ricans today may justly take pride in having more school teachers than soldiers. They have turned their barracks into schools and spend 22 per cent of their budget on education, or twice as much as on defence.

Living Standards and Health [6]

Although Costa Rica has made remarkable progress, the people are still very poor and the living standard in many areas is distressingly low. In the coastal plains a population that consists almost entirely of English-speaking negroes shares unfloored huts of wood or thatch with their domestic animals in an existence in which sanitation and personal hygiene are unknown (Fig. 69). About 2000 feet up on the Atlantic slopes the traveler sees the beginnings of the white population and of an improvement in conditions (Fig. 68). Some of the houses are equipped with wooden floors and privies, and, although domestic animals share the houses with the people, the hookworm infection is not so bad as on the coast. The high plateaus from 3000 to 6000 feet form the habitation of an almost white population, and the houses are far better, constructed of wood or brick with tiled roofs and floors of wood (Fig. 70). Animals are still allowed in the dwellings, but sanitation, water supply, and hygiene are much superior. The worst conditions prevail in the suburban districts. Here the people are very poor and the standard is very low. As in many Latin American republics there is an upper stratum of fine old aristocratic families, highly educated, cultured, and widely traveled. The women of these families are in many cases very graceful and beautiful and show no signs of tropical degeneration (Fig. 71). San José, the capital, is quite an attractive town and is well laid out. In recent years its utilities have shown great improvement under American and British influences, which have done much to break down traditionalism in the last two generations. We could discern in 1933 few unfavorable factors that could be definitely attributed to the tropical conditions. Professor C. L. Jones considers, however, that the people show a lack of individual ambition, which he lays at the door of a nonstimulating climate and unsatisfactory health. He notes that other deleterious influences are isolation, a static mental horizon, and physical and mental inbreeding.[7] The over-whelming importance of the coffee industry has tended to make the people traditionalists, while the problems of the country are too vast to be solved by so small a sovereign people. Some of the American colony also say that they feel the monotony of climatic conditions on these high tropical plateaus and that frequent visits to cooler climates are necessary. Nevertheless, one's reactions to Costa Rica and its people, after seeing the negro populations of the British, American, and Dutch West Indies or even the white and near-white peasants of Cuba, are favorable.

It is impossible at present to discriminate between the effects of climate per se and unsatisfactory health, but matters will be clearer if health conditions continue their rapid improvement. The Rocke-feller campaign against hookworm, and the efforts of the fruit com-panies and of Señor Nuñez, the Costa Rican Minister of Health, have had wonderful results. Yellow fever has long been under control, but the continued battle against malaria and hookworm indicates how difficult these diseases are to eliminate. The coastal regions form an ideal breeding ground for several types of malaria-bearing mosquito, and "the destruction of all places where stagnant water may lodge con-tinues a task far beyond the power of any human agency." [8] Neverthe-less, the fruit companies have brought the death rate amongst their employees down to 14.03 per cent, and the admittances to hospital for malaria fell from 269 to 111 per 1000 in the period 1925-1929.

The Costa Rican government began the attack on hookworm in 1910, but when the Rockefeller Foundation opened its campaign in 1914 it found that in regions up to 3000 feet 70 per cent of the urban and 77 per cent of the rural population were infected. Prior to 1918 the campaign is said to have cured 12,411 persons, or 46.5 per cent. As a result the total deaths in Costa Rica fell from 26.32 to 22.52 per 1000, infant mortality from 201.7 to 175.9 per 1000, and child mortality from 328.6 to 275 per 1000. "No other cause but the campaign for hookworm eradication was responsible for these results." Employers who find their employees happier and stronger pay eloquent tributes to the attack on hookworm. Nevertheless, the ravages of the disease still remain serious. Often too poor to afford shoes, the peasants are reinfected by the disease, which destroys their energy and keeps their standards of living low. Thus hookworm creates a vicious circle.

Figures by race for infection indicate how dangerous is the presence of the negro. It was reported in 1918 that in the thousands of persons examined 12.5 per cent of yellow, 50.3 of white, 75 of blacks, and 82.1 of mestizos were infected. Although medical science has done such excellent work, the death rate from all causes remains very heavy, and was 22.7 in 1926-1930 and 23.8 in 1931. The population of the Atlantic coastal plains is largely male and of vigorous age; yet, in spite of the splendid efforts of the American fruit companies, the death rates in the eastern coast lands are the worst in Costa Rica, Limon Province reading 31.6 in 1906-1925.

The birth rate of Costa Rica is the highest in Latin America, 46.2 in 1926-30. The death rate for the same period was 22.7 and the population increased by 47,364 in 1927-1931. Of this increase 97.82 per cent was natural and for the most part occurred in the white population of the plateaus. Dr. Charles Merz, the Government Statistician, writes that no European countries, much less Latin American countries, show so rapid an improvement in biological growth.

The whites of Costa Rica thus appear to be undergoing an expansion like that in Cuba, Puerto Rico, and several other tropical countries, but fortunately in this case medical science is not creating the overcrowding so lamentably obvious in Puerto Rico, for much of the republic is unsettled and there is sufficient area on the plateaus for the whites to expand.

The Negro Problem

So far we have shown that the Costa Ricans attribute their progress to their homogeneous population of whites or near-whites, who are improving their civilization and increasing rapidly on tropical plateaus blessed with a fertile soil and moderate climate. This is in direct contradiction to the general trend of events in Central America and the West Indies, where the Indians or negroes are steadily absorbing the whites. We further see that Costa Rica throughout most of its history has been protected from colored people both by isolation and poverty. With the conquest of these difficulties, however, the colored invasion, so usual in the Caribbean, commenced. Costa Rica is now in a difficult position. The banana industry of the Atlantic coast has added greatly to her wealth and has rescued her to some extent from dependence upon the one-crop industry of coffee. Furthermore, the fruit companies are responsible for the vitally important Atlantic railway. On the other hand, the banana industry has certain evil, monopolistic features. It is dependent upon the negro, and the negro, who is creeping up the plateau, brings serious problems of race and health in his train.

The negro invasion opened some fifty years ago with the construction of the Atlantic railway, as the Costa Rican peasant was unwilling to do the work and, under the old prescientific conditions of health, Italian workers failed. With the establishment of the banana industry the American fruit companies repeated the "ethnological crimes" of the old European slavers—they introduced thousands of negroes and failed to repatriate them. As a result there were 19,136 negroes and 2123 mulattoes in Costa Rica in 1927. Negroes then numbered 94.1 per cent of the population of the Atlantic province of Limon and were increasing very rapidly. There is no doubt, too, that the negro is moving up the

Fig. 66—Country school at Coronado, near San José, Costa Rica.
Fig. 67—Children at the school, Coronado.
Fig. 68—Village near Turialba, Costa Rica, on the "color border," altitude about 2000 feet.

Fig. 69—Negro house, Limon province, Costa Rica.
Fig. 70—Typical peasant house, near Cartago, Costa Rica.
Fig. 71—Costa Rican girls returning from Easter mass, San José.

plateau and is spreading hookworm and malaria. It seems impossible, moreover, for the weak and impecunious government to keep him back. A further difficulty lies in the fact that many of the negroes have become Costa Rican citizens, while others have now no nationality at all. British and American officials seem in despair over the situation. One stated that the negroes were breeding like rabbits and were rapidly ascending the slopes of the plateau. Another said that nothing could persuade the Costa Rican government to act. In 1933 the Costa Ricans themselves appeared to be in two camps. Leading statesmen and citizens, such as Nuñez, Víquez, and Guardia, took the view that the negroes did not wish to invade the plateaus and that many were leaving the republic owing to the banana disease. On the other hand, Costa Ricans such as José Guerrero were vigorously attacking both the fruit companies and the negroes, declaring that the banana industry caused the exhaustion of the soil, land grabbing, a monopoly of transport and commerce, physical misery to the worker, and a high percentage of mortality and disease. Guerrero wrote that Costa Rica had gained the respect and liking of the world owing to the orderly social and political life led by a people blessed with racial unity. In his opinion it was essential for the nation to act before the "shadow" on the Atlantic seaboard spread to the Pacific coast and other parts of the republic and before the international esteem for Costa Rica declined.[9] Opinions such as these have now induced Costa Rica to move. The government has circulated to its consuls a decree that prohibits the entry of all colored races and states that colored people who leave Costa Rica will not be permitted to return.[10] There still remains, however, the question of dealing with the negroes of Limon province and the adoption of measures that will prevent them from spreading to the white zone. Under improved conditions of health the white Costa Ricans are beginning to settle on the Atlantic plains, but they dislike the heat and undoubtedly prefer to leave the banana industry to the more rugged colored laborer. Since the banana industry has suffered from disease, the negroes of the coast lands of the republic are turning to cacao and other crops, and their numbers will probably increase. If this is the case, only an effective control of the lines of communication to the plateaus may save the white Costa Ricans from the "negrodation" that is becoming general in parts of Central America.

The South American Tropics [11]

A large part of the South American continent lies in the mathematical tropics. Highlands, however, cover substantial areas and carry milder climates northward toward the equator. In the South American tropics nature has been "supremely generous in her gifts. . . . No equally large area of the world has so high an average of fertility." The continent has "the finest system of natural inland waterways in the world," and the

mountains on the west are "exceptionally rich in useful minerals." [12]
Yet, rich as is the region, nature has provided compensating disadvantages. The huge area of wet low-lying tropics repels man by climate,
swamps, and dense vegetation, which hamper settlement and transport
and promote countless forms of pests and disease.[13]

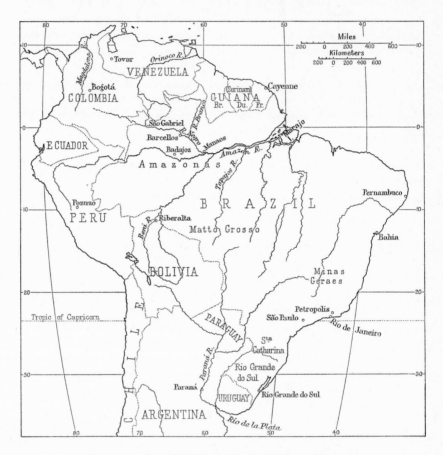

FIG. 72—Location map of South America (scale: 1:50,000,000).

In conformity with the existing conditions of white settlement in the
tropics, the whites inhabit the highlands encircling the Amazonian basin
on the north, west, and south, like the rim of a saucer.[14] Small groups of
whites are scattered along the great rivers of the lowlands. Indians,
negroes, and a conglomeration of racial mixtures, however, form the
bulk of lowland population. Even in the highlands the Indians and the
white-Indian mixtures—the mestizos—greatly outnumber the pure
whites. Before the coming of the whites, the cool highlands formed the
home of those Indian peoples who were the most developed South
Americans and lived the most advanced type of life.[15] There is no

doubt that the Indian detested and avoided the hot moist tropics as much as does the white. It is difficult, however, to decide whether this attitude was due to disease or to climate. Bates stressed the importance of both factors:

I have already remarked on the different way in which the climate of this equatorial region affects Indians and negroes. No one could live long amongst the Indians of the Upper Amazons, without being struck with their constitutional dislike to the heat. Europeans certainly withstand the high temperature better than the original inhabitants of the country; I always found I could myself bear exposure to the sun or unusually hot weather quite as well as the Indians, although not well fitted by nature for a hot climate. Their skin is always hot to the touch, and they perspire little. No Indian resident of Ega can be induced to stay in the village (where the heat is felt more than in the forest or on the river) for many days together. They bathe many times a day. . . . They are restless and discontented in fine dry weather, but cheerful in cool days, when the rain is pouring down on their naked backs. . . . They are very subject to disorders of the liver, dysentery and other diseases of hot climates; and when any epidemic is about, they fall ill quicker, and suffer more than negroes or even whites. How different all this is with the negro, the true child of tropical climes! The impression gradually forced itself on my mind that the red Indian lives as a stranger or immigrant in these hot regions, and that his constitution was not originally adapted, and has not since become perfectly adapted, to the climate.[16]

The racial mixtures of the South American tropics evolved comparatively recently. The Spaniards and Portuguese, who conquered the country from about 1520 onwards, were themselves highly mixed peoples,[17] and, wherever the steel-clad knight and the sandaled monk penetrated, a strange mingling of race and culture took place.[18] Mark Jefferson's researches on Chile bear tribute to the rapidity of the amalgamation. Here, as in other areas, white women were few in numbers and the Spanish trooper fared forth to the frontier accompanied by from four to six native women. As previously noted, in a single week in 1580 sixty children were born in a frontier post of 160 men.[19] Throughout South America a number of families still remain pure white, but the vast majority have some mixture of color. Even of the temperate areas Jefferson writes: "a generation after the Rio de la Plata region was settled the sons of Spaniards and native women were regarded as of pure Spanish descent."[20] In Brazil the Dutch counted as negroes only those persons who showed no white blood.[21]

Both Spain and Portugal used Indian labor but added to the racial conglomeration by the importation of negro slaves. As elsewhere, the slavery and the plantation system had bad effects on the whites by killing their initiative and creating easy-going habits. Unfortunately, in the higher areas, where Europeans could work, their vigor was offset by the presence of Indian peons and half breeds and by the evil tradition that the whites must do no manual work. The price paid by the resulting society is shown in the fact that most Europeans avoid those regions that involve competition with cheap labor and go to the uplands of southern Brazil or to the south-temperate lands.[22]

Population statistics for most South American republics are unreliable, and they are particularly untrustworthy as regards race. Table I in Chapter II gives some recent estimates. Gregory states that, taking the continent as a whole, the number of persons of pure Spanish blood is less than 10 per cent.[23]

From the point of view of present white settlement, by far the most important parts of the South American tropics are the highland areas of southern Brazil, where there is a large population of Italian descent. The region has been regarded as a vast melting pot, which will evolve a mixed race. This does not detract from the economic potentialities of the southern Brazilian highlands. As C. F. Jones points out, this area and the adjoining regions stand upon the threshold of a great development because of favorable climatic conditions, vast areas of fertile plains and plateaus, a variety of resources, water power, and a vigorous, literate population—inducements that will attract large numbers of Europeans.[24] Here extensive immigration from Europe might delay racial amalgamation for a time, but throughout the rest of tropical South America the process of racial mixture is proceeding apace. In the highlands the Indians and mestizos are slowly absorbing the white inhabitants, who are still fairly numerous. In the tropical lowlands the few white settlers are rapidly disappearing in a melting pot of negroes and Indians, in which the negro is likely to be the dominant type.

Racial Culture and Prospects

This submergence of the white peoples of the South American tropics raises the vital question of whether the Indians, negroes, and various mixed races are capable of improving or even of maintaining their existing culture. We have seen in the chapter on Costa Rica the significant fact that the standard of civilization is highest in the republics that contain the highest proportion of white blood. L. L. and J. S. Bernard make the important statement that

. . . there is a noticeable correlation between culture and the proportion of Negro blood, the higher culture, greater facility in self-government, and economic advancement occurring where the Negro element is smallest. These social goods are markedly deficient in the countries that show the highest proportion of Negro blood.[25]

According to Sorokin, "the studies of Ferguson, E. B. Reuter, and of some others, have shown that the greater the infusion of white blood into the negro, the higher is his intelligence quotient." [26] Despite the contrary arguments set out in Chapter XII, the perfect agreement of various tests, the historical, cultural, and mental evidence, the absence of geniuses (especially of the highest rank), and the "superiority" of mulattoes all seem to indicate that heredity makes the negro "inferior." "From the standpoints of cultural achievements, the results of mental tests, the number of geniuses produced, and the 'superiority' of halfbreed Indians over full-blood Indians, the red race makes a somewhat better showing than the negro, but one which is, nevertheless, 'inferior' to that of the whites." [27] If these views are correct the passing of white supremacy in the American tropics must be regarded as a calamity to the human race.

The South American tropics teach some valuable lessons as regards white settlement. First, it is obvious that climate is a fundamental control, apart from all questions of disease. The whites definitely prefer the comfort of the cool highlands. McBride and other writers note that in regions such as Bolivia the Spaniards sought the soft, mild temperatures of the many valleys that dissect the eastern Andes. Here, where neither heat nor cold was excessive, the immigrants and their European animals and plants were more easily acclimatized.[28]

There is some evidence that the high plateau has a bad effect on the white and that he cannot work at very high altitudes, but this point has not been proved.[29] It is clear, however, that Mediterranean whites and even northern races can survive in the South American tropics for many generations. In most countries of these tropics a number of families of southern European ancestry have remained pure. Also certain German communities have survived for a long time, both in southern Brazil and in more difficult and isolated regions. For example, in southern Brazil, Petropolis, the summer capital, a town situated near the tropic at a height of 2800 feet, looks German rather than Brazilian, and local German names have survived. About 1836 the region was colonized by Germans en route for Australia, and the people still have fair hair and blue eyes and look ruddy and robust.[30]

O. M. Miller gives an interesting account of an isolated German settlement at Pozuzo in latitude 10° S. in central Peru. Eighty families arrived here in 1857, and the population now numbers about 600. Miller states that his expedition was agreeably impressed by the well-constructed houses, trails, and bridges of the colonists, particularly as they had heard much about the degeneracy of these Germans. "It was surprising to meet, in such a situation, an extremely blonde, beautifully complexioned girl cleanly dressed in white, walking down the trail and carrying a pail in each hand like the traditional Tyrolese milkmaid." The expedition was somewhat disillusioned later, although conditions were by no means as bad as they had been led to expect. They found, however, that the great quantity of raw cane alcohol drunk by the men had had a deleterious effect on the physique of the second and third generations, though there were still many fine upstanding people in the colony. Unlike most communities of tropical whites, the women seemed very much more healthy than the men. Miller considered that there had been little intermarriage with the Indians and thought that the main reason why the colony had not developed successfully was its inaccessibility. It is important to note, however, his opinion that "climate plays an important part." He adds significantly that "the colony is situated at too low an elevation," although it is located at a height of 2800 feet.[31]

Isolation

Isolation is one of the most important reasons for the failure of white settlement in many parts of the South American tropics. As in Central America, one finds scores of instances where groups of white people have attempted to settle isolated regions but have failed to export their products and have departed or been absorbed. Recent examples, which ended in disaster, were Murray's attempted colonization scheme in Bolivia and the failure of the Tomenotti concession in Peru. Murray, once governor of the American State of Oklahoma, aspired to have the reputation of establishing an important colony in South America on a permanent basis. The concession, however, was isolated; the American families were inexperienced colonists and the nearest doctor was 300 miles away over mule tracks.[32] The Tomenotti concession consisted of two and a half million acres of most desirable country. It attracted educated American families, but these people, finding themselves isolated in eastern Peru, sacrificed their capital and left at the first chance.[33] Many such experiments have failed, even when situated, like Lane's "New Australia," outside the margin of the tropics. European governments should rigidly set their faces against such small isolated efforts.

These failures support the views of R. R. Platt of the American Geographical Society, an authority on South America. Platt considers that the chief obstacle to the white settlement of many parts of the South American tropics is isolation rather than climate.[34]

In Chapter XVI attention is called to Earl Hanson's favorable opinion of the whites on Marajo Island at the mouth of the Amazon in the tropical lowlands. These people lead a healthy and energetic pastoral life. Unless modern science can really defeat malaria and revolutionize conditions as regards comfort, however, white settlement has little hope in the low equatorial tropics of South America despite the battle that is being waged by such organizations as the United Fruit Company and the Ford Company against disease and discomfort. Ford's settlement on the Tapajoz River now embraces some 4000 persons and is replete with the most modern hospitals, sanitation, and shops. The employees are guarded against disease and enjoy an excellent diet, which includes fresh meat, vegetables, and bread.[35] The reports of the United Fruit Company, which conducts numerous "banana" settlements in the low tropics, describe a most efficient organization, conducted on highly scientific lines. In 1932 both the president of the company, Mr. Cutter, and its medical scientists said that the company's high expenditures on medicine and sanitation had more than paid. They added, very significantly, that an adequate standard of living was almost as vital to the employee in the low tropics as was the work of the medical scientist and sanitarian in safeguarding health. No private organization has done more to improve conditions in the low tropics than the United Fruit Company, but it must be remembered that its white employees are sojourners rather than settlers.[36]

A review of the problem of white settlement in the South American tropics indicates that both Mediterranean and northern whites can survive and even maintain fair standards under great difficulties of climate, isolation, and diet. Poor health and lack of comfort in the lowlands and isolation in the highlands present almost insurmountable obstacles, however, and, except perhaps in southern Brazil, the scattered white communities will almost certainly be absorbed in an Indian-negro-white race.

CHAPTER X

TROPICAL PLATEAUS: II. AFRICA

It is difficult to estimate the number of whites in tropical Africa.[1] There are probably now more than 50,000 British in Southern Rhodesia, 14,000 in Northern Rhodesia, 27,000 on the East African plateaus, and 8000 in West Africa. The French have 181,000 Creoles in Réunion, 22,000 whites in Madagascar, and 15,000 in their vast territories in West Africa.[2] When Sir Harry Johnston wrote in 1910 there were still 50,000 whites in Mauritius, but he considered that the island would become the home of a brown people, half negro and half Indian, with a strain of white blood.[3] The chief French populations lie outside the tropics to the north. The Portuguese and Italian colonies in tropical Africa contain a number of whites, and the Italian conquest of the plateaus of Abyssinia may have far-reaching consequences.

History

Up to the middle of the eighteenth century no modern European nation wished to colonize any part of tropical Africa. The whites were seeking trade, particularly the trade in negro slaves, and they fought those who would not deal with them.[4] At the end of the eighteenth and the beginning of the nineteenth century a new factor, evangelical missionary enthusiasm, entered the field, and a missionary, David Livingstone, took the leading place in the final opening of the continent. As soon as they had determined the main geographical features, the European nations began the "scramble for Africa," and their exploitation of the continent resembled in many ways the earlier conquest of the Americas. Down to the great war the eyes of the world were focused upon Africa. The trader and the missionary pressed forward, and plantations followed in their train. Once again the European nations assumed political supremacy and exacted plantation labor from colored peoples, and, as in the New World, racial problems became prominent. Unlike the West Indies, however, large areas of tropical Africa were closely populated by indigenous races, which the whites and their diseases were unable to exterminate. Despite the survival of the native peoples, some European nations introduced colored exotic stocks, such as Indians and Chinese, with the result that the racial kaleidoscope became even more complex.

As in the New World, the close of the nineteenth century and the opening of the twentieth saw the prescientific invasion merge in the scientific. Medical and sanitary science fundamentally altered health conditions. Railway engineers linked together distant territories in such regions as South Africa, Nigeria, and East Africa.[5]

Europeans, or peoples of European origin, now govern practically the whole of the African tropics, but they rule as aliens or sojourners except in a few regions that especially favor white settlement. Of these the plateaus of British East and Central Africa are particularly interesting and important.

The British Plateaus

In eastern and southern Africa, between latitudes 5° N. and 23° S., Britain rules a region of more than 1,100,000 square miles, consisting largely of tropical plateaus that seem to offer possibilities for white settlement. The territories and inhabitants included in this region in 1930 are shown in Table XI.

The climates of East and Central Africa vary greatly with latitude and altitude. Table XII gives the statistics for important white settlements in the interior and for Mombasa on the coast.

It will be seen that for Nairobi, Salisbury, and Kimberley the climatic figures are comparable with those of the plateaus of Costa Rica or tropical Queensland. There is, however, one fundamental difference—the presence of a colored people of lower cultural and economic status. H. Clifford Darby sums up the resulting effects. Southern Rhodesia, Northern Rhodesia, and Nyasaland form "three archipelagoes of settlement" in a sea of bush and scrub, with smaller island clusters in Angola, Kenya, and Tanganyika. In these subtropical highlands the white man is establishing a culture that is essentially dependent upon the exploitation of native labor, and the white man must always be in the position of master or foreman.[6]

Climate, Health, and Energy

Opinions vary as to the effects of the plateau climate upon the white inhabitants, and the presence of the native population greatly confuses the outlook. Most authorities express cautious views on the present evidence.[7] Dr. A. M. Fleming, the principal medical officer for Southern Rhodesia, wrote about 1923 that the country was formerly regarded as unfit for white men but that this view had been discredited, fever having been conquered. In his opinion, "It would be hard to find a collection of people whose general physical fitness was so apparent, or who exhibited less evidence of degeneration." [8] Dr. W. M. Hewetson, writing in 1922, stated that Rhodesia contained "a blonde community, small in numbers, . . . but highly selected and approximating already to a fixed type, with characteristics of its own showing distinctly; a high standard of initiative . . . and an average productivity much above the rest of South Africa." [9] In a careful climatic analysis Hewetson noted factors such as the monotony of the climate, the good effects of winds, and the

TABLE XI—TROPICAL AFRICA: AREA AND POPULATION STATISTICS*

| | AREA SQ. MILES | EUROPEAN POPULATION | NATIVE POPULATION | |
			All colored	Native
Southern Rhodesia......	150,354	49,564	1,047,000	1,043,000
Northern Rhodesia......	290,320	13,454	1,331,830	1,331,229
Kenya..........	224,960	16,885	3,081,650	3,024,575
Tanganyika......	360,000	8,228	5,055,038	5,022,640
Uganda.........	93,981	2,023	3,530,987	3,515,910
Total...........	1,119,615	90,154	14,046,505	13,937,354

*Data from the South and East African Year Book and Guide, 1932 and 1937.

TABLE XII—AFRICA: CLIMATIC DATA FOR CERTAIN STATIONS*

| STATION AND LENGTH OF RECORD | LAT. | ALT. (feet) | TEMPERATURE (degrees Fahr.) | | RELATIVE HUMIDITY (per cent 24 hours) | ANNUAL RAINFALL (inches) |
			Mean ann.	Range		
Kisumu 1931–1935.... Kenya	0°	3,733	72.9	2.3	64	44.69 (32 years)
Nairobi 1916–1935.... Kenya	1°16'S	5,495	66.8	6.5	66	34.90 (20 years)
Mombasa 1931–1935... Kenya	4°4'S	53	80.6	7.9	77	47.00 (45 years)
Fort Johnston........ Nyasaland	15°0'S	1,558	76.0	13.0	..	33.50
Salisbury 1921–1930... Southern Rhodesia	17°49'S	4,865	64.0	15.6	64	31.25
Kimberley (5 years)... Griqualand	28°42'S	4,012	64.2	25.2	51	18.26
Durban.............. Natal	29°51'S	260	72.4	13.3	..	39.48

*Statistics from: The South and East African Year Book, 1938; A. A. Miller: Climatology, London, 1931; and the Köppen-Geiger "Handbuch der Klimatologie," Vol. V, Part 10, 1933.

unknown influence of atmospheric electricity. He was unable, however, to reply "yes" or "no" to the question, would the Rhodesian whites succeed in setting up "a blonde independent state in the tropics." The cost of life had been heavy. The birth rate was 23.5 per 1000 as compared with 27 in England, and miscarriages seemed more common. While he believed that the main hope for the future lay in locally born white children, the reports of the Medical Inspector in the Department of Education showed that Rhodesia was "up against it." In the words of the inspectors, "We are beyond the natural range of our species." [10]

The evidence before the Joint Select Committee on Closer Union in East Africa [11] was also hesitant and inconclusive. Most of the witnesses, even after years of African experience, declined to commit themselves on the subject of white settlement and climate. They admitted that the third generation of native-born whites was beginning to appear, but said that they would like to see how this and the fourth generation developed. Dr. H. H. Hunter of Uganda thought that people of European ancestry could do manual work on the African plateaus. Sir E. H. M. Leggett considered that the climate presented an insuperable difficulty and that the whites could not carry out manual labor. Many writers on Africa, however, are beginning to subscribe to the views of Australian tropical doctors on the importance of hard physical work. Hewetson, for example, believes that manual labor in itself is not detrimental and that it is obviously one of the chief duties of the government to encourage exercise and sport.[12] Sir Daniel Hall puts the position even more strongly: "The poor white class has arisen in South Africa precisely because public opinion has ruled out manual labour upon the land as a fitting occupation for a white man. If an aristocratic class is created that cannot be allowed to dig, some members of it inevitably will become not ashamed to beg." [13] Agriculture is, and must remain, the prime source of employment in Kenya, and if a permanent white population is to be maintained there must be opportunities in the only industry in the country for all sorts and conditions of men." [14]

Isolation and Comfort

The truth is that the problem of white settlement is obscured by many other factors, not a few of which are social or economic in character. Malaria, sleeping sickness, blackwater fever, and other diseases greatly impede the settlement of some of the best areas. H. C. Darby notes, for instance, that "in the school medical examination of Southern Rhodesia half the children gave indications of having had malaria." [15] Isolation is also detrimental in the pioneer regions and is particularly harassing to women. Hewetson describes the problems of the outback farmers. These people, he says, have to live in isolated two-roomed houses and often possess no telephone, horse, or motor. They secure their supplies with great labor. They face grave difficulties and expense in obtaining dental and medical service, or family education. Their womenfolk live in constant fear of assault. Housing conditions are frequently disgraceful and call to mind the Australian "rural slums." Hewetson [16] condemns in round terms the use of the "satanically convenient, but pernicious and damnable galvanized iron, about the best conceivable material for transmitting heat." The coat of arms of the new Rhodesia should be "a sheet of corrugated iron rampant." "The man," says Hewetson, "goes out in a pith helmet and leaves his wife and children to stew in an inverted iron pan." Other things being equal, there was a remarkable difference in the bloom and appearance of children living in iron-roofed from those living in thatched houses. The railway houses in particular were always a scandal.[17] These things, together with the constant strain of supervizing native servants, make great calls on the nervous strength of the women. Authorities disagree as to whether the sunshine and the high altitudes of the plateaus tend to increase nervous tension.

Opinions also differ regarding children. As in most parts of the tropics, babies do very well in Rhodesia, but some residents think that in later years children become listless, fretful, and more susceptible to malaria.[18] On the other hand, several men and women informed the Joint Committee that the children were perfectly well and that the only reasons for sending them away were education and the necessity of preventing them from mixing with the natives. Lord Francis Scott gave most favorable evidence to the Joint Committee. He considered that there was no white deterioration in Kenya and that the children were, if anything, of better physique than in England. There was no reason at all from a health point of view why the white race should not go on doing extremely well.[19]

Racial Problems

General Smut's picturesque exaggeration holds an element of truth: "The question of white and black on the African continent is going to be the most interesting and enthralling problem of the twentieth century."

The evidence from the East African plateaus appears to indicate that the gravest obstacles to white settlement lie in neither health nor climate but in the presence of colored peoples. Witness after witness emphasized this point to the Joint Committee, and almost every authority states unequivocally that the great economic and social problems arising from interracial relations are the crux of the matter.

A neutral observer, R. L. Buell, thus summarizes the subject: "The native is deprived of land which he has regarded as his own, and because of the land shortage . . . he has been obliged to work for the European employer." White immigration has produced the same problems as elsewhere, and the same type of restrictions. The government establishes native reserves, which encroach on native lands and then become inadequate. The native males are reduced to the status of migratory wage earners bound down by many restrictions, and home and family life disintegrate. The whites, on the other hand, become a class of "old

Virginian gentry," holding large quantities of undeveloped land, owing to the scarcity of labor and the desire to speculate. Beneath the white planters and between the races emerge a poor-white and mixed population marked by all the horrors of racial feeling and miscegenation.[20]

Unlike Buell, some writers consider that white influence has been beneficial in the African tropics and that these regions contain room for both white and black. Nevertheless, the majority of those who understand the local conditions are alarmed for the future of the whites, owing to racial relations, the development of the native population, and the altered policy of the British government. Although the poor-white question has not arisen as in South Africa,[21] "there are elements at work that sap the energies and weaken the morale of the privileged European." The report of a recent commission on education states:

"We found among witnesses everywhere a lively and almost alarmed sense of the danger of moral degeneration which threatens the youth of a country where the services of others are so easily come by, and where the labor that serves the first needs of life is apt to be despised as menial and dishonoring." [22]

It is indeed questionable whether a race freed entirely from the necessity of manual labour can retain, without some special effort, its full virility. The upper strata of every society are continually recruited from the layers beneath. This is impossible in a land where a white aristocracy rests on a foundation of black labor. . . . There is, furthermore, the direct psychological effect of the native. The Rhodesian child is bereft of a large portion of the white inheritance.[23]

The Commission declares further that children growing up in such a situation may come to have different and probably lower standards than their pioneer forefathers. Yet, the maintenance of such standards will be the deciding factor in these white settlements.

Other matters that are seriously alarming British settlers in East Africa are the growth and development of the native population and the changed attitude of the British government. The whites have become fearful of their position "between the upper and nether millstones; between the direction from interests and policies outside, and the rapid increase and rise of a native race." [24] They state with justice that the British government encouraged white immigration in the years following 1904 and then, after the whites had become firmly established, evolved such doctrines as the "dual mandate" or "dual policy," and the "permanent trusteeship." These, stripped of official verbiage, mean in plain speech preference for the majority—in other words, preference for the native. The mass of evidence in the various reports leads to only one conclusion: that the fears of the white settlers are fully justified. The so-called White Paper of 1923 stated, for instance, that the primary duty of the Colonial Government in Kenya is the advancement of the African. In the words of this report:

Primarily, Kenya is an African territory, and His Majesty's Government think it necessary definitely to record their considered opinion that the interests of the African natives must be paramount, and that if, and when, those interests and the interests of the immigrant races should conflict, the former should prevail.[25]

The White Paper of 1927 laid down "the Imperial duty of safeguarding the interests and progress of the native population as trustees for their welfare until such time as they can take part more fully in their own Government and in the common affairs of all races inhabiting the territories." [26] This policy is restated with certain modifications in a White Paper of 1930 [27] and other official documents.[28] Professor Wellington summarizes the present position thus:

> . . . the British government has declared that it will maintain "the dual policy" of regarding native interests in East Africa as paramount and that the interests of the European settlers will be furthered in so far as they are in harmony with the measures taken to ensure the development of the native people. Many settlers feel that the importance of their position lies in the "strong settlement" policy of encouraging more and more European immigrants. Others think that the labor shortage will become more acute unless a halt is called. Certainly the situation requires the utmost caution. East Africa needs the outpost of European civilization; but whether this community can be greatly increased on its present basis of native labor, without detriment to the native peoples, is extremely doubtful.[29]

On the African plateaus the native population seems likely to increase more rapidly than the white, while the imported Indians will continue to foment political disturbances as they are doing in places such as Fiji. In these circumstances, the minority population of whites will possibly seek to throw in their lot with the powerful and self-governing whites of South Africa, for these communities will continue the control of the negroes as do the whites of the United States.

Biologically the future is a mark of interrogation. The British whites of East Africa may, perhaps, evolve into working communities and hold their own against the negro. It seems more likely, however, that the negro will undercut and absorb or drive out these whites as he has done in most parts of tropical America and the West Indies.[30]

The South African Analogy

In comparison with the natives the British and Dutch of South Africa are numerically far stronger than are the whites of the tropics to the north. Nevertheless, the experience of the South Africans indicates the problems that will probably result from the British penetration of the tropical plateaus. In 1858 the fundamental law of the Transvaal Republic declared that "the people will not tolerate equality between the coloured and white inhabitants either in church or state," and this racial feeling still overshadows every aspect of South African life.[31] The whites fear the growing numbers, enlightenment, and economic abilities of the negroid peoples—such, for example, as their increasing ability as artisans.[32] The natives on their side lack historical knowledge. They fail to appreciate those advantages that have come with the white immigration,[33] and hatred radiates from the great labor centers, which Lord Selborne aptly likened to European universities. It is true that authorities such as Lionel Curtis and Margery Perham now see hope in the young generation of liberal South Africans, but, no matter how enlightened these young leaders may be, they face a task of appalling difficulty in reconciling the interests of the races, in guiding native progress, and in combating the bitter opposition of the more ignorant and isolated Europeans, and the poor whites.[34]

Although it is almost impossible to effect, the segregation of the races appears to be the only solution that offers any hope. General Hertzog is quoted as stating in 1925 that "a bloody revolution" seemed likely "unless through his policy of native segregation the white man's economic safety was assured." [35]

Other authorities stress the same difficulties in both the temperate regions and the tropics. C. T. Loram writes:

A supply of native labour is indispensable to the pioneer in Central and South Africa. . . . The debilitating influence of a tropical and subtropical climate, the prevalence of insect-transmitted bacterial diseases, and the depredations of stock-consuming wild beasts make farming impossible in the pioneer belts without the aid of the native. Besides, he is there. Why not use him? [36]

According to J. H. Wellington, "Native labor is almost indispensable to the white settler in the pioneer zone on account of the high summer temperatures and the scarcity of white labor." [37]

The Poor-White Problem in the South African Subtropics

Already in southern Africa the intermingling of white and colored has produced those disharmonies that are customary when races of widely different civilization, culture, and economic status associate. W. C. Willoughby writes:

For a generation or two the illgotten gains of the slave-owner seem to spell prosperity; and then dry rot sets in: industry and enterprise languish, and the community is afflicted with parasitic problems wellnigh insoluble, like the decadence of the southern portions of the United States. . . . What can be done with a crowd of poverty-stricken Whites who have nothing but their own muscles to put upon the labour market and are still dominated by the notion that manual labour is only fit for "niggers"? [38]

Buell notes that poor whites comprise some 5 to 10 per cent of the European population of South Africa. They are Europeans who, because of general lack of education or efficiency, are unable to maintain European standards either as tenants on European farms or as workers in the cities, where they dwell in great poverty.

Willoughby does not wholly condemn the South African hybrids. He denies that they combine "the vices of both races and the virtues of neither," although the hybrid is generally born of a vicious father, who deserts the mother and leaves the offspring to be spurned by other races.[39] The South African Census of 1921 indicated that this mixed population, which then numbered 546,000 or 7.9 per cent of the total population, was increasing at the low rate of 3.73 per cent a year. Deducting white immigrants, however, the total white increase in South

Africa from 1911 to 1921 was not as great as the colored increase. The Director of the Census of 1921 wrote: "It will require very little calculation to show that if the white race is to hold its own over South Africa, it will be necessary to secure an immense development of white civilization during the next fifty or perhaps only the next twenty-five years." According to Buell "the European race can only hold its own numerically by seeking accessions abroad. Failing this, it must forever abandon the prospect of maintaining a white civilization except as a proportionately diminishing minority." [40]

An exhaustive investigation, the Carnegie Report on "The Poor White Problem in South Africa," throws important light on this subject. [41] The surveyors, who included medical scientists, educationists, sociologists, economists, statisticians, agricultural experts, and others, obtained data covering most of the Union, in which they estimate that the poor whites number about 220,000. They consider that "maladjustment to changed conditions" is "the main cause of the problem" and that isolation and insufficient and unsuitable education have produced psychological traits that are largely responsible for the maladjustment to the demands of modern life. [42] The investigators deny that the warm climate creates any deterioration and specifically refute Dr. Ellsworth Huntington's views on the poor-white problem of South Africa as set out in his "Civilization and Climate." Murray, for example, emphasizes the fact that the poor-white problem first appeared in the Karoo, which is a region of cold winters and sharp frosts. [43] In the opinion of the surveyors:

. . . neither epidemic diseases nor insufficient or unsuitable diet, nor climate play an important part among the great primary causes of impoverishment of a section of the white population in South Africa. But conditions of poverty and ignorance lead to lack of food and to wrong diet. This weakens the resistance of the poor white to disease, reduces his working power, and so makes the problem more acute. [44]

The report lays considerable emphasis upon the deleterious effects of bad housing and diet, and notes the manner in which an inadequate diet increases the incidence of malaria. [45] An important finding is that the majority of poor whites are of normal intelligence and about one third possess more than average intelligence. Unfortunately, however, the intelligence of the whole group is lower on the average than that of the entire European population, and the percentage classed as subnormal is about twice as large as that of the European population as a whole. [46] In discussing the relation between the poor whites and the non-Europeans the report discloses a main root of the difficulty. Under European rule the native population is increasing greatly, and in many cases the areas inhabited by the natives have become too small to support them all. Thus the native comes into competition with the European, and, although he is on the average a poorer laborer, he accepts lower wages and creates for the European a condition of poverty that is demoralizing. [47] Economic equality and propinquity of dwellings tend to produce social equality and miscegenation, and "the social line of colour division is noticeably weakening".[48] The Carnegie Report thus indicates that racial contacts in South Africa are repeating a process found in many climatic zones.

We have emphasized this question of the poor white in the South African subtropics because of its great significance in the tropics of that continent. If the whites, who are numerous and firmly established in southern Africa, are facing grave difficulties and doubtful prospects, what are the hopes of the little "white islands" of settlement on the tropical plateaus to the north? [49]

OTHER PARTS OF THE AFRICAN TROPICS

Evidence from the other regions in tropical Africa supports in general the lessons taught by the eastern and central plateaus.[50] South West Africa and Portuguese Angola contain tropical highlands, which can be exploited by whites. The central highlands of Angola [51] attain a width of some 400 miles and rise to heights of 4500 feet. The mean monthly temperatures range between 59° and 70° and the rainfall is from 40 to 55 inches a year. In these highlands Lubango, which is connected by rail with Mossamedes on the coast, was settled by white immigrants from Brazil and Madeira in 1885, and today its 3000 whites substantially outnumber the natives. T. A. Barns attributes some of the success of these settlers to diet: "General health here as elsewhere in Africa depends, to a great extent, on good fresh food well prepared. . . . The Portuguese have never gone in for tinned foods." [52] Another interesting settlement is that of the restless Boers who colonized Huila (lat. 14° S.) about 1880. These and other small communities may continue for some time as isolated "white islands," but ultimately they are almost certain to be submerged.

CHAPTER XI

THE AMERICANS IN PANAMA

Throughout the world scientists have recognized the American success at Panama as epoch-making in regard to health and sanitation; yet they have tended to look upon the experiment as a geographical and economic freak. In reality Panama is a great, many-sided achievement by a white nation in the low tropics, and its results have already had excellent effects on both sojourners and settlers throughout the tropical world.

CLIMATE AND PHYSIOGRAPHY

The Panama Canal lies in latitude 9° N., close to the thermal equator. As the region possesses a dry season (January-April) and a wet season (May-December), Austin Miller classes it as tropical rather than equatorial, but Table XIII below indicates that the climate is almost as extreme as the climates of the true equatorial coasts. The Canal Zone consists of a strip of land some forty-five miles long and ten miles wide (Fig. 73). The Atlantic coast area is made up of low, swampy alluvial flats with lagoons extending inland for several miles. The Pacific coast has more elevation, but high tides create many swamps. Inland the Chagres River and its tributaries flow through numerous valleys and low hills, where the heavy rainfall produces countless pools, swamps, and springs and dense, wet tropical jungle. On the whole the soil is poor, and this, together with the fact that the rainfall is seasonal towards the Pacific, accounts for difficulties and failures in agriculture.

The two chief American settlements are at Balboa Heights, near Panama City on the Pacific, and at Cristobal-Colon on the Atlantic side. In 1932 there were, exclusive of naval and military ratings, 6556 whites at Balboa and 1849 at Colon. While no great differences in health appear between the two stations, scientists point to substantial contrasts in the local climates, as the dividing hills from 200 to 1000 feet in height shut off the Atlantic trade winds and create more continental conditions on the Pacific side.

Table XIII indicates that Balboa Heights is slightly cooler, drier, and less humid than Colon. Also it has the advantage of a higher daily temperature range, although Colon is more windy, owing to the northeast trades. The French canal builders, who selected the airy Balboa Heights for their hospitals and other buildings, chose a site of local climatic advantage, a fact that has probably helped the American efforts. At the same time there is no doubt that the climates of Balboa Heights and Colon are intensely tropical. Although these American stations may

146

not experience the severe summer temperatures of monsoonal places, such as Lahore (India) or Wyndham (Western Australia), where the average temperatures of the midsummer months approach or exceed ninety degrees, the heat and humidity are trying for whites throughout the whole year.

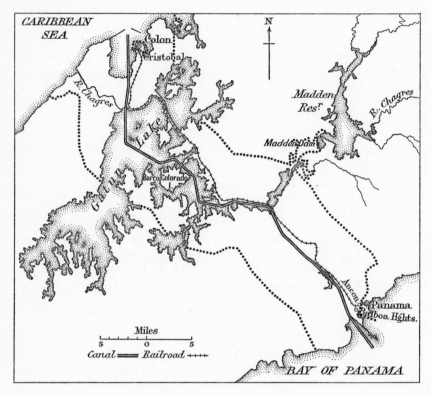

FIG. 73—Map of the Panama Canal Zone. Scale: 1: 650,000.

Such is the climate and physiography of a region once known as "the pest hole of the world." In 1880 the Dean of the Medical Faculty at Panama stated: "First you have the wet season lasting from about the 15th of April to the 15th of December, when people die of yellow fever in four or five days. Next you have the dry season . . . when people die of pernicious fever in from twenty-four to thirty-six hours." [1] As late as 1903 the Panama Canal district was officially described as "one of the hottest, wettest and most feverish regions in existence. Intermittent and malignant fevers are prevalent, and there is an epidemic of yellow fever at times. The death rate under normal conditions is large." Dr. H. R. Carter in his "Yellow Fever" called the region "a permanent regional focus" for that disease, "because yellow fever existed at some place in it at all times; and from such infected places other places in the region were infected from time to time." [2]

TABLE XIII—PANAMA: CLIMATIC DATA, WITH DATA FOR COMPARISON
WITH OTHER REGIONS*

STATION	LAT.	ALT. (feet)	TEMPERATURE (degrees Fahr.)					RELA-TIVE HUMID-ITY (per cent)	RAIN-FALL (inches)	WIND (miles per hour)
			Mean ann.	Jan.	July	Daily range dry season	Daily range wet season			
Balboa...	9°N	100	78.6	78.2	78.7	19.1	14.5	83.1	68.8	7.6
Colon....	9°N	36	79.8	79.8	79.9	6.8	8.9	83.3	128.4	10.5
Colombo.	7°N	24	80.2	79.0	80.0	..	..	78.0	83.1	..
Batavia..	6°S	23	79.0	77.9	78.7	1.8		85.0	72.1	..
Cairns...	16°S	16	76.5	82.2	69.9	..	..	72.0 (9A.M.)	88.4	..

*The climatic data for the Panama Canal Zone have been kindly furnished by R. Z. Kirkpatrick, Chief Hydrographer, Panama Canal; those for Colombo and Batavia are from Kendrew: The Climates of the Continents and the Köppen-Geiger "Handbuch der Klimatologie," Vol. 2, Part H; and those for Cairns from the Commonwealth of Australia Council for Scientific and Industrial Research, *Pamphlet No. 42.* On the climate of Panama see also Annual Reports of the Governors of the Panama Canal, Washington; C. F. Brooks: Notes on the Climate of Panama, *Geogr. Rev.,* 1920, Vol. 10, pp. 268–269; and F. D. Willson: The Climatology and Hydrology of the Panama Canal, *in* G. W. Goethals: The Panama Canal, New York, 1916, Vol. 1, pp. 223–334; [H. L. Abbot: Climatology of the Isthmus of Panama, Including the Temperature, Winds, Barometric Pressure, and Precipitation, *Monthly Weather Rev.,* Vol. 27, 1899, pp. 198–203; the same, Climatology of the Isthmus of Panama, *ibid.,* Vol. 31, 1903, pp. 117–124.—R. G. S.].

EARLY HISTORY OF HEALTH

From 1520 onwards the early Spanish settlers established between the Atlantic and the Pacific two overland trade routes, which became the main lines of communication between Spain and the west coast of the Americas and the Philippines. Primitive means of transport were used up to the middle of the nineteenth century, when, after the rush to the California gold diggings, an American company constructed the Panamanian railway in 1850-1855.

From the very earliest days of white occupation the region was damned through the loss of unacclimatized Spaniards (often the highest officials), and when the area boomed again in the gold rush its unsavory reputation grew apace. Many of the gold diggers perished in crossing the isthmus. The Fourth Infantry of the United States Army lost 80 out of 810 men, largely as the result of marching halfway across, and so appalling was the mortality among the builders of the railway that it was said that every cross tie represented a life. The company, for example, imported 1000 negroes from the west coast of Africa. In six months they died. It then imported 1000 Chinamen. In six months they too were dead.

The idea of a canal across the isthmus dates back to Spanish times, and several surveys were made before 1881 when De Lesseps and the

French attempted to repeat their success at Suez. Again, however, the newcomers suffered colossal losses. Malaria, yellow fever, dysentery, typhoid, smallpox, uncinariasis and cutaneous infections were endemic and were primarily responsible for the French debacle. Each influx of non-immunes led to a recrudescence of yellow fever, which by its deadly and spectacular character terrified new arrivals from the temperate zone. Malaria proved an even more serious obstacle owing to the fact that it created chronic disability among workers of all nationalities. Intestinal diseases also caused heavy mortality. It has been estimated that in all 16,000 men perished in a force that averaged only 10,000.[3] The French were not wholly to blame for these disasters. It is true that their force suffered from lack of screened houses, water closets, and bathrooms and that their administration left much to be desired. In those early days of scientific medicine, however, the role of the mosquito in yellow fever and malaria was unsuspected and the control of intestinal disease but little understood. Also the company had no power to enforce sanitary measures in the adjacent Colombian territory.

THE AMERICAN REGIME

On May 4, 1904, the Americans purchased the property of the French company, and United States personnel began to arrive. The new regime commenced with the advantage of a treaty agreement with the young Republic of Panama, under which the United States secured unrestricted sanitary control over a strip of territory covering five miles on each side of the center of the canal, together with the cities of Panama and Colon. Also, during the previous ten years two discoveries in the field of epidemiology had paved the way for a scientific attack on yellow fever and malaria. The control of intestinal infections was also improving, and the new-comers possessed practically unlimited funds.

The Americans at once established a Sanitation Department under the governor of the Canal Zone and later placed this under control of the Isthmian Canal Commission as an independent department, with Colonel W. C. Gorgas in charge. In spite of the gravest difficulties and setbacks, the Americans pushed forward with splendid determination and ability. They completed waterworks, sewers, and paving in the city of Panama and spent millions in the cities and zone. In a very few years they had completely eliminated yellow fever by controlling the mosquito *aedes aegypti*, the last case to develop locally occurring in Colon in May, 1906.[4] As will be shown later, they were less successful in their attack on malaria, for the conditions of soil and climate remained ideal for the breeding of the anopheles mosquito, and the disease still continues to be one of the largest problems that the health authorities of the isthmus have to combat. Yet, although it has proved impossible to eradicate the anopheles from the entire zone and residents not connected with the government are required to reside at least one mile beyond the borders of the sanitated towns, the white inhabitants are perfectly safe provided they do not remain outside the protected areas at night. How well the Americans have handled the problem is shown by the fact that the hospital admission rate for malaria per thousand white employees fell from 821 in 1906 to 14 in 1917. Since the latter date it has varied between 11 and 31. From 1921 to 1931 only four deaths occurred.[5]

Very striking is the fact that the Americans obtained good results not only in the Canal Zone but in the crowded negro and mestizo cities of Panama and Colon. In Panama with its mixed population of 74,000 the death rate fell from 65 to 18.4 (1926-1930). The latter figure compares well with the statistics of some of the cities of the southern United States with mixed populations. By 1926-1930 the Americans had reduced the combined death rates of white and colored to 7.86 per thousand as compared with 29.8 in 1905-1909.[6]

The achievements of the Americans attracted great attention, and their technique spread throughout the tropics. As early as 1912 Sir R. P. Ashton paid them a glowing tribute and stated that the British authorities in India "could not do better than apply to the United States Government for the loan of one of Colonel Gorgas' officers to advise them. Such a man would bring ripe experience, and ideas new to India. He would be untrammelled by the fear of imperilling his promotion, by telling home truths, however unpalatable." [7]

American Overoptimism

Elated by their successes, a number of American scientists began to claim that "by far the larger part of the moribundity and mortality formerly attributed to tropical climates was due not to climate per se but to isolation, tedium, nostalgia, venereal disease, alcoholic excess, poor municipal conditions, and, most important of all, to infection with specific parasites, whose invasion is now almost wholly preventable." [8] Unfortunately, there now seems little doubt that General Gorgas and his supporters ignored important geographical and economic factors, that they unduly minimized the effects of climate per se on whites in the tropics, and that their claims were too wide. Even at the time, his sweeping assertions exposed Gorgas to much criticism and destroyed his friendship with W. E. Deeks, who was head of the Isthmian medical service, 1906-1914, and subsequently founded the great medical service of the United Fruit Company. Among other criticisms Deeks pointed out that the Panama force was a young picked group and that the characteristics of the second generation had still to be seen.

For a moderate and accurate summary we may quote an opinion of Colonel C. F. Mason [9] as both defining and limiting what the experiment achieved. The Americans, he stated, practically eliminated tropical and some other specific diseases, and he produced statistics of sickness and mortality that compared favorably with those of healthy communities in the temperate zone. He could not, however, follow Gorgas' claim that the Caucasian race under proper conditions could now live and work in the tropics as well as in the temperate zone and could establish important communities there. Mason considered that results similar to those achieved at Panama could be secured anywhere in the tropics with equally expert supervision and an equally great expenditure but that the tropics would never be a suitable permanent dwelling for the Caucasian race. Even with the conquest of disease there remained the influence of climate per se: the constant heat and moisture without a seasonal change. Some few persons apparently escaped injurious effects for long periods, but not the majority. The effects on second and third generations living under the climatic conditions of Panama could not be calculated as like conditions had not been observed before, but the known effects of heat and moisture in India were contrary to Gorgas' conclusions.[10] This summary of Colonel Mason's takes the argument beyond the field of health and sanitation into the whole arena of white settlement in the tropics.

History of Manual Labor

The White American Artisans

So striking were the American results in health and sanitation that they tended to obscure other important successes. To take an outstanding example, contemporaries considered that of all difficulties the labor problem seemed the hardest one to solve. Yet, even here, the Americans were successful, and their success produced results of worldwide significance.

At the outset the government decided to bring high-grade Americans to Panama, but the French losses and the American setbacks of 1904-1905 advertised the place so widely as "a pest hole" that it became necessary to offer unusually attractive living conditions and wages and to appoint recruiting officers to secure skilled and healthy men. At first, according to Colonel Goethals, the canal got "the roamers"—men, who, although in receipt of wages 40 to 50 per cent in excess of those of the homeland, stayed only a year and then gained free passages back to the United States. In these early days neither the personnel nor the conditions were satisfactory, while the officers had much to learn about tropical labor and life. Housing was poor, there was little facility for pleasure or recreation, and, despite the climate, the shops demanded extremely hard and fatiguing work. Nevertheless, there was something to be said on the side of the climate and the employers, for the workers included many loafers who expected the shops to be "a government proposition," and many who did things that they would have been ashamed to do in the homeland, such as yielding to alcoholic excess.

Gradually the authorities weeded out the drinkers and retained the sober and industrious, for it soon became evident "that the effects of intoxicants were far more deleterious than in the United States." Results quickly showed that it was all nonsense about the Zone killing men. If the workers took care of themselves, it was as healthful as any part of the United States.[11]

By 1907 the Americans in the Canal Zone were generally interested in their duties, and the fear of sickness had disappeared. The United States force of 5000-6000, which by that time included 1200 women and children, was better nourished than the colored employees and hence showed greater vitality and a far lower death rate. Later the Americans averaged a sixth to a seventh of the labor force and were employed in supervising skilled work and as mechanics, carpenters, plumbers, masons, electricians, steam-shovel men, locomotive engineers, constructors, firemen, and policemen. It will be noted that some of these occupations involved heavy manual labor. Numbers reached their maximum from 1908 to 1913, when there were more than 5000 Americans employed on the canal and the railway. By 1912 there were more than 4000 women and children in the Zone, a fact that prevented some of the worst evils of tropical white settlement and "contributed greatly to the successful building and operation of the Canal."

The good results were due not merely to novel and painstaking control of health and sanitation but to wise and generous furtherance of economic and social life. In 1913 Scott called the Americans employed on the canal "the most pampered body of workers in the world." They received, he said, "an eight-hour day with a two-hour intermission at noon; first-class board cheaper than in the United States, free quarters, free medical service on full pay, nine holidays on pay, ... wages and salaries from 30 to 80 per cent higher than in the United States, an annual vacation of forty-two days on full pay for gold employees, and the necessaries of life for sale at lower prices in the Government Commissary than in the United States."[12]

Much of the American success must indeed be attributed to the granting of adequate remuneration and to novel and highly efficacious housing and diet. In the early days there was much discontent over the use of some 2000 dilapidated houses left by the French, but the Commission gradually provided excellent, airy houses of a four-family type rent-free. These houses, which can be seen today in Colon and Balboa, were of a convenience hitherto unknown in the tropics. So open were they to air currents that no electric fans were necessary, and all were thoroughly screened and fitted with modern plumbing and sanitation. As early as 1910 Ashton was impressed by these "houses all built like huge meat safes" and by the fact that there were no crows, pigs, and pariah dogs to make up for neglected sanitation as in the East.

The Americans also greatly improved the diet. Not only did they reduce the early alcoholic excesses, but the Government Commissary sold at extremely low rates a wide variety of foodstuffs, which were secured with increasing facility as the canal became one of the great highways of the world. There is no doubt that the dietetic principles evolved in Panama will be of increasing importance in tropical settlements. As is explained elsewhere, the light meals of fish, milk, fruits, and green vegetables are infinitely preferable to the hot, heavy diets so widespread in British and Dutch tropical lands.

From 1914 on, the government reduced the force to a normal operating body of some 2400 persons on the canal and 450 on the railway. In 1921-1922, to the great indignation of the employees, it fixed salaries and wages at tropical service rates (25 per cent in excess of home remuneration) and charged for housing, light, and other services. Scott vigorously attacked the old labor force on the ground that they regarded themselves as "national heroes." The employees, on the other hand, asserted that the United States Congress thanked and rewarded officers of the army and navy, while it completely failed to recognize the services of the high civilian officials or of the ordinary American citizens, who did as much to build the canal as the military folk. The evidence in the controversy is disappointing in that it is biased and throws little light on such problems as the effects of climate per se. The employees, for example, attempted to substantiate two contradictory propositions. On the one hand, they clamored that the government was trying to substitute negro aliens for white Americans, whereas "the truest economy would be found in the employment of the more efficient and highly paid American citizen." On the other hand, they claimed that the government must maintain the old lavish wages, allowances, and free services, as the climate destroyed the health and efficiency of these same whites. Apparently the Panama Canal Commission recommended to the Secretary of War that on grounds of economy the governor of the canal should train and employ tropical (negro) labor "in much greater numbers and in much higher positions." A strong move by the American employees defeated this proposal in spite of the fact that they themselves produced a mass of rather nebulous evidence to prove that the effects of the climate were deleterious. At any rate, the United States government increased the white personnel by more than 400 in 1923, and it has since remained at about 2700. It will be explained later that, under unusually good conditions of health, sanitation, housing, diet, wages, and leave, these whites show little evidence of the so-called tropical degeneration, in spite of the fact that, in flat contradiction to the old theories, a number of employees (in some cases of the second generation) engage in hard manual labor and take comparatively rare vacations. On retirement many prefer to live and die in the Zone.

On the whole, the thirty years' history of the American whites in Panama leads to some unexpected conclusions. Although Gorgas' views proved unduly optimistic, the experiment showed that under scientific health control and good economic and social conditions large numbers of whites from the cool-temperate zone could live their lives in the low tropics and engage in strenuous manual labor that in the past had been conducted only by the colored peoples. As we shall see (pp. 164-165, below), the children of these tropical residents show no degeneration and some individuals remain almost permanently in this humid tropical zone.

Southern European Whites [13]

Although a number of white Americans were prepared to engage in hard manual work, the government turned in the first instance to the negro for unskilled labor. Many of the negroes from the United States were arrogant, unreliable, wasteful, and prone to assert their rights as American citizens, while the work of the mixed peoples of Central and South America proved thoroughly unsatisfactory. The authorities, therefore, sought British and French negroes from the West Indies. Of these the supply soon exceeded the demand, but their efficiency was so low that it was decided to import white labor of southern European origin. Agents were sent to Cuba, and there enlisted a body of 400 Spaniards, whose work proved so satisfactory that Spaniards, Italians, and various others from southern and central Europe were brought in from the old world. From 1906 to 1908 the Americans imported nearly 12,000 contract laborers, of whom 75 per cent were Spaniards and the remainder mainly Italians and Greeks. The maximum employed at any one time was approximately 5500 in the year 1908. Owing to voluntary departures the supply did not meet the demand until 1911, when the Commission began to reduce the force and to repatriate. There were still 1200 employed in 1914.

At first difficulties arose with the newcomers, as many would not live in screened quarters. Also there were insufficient women, and the incidence of malaria was high, owing to the number of workers who slept in native huts. As Dr. Deeks wrote in 1911:

Those of the European laborers who so desire live in well kept and carefully screened barracks, and, for families, screened quarters are provided. But no amount of advice seems to be effective in securing among them individual prophylaxes against disease. Every sanitary regulation needs to be rigidly enforced. They often prefer to sleep in hammocks, or even on the ground under their quarters or in other places. They mingle freely at night with the natives, and cannot be kept indoors. As a race they are not addicted to strong liquor but . . . an increase of malaria among them is always accompanied by an excess consumption of rum, and very inferior rum, in the belief that the drink is an efficient medicine.[14]

Even today at the Madden Dam the contractors encounter the same difficulties with the central Europeans in the working force.[15] On the other hand, the American authorities themselves had much to learn. The first batch of Spaniards went down with malaria in the healthful season. The second arrived in the wet season, but remained healthy because they were screened. In spite of such difficulties, the experiment proved extremely satisfactory and had great influence on the progress of the canal. Although the southern Europeans received twice as much for exactly the same work as that done by the negroes, their efficiency was estimated to be three times as great. Almost all observers spoke well of the Europeans. They were intelligent, reliable, and stuck closely to their work. P. S. Wilson, Inspector of European Labor during the construction period, stated, for example, that they worked hard in any weather and were particularly good in track gangs. Later many brought out their wives and children and formed a happy, cheerful, and contented labor force.[16] Major R. E. Wood of the Quartermaster's Department, Panama Canal, 1905-1915, it is true, gave the opinion that the efficiency of the whites declined and that "at the end of the construction period there was no great difference between the two classes of labor," [17] but his view is strongly contested by several who were in positions of authority during this period. P. S. Wilson considered that the Spaniards were excellent and did not deteriorate, with the exception of some old men who would have deteriorated in any case. The Cubans, Greeks, and Portuguese were also very satisfactory.[18] Vaughan Cornish supplied some interesting details from his experiences in the construction days. He stated that results showed the inability of Russians and Baltic folk to stand the conditions, while the French did not like pick-and-shovel work. The Greeks, Italians, and Spaniards did best. Physically the Italians were excellent and stood the climate well, but they were somewhat intractable. The Spaniards, who were mainly Galicians and Castilians, were sober, patient, and quick to learn.[19]

It appears that the greater part of the southern Europeans left when the Commission reduced wages. Some went to Guatemala with the United Fruit Company, where they did not prove satisfactory, as they failed to fit in with conditions of health, food, and language. A number are still at work in Panama. One highly skilled gang of Spaniards continues to give splendid service in wrecking work on the canal, and in 1933 the contractors at the Madden Dam were using some 122 central and southern Europeans, about 10 per cent of the force. The contractors and their officers gave interesting information on the relative value of the different types of labor. They employed Americans in all important mechanical positions, as Jamaican negroes injured the machines. They estimated that the southern Europeans were from 75 to 100 per cent more efficient than the Jamaicans. This white superiority was evident even in drilling and other extremely hard work. Unfortunately, the health of the Europeans was as much as 80 per cent poorer than that of the negroes, the Europeans being prone to malaria, owing to the old trouble of seeking women in the native camps. Nevertheless, it was gathered that, in spite of low pay, heat, hard work, and ill-health, the southern Europeans formed the backbone of the Madden Dam force.

In the opinion of several highly qualified American authorities, the United States made a fundamental error when they reduced wages and repatriated the southern Europeans in favor of the less expensive, but less efficient, West Indian negroes. The issue certainly showed that this action augmented the difficulties of health and sanitation and added immeasurably to the profound problems of racial relations and population increase.

Negro Labor [20]

Although white artisans from the United States and white laborers from southern Europe did much of the construction work at Panama, the bulk fell to the negroes. Several factors induced the Americans to utilize this type of labor. First, the history of industry in the United States provides an almost continuous record of northern whites avoiding manual effort by the importation of negroes, southern and central Europeans, Mexicans, Filipinos, and other peoples prepared to undertake hard and monotonous work. Second, the Americans had found the negro extremely useful and suitable in the hot southern states, and they were used to managing the colored race, which formed more than 10 per cent of their population at home. Third, the Spanish conquerors and the previous constructors of the canal and railway had all brought in and utilized negro labor, so much so that Colombians had long regarded Panama as the "black province" of their partly white republic.

As stated in a previous section, early efforts to introduce United States negroes were unsuccessful owing to the fact that many of them had proved unreliable, arrogant, extravagant, and jealous of their rights as American citizens. Nor was it easy to procure British and French negroes from the West Indies. The planters naturally wished to retain this labor, while the failure of the French canal company, which left 20,000 West Indian negroes stranded, had given Panama a very bad name. In the end, however, Jamaica sent negro artisans; Barbados supplied 19,900 workers, 30 to 40 per cent of the negro males in the island; and Guadeloupe and Martinique sent some 7500 French negroes. As wages were 10 cents or more an hour for pick-and-shovel work, together with free quarters and medical attention, commissary privileges, and repatriation after 500 working days, more than 30,000 workers were quickly secured.

There seems no doubt whatever that at the outset the efficiency of this colored labor force was extremely low. In 1906 the Canal Commission reported: "Another year's experience with negro laborers from near-by tropical islands and countries has convinced the Commission of the impossibility of doing satisfactory work with them. Not only do they seem to be disqualified by lack of actual vitality, but their disposition to labor seems to be as frail as their bodily strength." [21] It appeared that the Jamaicans lacked initiative, while Gorgas considered that they had poor resistance to disease. It was immediately after this report that southern Europeans were secured.

During 1907 and 1908, however, the authorities changed their tune. They began to attribute the negroes' lack of strength and initiative to improper diet and to poor handling by inexperienced American foremen. The negroes now showed "a better disposition towards labor." The different divisions began to compete eagerly for labor from the West Indies with such keen rivalry that on one occasion members of the Municipal Engineering Division and the Building Department engaged in a street fight.[22] R. E. Wood asserts that as time went on the efficiency of the West Indians increased. "They developed steadiness . . . [and made] tremendous improvement . . . learned many of the trades and . . . developed into first class construction men." Yet even Wood, who considered the efficiency of the southern Europeans and negro forces about equal, admitted that their ability was "not comparable with the efficiency of unskilled labor in the United States."[23] Down to the present time opinions on the relative merits of negro and white labor have differed greatly, and, as indicated above, the relative proportion of white and colored workers has remained fairly stationary since the construction years.

The difficulty of reaching a definite conclusion on the merits of white and colored labor in Panama can be shown by two contradictory results obtained in tests of a very similar nature. In November, 1909, Messrs. Hebard and Alberts, who offered 35 cents a cubic yard for the removal of material on contract, found that French and British West Indian negroes were far superior to southern Europeans, while Central Americans could not do the work at all. On the other hand, the views of the contractors and overseers at the Madden Dam concur as to the immense superiority of white Europeans over negroes, even in very heavy manual work.

From 1904 to 1914 the Americans introduced 31,071 West Indian negroes, together with 11,873 southern Europeans and 2113 Central and South Americans. At the close of the construction period in 1913 the authorities repatriated large numbers of negroes and the fruit companies took several thousands for their Central and South American work. The plans as formulated anticipated a reduction in personnel by no less than 9659, but, as "the reduction was not as extensive as was anticipated," thousands of negroes abandoned their rights to repatriation and remained to complicate the racial, health, and other problems that are becoming more and more menacing to the American and Panamanian governments.

THE CANAL FORCE TODAY

The concluding sections of this chapter will deal with the present position of the white and colored workers and with some of the major problems that the Americans are facing today in the Canal Zone.

Numbers

The Census of 1930 stated that there were then 18,634 white and 20,519 colored persons in the Canal Zone and that the white employees numbered 3589 and the colored 11,935. Of the total number of whites 13,152 were men, 3193 women, and 2289 children under fourteen years of age. As about 9700 of the males were army and navy personnel stationed in Panama for comparatively short periods, there seem to have been some 3400 white males who were permanent residents. Of the total 18,634 whites, 1878 had been born in the tropics, 1684 having been born in Panama or in the Canal Zone. As most of the tropical-born were probably children of the permanent body of canal and railway employees, it is likely that these tropical-born whites formed quite a high percentage of the permanent residents.

Length of Residence

From the report of the governor of the Canal Zone it appears that the turnover of white employees was rather more than 13 per cent in 1931, which makes an average service of seven to eight years.[24] "The Canal Diggers in Panama," a statement of the case for the American employees, gives important details up to the end of 1927. It appears that of 2316 employees on the canal in December, 1927, 1095, or 47 per cent, had completed ten years. Periods of service were naturally longer on the older Panama railway. Of 429 Americans 240, or 56 per cent, had completed ten years, and 52 of these had exceeded twenty years. In addition there were a few cases of very long service: 29, 32, and even 36 years. From these statistics the employees claimed that the retiring age of 62 was too high. They stated that "25 years' service in the tropics is the maximum that should be required for voluntary retirement" and that employees in occupations requiring considerable physical activity should be retired when they reach 55 and all others when they reach 60 years.[25]

Probably such provision is wise under present conditions in Panama, but there is little doubt that the establishment in the Canal Zone of a physiological research institute to study problems of acclimatization would result in a better selection of persons capable of living a long life in the tropics. It is already most significant that some employees can work for far more than 25 years and that others on retirement wish to continue residing in the Zone. We saw in the workshops men who for years had retained good health, though laboring under very hot and dusty conditions. One group of molders, who were working infinitely harder than their negro assistants, averaged 17 to 18 years of service with a maximum of 29 years.

Advantages at Panama

There is every reason why the Americans at Panama should be the happiest body of tropical whites in the world. Not only is the canal economically profitable in normal times, but the United States government is prepared to foster it on grounds of national defense, with the result that the canal employees secure substantial concessions. The Canal Commission, for example, pays salaries and wages on a so-called "tropical scale," which is 25 per cent above home rates for the same type of work. Although the authorities now make a number of charges, such as rent for bungalows, they provide pensions, generous leave, cheap fares for the personnel and for their automobiles to and from the United States, and other concessions that increase substantially the high remuneration paid under the "tropical scale." The housing provided for white Americans is generally good and is splendidly suited to tropical conditions. The single or four-family bungalows are adequately screened, yet completely open to the air. Even the government restaurants are screened and wide open on three sides. As a result, electric fans are neither necessary nor desired. All the houses are fitted with modern sanitary plumbing and baths. American methods at Panama put British Indian, British Malayan, and north Australian sanitation (or lack of sanitation) to shame. In this respect the Americans seem to be approached only by the Dutch (Figs. 74, 75).

Very modern, too, and very sensible are American modes of dress. One sees neither heavy helmets nor shirts reinforced against sunstroke. The dress of men, women, and children is light and airy in the extreme, and men enter restaurants, even in the evenings, in white trousers and white open shirts without collars or ties.

As Panama has become one of the chief world highways, the diet is now adequate and of wide range. The government restaurants offer delicacies and varied meals at moderate cost, with ample vegetables and fruits, and it is the fault of Americans themselves if some live mainly on canned food. In 1933 we failed to discover the lack of milk complained of three years previously in the Columbia University survey. The canal authorities have certainly done their best to make the isthmus independent of imported food supplies. They have established plantations, experimental gardens, cattle ranches, and a dairy farm, but there are considerable difficulties, as the rainfall is variable and a great deal of the soil very poor. Much has also been done to provide those facilities for amusement that are so essential to any community likely to suffer from isolation. There are good clubs, motion pictures, tennis, golf, and excellent bathing, for swimming is an almost universal sport.

It is difficult to estimate how far the American success may be due to adequate vacations and generous concessions to those wishing to take leave in the United States. Most of the employees and their families spend a few months in the United States every two or three years and claim that they benefit even from vacations spent in the trying summer climate of the eastern United States. Others again told us, as did British people in Singapore, that unless they take vacations they suffer more and more from "tropical memory"; yet others, hard-working and apparently healthy, stated that they had taken little or no leave at all. Again, the question seems one of individual powers of acclimatization, but for the majority of whites, vacations in the cool-temperate zone seem necessary.

Occupations, Manual Labor

The Columbia University survey of the Canal Zone schools, 1930, includes an analysis of white occupations in Panama, and this summary throws important light on the types of labor that white settlers can now undertake. A list of 2918 American male workers includes 10 artisans, 14 blacksmiths, 61 boilermakers, 17 builders, 80 carpenters and wood-workers, 187 electrical employees, 301 machinists, 17 painters, 34 plumbers, 12 sheet-metal workers, 57 miscellaneous metal traders, 34 farmers, and 87 laborers.

As stated above, we saw in the workshops whites, who for years had engaged in strenuous manual labor, and good specimens of the second generation are also now working in the shops. We were told that the whole canal could be run with white labor, but it would involve great additional expense and would cause labor difficulties if white Americans proved dissatisfied with the harder and more monotonous types of work.

On the other hand, the American leaders at Panama are beginning to realize how fallacious is the British doctrine that white residents of the tropics must avoid any hard exercise except for sport. In the words of the Columbia report:

In spite of the rather common belief that exercise in the tropics is dangerous, quite the opposite is true. Exercise is probably of greater value in hot countries than it is in the temperate climes since it takes the place to a considerable degree of the stimulation which comes from an atmosphere much cooler than the body. In the last 14 years only 48 heat cases have been reported to the dispensaries and hospitals of the Zone, a much smaller number than is reported in New York City on any hot summer day.[26]

There is little doubt that the dictum applies both to men and women. I was told again and again in Panama that the most happy and healthy women were those who did hard work.

In 1930, 518 women were employed by the Canal Commission, but these were mainly engaged in clerical occupations. With colored servants and fair financial resources it is probable that many American women do insufficient housework. Once again it appears that the Americans may be paying dearly for the introduction of negro labor.

Captain Guy Johannes, head of the penitentiary, supplied some interesting information as regards manual laborers. Although he himself considered that white people could not stand the climate indefinitely, he stated that with careful supervision the government was able to employ white prisoners on outdoor manual labor—on the roads, for example—from 7 a. m. to 3 p. m. Before setting the men to work the authorities made thorough medical examinations and took any necessary

Fig. 74—"Gold force" houses, Ancon, Canal Zone.
Fig. 75—"Gold force" houses, Colon, Canal Zone. Note the screening.
Fig. 76—Inundation caused by the Panama Canal. The malarial mosquitoes that breed in such places are a menace except in especially protected zones.

precautions. They also supplied the prisoners with a carefully balanced diet, which was more substantial than that given to sedentary workers. Captain Johannes considered that with this handling the health of prisoners greatly improved under hard outside labor.[27]

Health

A substantial volume would be insufficient to present the varying opinions on the problem of the health of the whites. Despite the conquest of yellow fever and the progress made against malaria and other diseases, there still exists a very general belief that the favorable health statistics fail to present a true picture. Many American scientists with long experience at Panama consider that the white man is not in his natural clime and that all the authorities have achieved is to make some parts of the Canal Zone habitable and fairly safe.

The exponents of these views allege that the statistics are worthless because people threatened with invalidity or death depart to the United States. They assert, although figures are as yet lacking to confirm it, that Americans tend to die soon after retirement. They bring forward all the usual arguments that the white man, and still more the white woman and white child, deteriorate under the effects of tropical heat, humidity, and light.

We may admit at once that the Americans have not succeeded in making most of the isthmus healthful. As Dr. D. P. Curry, Acting Chief Health Officer, wrote in August 1925:

We have not by any means converted the entire Isthmus, or even the Canal Zone, into a "tropical paradise," where white men, bred in colder climes, can come without fear of injury to their physical condition. The efforts of the Health Department are and always have been necessarily limited, for economic reasons, to the sanitation of the immediate surroundings of the more important industrial and residential communities [Panama, Colon, Gatun and Pedro Miguel]. It is only within these sanitated areas that employees and their families are assured of reasonable protection against the so-called tropical diseases, such as malaria, hookworm, dysentery and a number of other infections. Beyond these strictly circumscribed areas the danger of infection is as potent as ever.[28]

There is no doubt that, great as are the American scientific achievements, the "safe" areas of the Zone are still only a number of camps continually armed and guarded against external disease. Malaria is increasing, and the growing range of the automobile is augmenting the risk of infectious disease. On the other hand, the fears and dangers of tropical disease are undoubtedly magnified. A few cases of malaria will create a panic whereas a similar number of pneumonia cases would be taken as a matter of course.

Another difficulty is the presence of a large Central American and negro population. In the years 1923-1928 venereal disease ranked second to malaria as a cause of admissions to hospitals of white and colored employees. This does not imply a criticism of the behavior of

12

the American whites. It is noteworthy that despite the proximity of an unlimited liquor supply in Panama and Colon, there seems to be less heavy drinking than in British tropical domains such as Burma or northern Australia.

As for the much criticized health statistics, the figures given in the accompanying table of mortality (Table XIV) lead to the following conclusions. First, the white death rate for the Canal Zone is showing a

TABLE XIV—PANAMA AND, FOR COMPARISON, OTHER LOCALITIES:
DEATH RATES PER 1,000 PEOPLE*

Canal Employees (white).............	1908–12	5.8
	1917–21	3.28
	1927–31	6.36
Canal Employees (colored)............	1908–12	8.1
	1917–21	7.16
	1927–31	10.02
City of Colon........................	1931	16.07
City of Panama.....................	1931	17.64
New Zealand (lowest death rate)........	1932	8.0
Queensland (tropical and sub-tropical)...	1932	8.35
Tasmania (cold temperate)............	1932	8.9
Northern Territory, Australia (tropical)..	1932	14.85
United Kingdom.....................	1933	12.5
United States.......................	1933	10.7
New York..........................	1930	10.8
Knoxville, Tennessee.................	1930	14.1
Charleston, S. C.....................	1927	18.7
Ceylon.............................	1933	21.2

*Data for Canal employees from Report of the Health Department of the Panama Canal for the year 1931; for Colon and Panama from Report of the Governor of the Panama Canal, 1933; for New Zealand, United States, United Kingdom, and Ceylon from the Statistical Yearbook of the League of Nations, 1936/37; for Queensland, Tasmania, and Northern Territory from Official Yearbook of the Commonwealth of Australia, 1935; for New York City and Knoxville from Statistical Abstract of the United States, 1937.

slight increase. It is, however, so much below that of the lowest country (New Zealand) that the rate would still be favorable even if considerably more whites were to die in the Zone instead of leaving, as alleged, to die in the United States. Second, the colored death rate provides evidence of similar nature. It is admitted that the negroes are an aging force and do not leave the Zone to die. Yet the death rate of these colored employees on the canal is lower than the death rates of the United States or of England and Wales, or of American cities such as New York, Knoxville, and Charleston, and far lower than the rates of other tropical regions, such as the Northern Territory of Australia or of Ceylon.

As regards the problem of the effects of climate per se, it is obvious that the Canal Zone attracts a certain number of men and women who should not go to the tropics at all. One meets many people who have never become acclimatized, and it is these who provide the worst cases of the so-called tropical neurasthenia, profuse menstruation, alcoholism, and the like. On the other hand, one finds many men and women who have lived and worked for years in the Zone and ask nothing better than to remain there after their retirement, if houses and commissary privileges can be secured. Medical opinion naturally varies as regards not only the first but also the second and third generations. Probably the most accurate view is that certain whites may be able to adjust themselves to permanent residence in the low tropics but that the adjustment will necessitate physical alterations, possibly involving some degeneracy. American scientists consider that tropical whites would tend to have smaller and looser bones than whites of the temperate zone and that they would be thinner, taller, and more anemic and would have less hair. This forecast is not unlike Bryan Edward's picture of the West Indian Creole or Sir Raphael Cilento's description of the loose-limbed tropical Australian.[29] Trenchant and vigorous is the opinion of another leading American doctor. Certain whites could probably establish themselves permanently in the low tropics, but "the third generation would be pretty weedy." [30] Yet, in spite of such dicta, it is hard to find any specific evidence of degeneracy, either among Americans of the second generation or among the children of the third generation who are now beginning to appear.

White Births

Owing to a number of complicated conditions it is difficult to form conclusions from the white birth statistics. This is a pity in view of the often repeated fallacies that whites breed poorly in the tropics and that the third generation cannot breed at all. Certainly, the white birth rate fell from 16.37 per 1000 in 1918-1922 to 9.39 in 1928-1932, but a fall occurred in most white countries. The median family in the Canal Zone now numbers only 2.68, and, although there are a few families of six, seven, and even eight children, only 22 per cent of couples have three or more children; 45 per cent have but one or two children and 33 per cent no children at all. It must be remembered, however, that the birth-rate figure for 1930 was more than half the United States birth rate for 1932 and this despite the fact that it was calculated on a white population of 16,511, which included some 9000 unmarried navy and army personnel. It would be essential to examine closely the economic background of the Panama community and the access to preventatives and similar controlling factors before attributing the small families to tropical degeneracy or to climatic control.[31]

White Children

The visitor to Panama is astounded to find the American stations overrun with most healthy-looking white children. Everywhere outside the cool, airy bungalows fair-haired and bareheaded tots, even in the heat of the day, play in scanty garments resembling bathing dresses.[32] The Americans have indeed proved at Panama—and their medical missionaries are proving the same thing in Central Africa—that in many parts of the tropics, given proper light clothing, heat prostration and sunstroke are myths. One would be reluctant, however, to apply these methods in the glaring heat of India or Burma. Perhaps the absence of sunstroke on the canal may be due to the high humidity; at any rate only light headgear is necessary, even in the middle of the day.

Statistics show that, with proper medical attention, sanitation, and diet, children thrive at Panama in their early years. There is no occurrence of many of the dangerous diseases of cool-temperate countries (for instance, there is no pneumonia after whooping cough), and such illnesses as do occur are mild.

The Columbia report of 1930 stated that the most serious problem was undernourishment, due to inadequate supplies of milk and to the fact that a great lack of vegetables prevented a properly balanced diet. While the milk supply was all pasteurized and of excellent quality, it was very expensive and wholly inadequate in amount. At twenty cents a quart it was beyond the reach of many of the poorer families. The employees also allege that at about eight or nine the children begin to show the effects of the climate; begin to lose their powers of concentration, and become more pallid and less robust than children in the United States. If things are as bad as the employees state, it is hard to account for the results obtained by the research workers who compiled the Columbia report. "The results of the testing program," they wrote, "have indicated that the group of white boys and girls in the grades and in the high schools are, on the average, achieving above the norms established for schools in the United States."[33] The achievement of the Canal Zone high-school students in social studies "was extraordinary." No doubt this result is partly due to the fact that the parents are a select body, that the curriculum is one in which the tests favored the pupils, that the teachers also are a select and particularly able body, and that the children go north on occasional vacations and possess the advantage of living on one of the great highways of the world. Yet when all allowances have been made, the fundamental question remains unanswered. If the effects of tropical climate are as devastating as alleged by the canal employees, how is it that their own children "both of a given age and of a given grade are achieving beyond the norms established for children in the United States"?[34]

A really legitimate grievance on the canal is that the white children lack opportunity to prepare themselves for professions or trades. In

1933 a junior college was only just being established. There are no summer schools, and facilities for adult education are urgently required. The Columbia report made recommendations to bring the school curricula into line with the needs of a population residing more or less permanently in Central America, but it lies with the government to provide openings for these tropical-born white children, who, in the majority of cases, are now compelled to leave their parents and seek their living in the United States.

The Color Problem

By the importation and wide utilization of negro labor the United States sowed at Panama the seeds of two extremely grave problems: negro health and colored population increase. The effect of the presence of the negro on the health of the white races was one with which the Americans were well acquainted, for it had long proved one of the gravest problems in the southern states. Unfortunately, they ignored their own experience, and as early as 1911 Dr. Deeks recorded at Panama the inevitable result. "As elsewhere in the world," he wrote, "the enforcement of sanitation amongst the negroes is a gigantic task. . . . As long as he has a roof over his head and a yam or two to eat he is content, and his ideal of personal hygiene is on a par with his conception of marital fidelity." [35]

The increasing efforts of the American authorities to enforce medical hygiene, sanitation, screened housing, education, and the like, produced wonderful results at the outset but they were not as effective in later years. The death rate from disease per 1000 colored employees fell from 47.76 in 1906 to 29.62 in 1907 and 9.24 in 1908. It reached its lowest (4.19) in 1915, and then rose again to an average of 10.02 in 1927-1931. This death rate varies from 40 to 118 per cent higher than that of white employees, partly because the whites have many advantages of race, environment, and employment. Also, although the average age of both forces is increasing, chronic degenerative diseases are affecting the colored workers to a proportionately greater degree. There would probably be little danger if the population numbers remained stationary. As, however, the number of negroes is increasing rapidly, the United States appears to be facing in Panama the health problem that was so important a factor in the adoption of the "White Australia" policy. It is significant that American health authorities are already severely alarmed and fear greatly that difficulties will rapidly become menacing as the colored peoples increase.

Table XV makes it clear that the populations of both the Canal Zone and the Republic of Panama are showing a large natural increase. The Columbia report notes that in the Canal Zone "the stable part of the population is rapidly growing, and, as the Government finds it possible to provide for the housing, larger numbers of employees will be permitted to live within the Canal Zone limits." [36] The population of the Republic of Panama increased by 4.78 per cent between 1920 and 1930, when it reached 467,459.

The fundamental problem facing the Americans is that of disposing of the increasing numbers of negroes. At the end of the construction period the government permitted some thousands of West Indian negroes to attempt agriculture on the shores and islands of Gatun Lake and in other parts of the Canal Zone, hoping thus to help dismissed employees, to deal with overpopulation, and to increase supplies for the Zone community. As, however, the negroes occupied areas beyond the control of antimalarial measures, the American doctors now think

TABLE XV—PANAMA: SELECTED VITAL STATISTICS*

	1918–22	1923–37	1928–32
Canal Zone			
Live births, white per 1000.......	16.37	12.89	9.39
"　　" 　colored per 1000......	28.65	22.01	14.96
Total births....................	22.54	17.76	12.49
Deaths.......................	8.10	8.28	7.62
Panama			
Live births, per 1000............	36.41	32.24	32.99
Deaths, per 1000...............	21.06	17.55	18.06
Colon			
Live births, per 1000............	29.89	23.76	28.13
Deaths, per 1000...............	18.48	14.08	15.82

*Data from the Report of the Health Department of the Panama Canal for 1932.

that it has resulted in a definite increase of malaria and recommend that no more permits be issued.[37]

The Report of the Governor, 1932, gives a gloomy summary of the whole position:

The Canal Zone, and the adjoining cities of Panama and Colon, in Panama, face a condition of permanent unemployment. The construction of the canal occasioned the coming of thousands of West Indians as well as numerous Europeans and orientals. Upon the completion of the construction work the United States offered repatriation to all discharged employees, or former employees. Many did not accept repatriation, and many who went home returned later to the Isthmus. For a time, increased business in Panama absorbed many of them. This has now slumped sharply, throwing many out of work. In the meantime, the extension of highways from the capital to the interior has resulted in a movement from the country to the city, rather than from the city to the land. A further factor has been the natural growth of population in a prolific people without control and without the offsetting losses from disease which occurred prior to the American era of sanitation. Similarly, but to less extent numerically, the American population in the Canal Zone has increased, and many young men and women of canal families are approaching maturity without employment. The search for work is sharp and there is increasing competition between Americans and aliens for work which may be performed almost equally well by either.

This situation has become acute with the general slump in business, the falling off in canal traffic and related activities and the diminished appropriations for new construction and replacements. It is not practicable to care for any number of these people by allowing them to settle on land in the Canal Zone; many could not make a living in the jungle and the increases of malarial infection which have resulted in the canal towns from the presence of settlers on the land have led to the decision to license no more settlers. The most obvious form of relief is an increase in public works.[38]

The Americans utilized the negro at Panama to save themselves expense and hard labor. There is a serious danger that in the long run the policy will involve the United States in both racial and economic loss.

Summary and Conclusions

The Panama Canal Zone is one of the most difficult and unhealthful regions for white settlement in the tropics, although a few places (notably Balboa Heights) have some local advantages over the general tropical coast. From 1904 onwards the Americans solved the main health problems for both white and colored people by perfecting a technique that has had worldwide effects. Health conditions, however, are still unsatisfactory except in certain small, highly sanitated areas. In these men, women, and children can spend active lives of normal length, although most people require vacations in the cool-temperate zone.

The Americans constructed the canal with American, negro, and European labor, and rely almost wholly on the first two today. Their results show that under satisfactory conditions of living and remuneration some northern whites can carry on the hardest manual labor for many years in the tropics and that the majority of men, women, and children are the better for strenuous physical exercise. The southern Europeans were better workers than the negroes, and it was possibly a mistake that the former, and not the latter, were sent away.

The success of the Americans has been due not only to their highly expert medical supervision, hygiene, and sanitation but to new and revolutionary ideas on housing, clothing, alcohol, and diet. Wonderful results are evident both in children and adults. Despite the allegedly deleterious influences of the tropical climate, the white children of the Canal Zone "both of a given age and of a given grade are achieving beyond the norms for children in the United States."

The most serious problem facing the Americans is that of the negro. The West Indians are increasing with rapidity and are already exerting a bad effect on the Canal Zone whites both as regards population pressure and health.

We have taken Panama as the most advanced and promising of white settlements in the low tropics, and we may apply its main lessons to these regions as a whole. First, it is clear that modern science is greatly improving regions that were once regarded as the plague spots of the world, with the result that health is making astonishing progress. Dr. G. J. P. Barger, who was stationed for many years at Bolenge on the equator in the Belgian Congo, states with accuracy: "We are living in Africa in a day when most of the vital problems of safe and healthful living in the tropics have been solved for us, so far as the knowledge of principles is concerned." [39] To take, for example, British West Africa (Gambia, Sierra Leone, Gold Coast, and Nigeria), in the five years 1903-1907, the death rate for non-native officials was 23 per 1000, the invalidings 63 per 1000, and the average length of service 2 years and 11 months. In the five years 1928-1932 the death rate had lowered to 6.5 per 1000, the invalidings to 10.7 per 1000, and the average length of service to 8 years and 2 months.[40]

This progress in health is of great importance, but the whites will remain sojourners as long as they face malaria and are forced to live in medically fortified camps and to take ceaseless precautions against tropical diseases. Furthermore, as in Panama, scientific medicine is rapidly increasing the native populations of tropical Africa, America, Asia, and the East and West Indies, and this factor alone will prevent the establishment and growth of communities of working whites. Throughout all the low tropics absorption is likely to be the fate of white communities that attempt to create permanent settlements.

PART III

SOME FACTORS GOVERNING WHITE SETTLEMENT IN THE TROPICS

CHAPTER XII

RACIAL PROBLEMS

Part I of this book presented the problem of white settlement in the tropics and touched briefly upon certain historical points. Part II examined a number of white settlements in different tropical regions in order to ascertain why, in a general welter of failure, these white communities survived for considerable periods and, in some cases, met with encouraging success. Part III will attempt to analyze the chief known factors that govern white settlement. For this purpose cautious use will be made of the data provided by history and general observation, and, where possible, the argument will also be based upon the findings of statistical and laboratory research.

The essential facts of white settlement in the tropics fall into three groups. These are the qualities of the immigrant peoples, the environmental phenomena that the immigrants encounter, and external influences—as, for example, the political pressure exercised by the great nations of the temperate zones through political sovereignty, economic policies, markets, and the like. Although these topics necessarily overlap, the following arrangement must suffice in dealing with them. First we shall examine some characteristics of white peoples in the tropics, together with some of the traits exhibited by white and colored mixtures of various types. Then we shall turn to the problem of environmental influences, under such headings as soils, climate, acclimatization, health, diet, comfort, and political and economic phenomena located within the tropics. Some of these factors are strongly influenced by cultural and possibly by ethnic characteristics. Nevertheless, they are primarily questions of environment. Tropical flora and fauna are treated incidentally and mainly in their geographical and economic aspects. These controls are of primary importance to white settlers, but the field is very great and very varied and the scientific problems involved are matters for the botanist, zoölogist, and entomologist. Certain political and economic factors that are largely external to the tropics, although of fundamental importance to tropical settlement by whites, can only be briefly touched upon.

THE RACIAL PROBLEM

In the present chapter a number of obscure questions that may be grouped under the unsatisfactory heading of "race" will be discussed. Unfortunately the existing knowledge on these matters is slight and uncertain and rests upon history and general observations rather than upon statistics or laboratory research.

In a recent work, "We Europeans," Julian S. Huxley and A. C. Haddon outline some of the difficulties that face an inquirer into the racial aspects of human settlement. According to these authorities the whole ground is extremely dangerous, for "a vast pseudo-science of 'racial biology' has been erected which serves to justify political ambitions, economic ends, social grudges, class prejudices." A survey of the scientific facts now available on the subject of race in man exposes "the extent of our scientific ignorance on this fundamental subject." Yet, "in spite of the extent of our ignorance a certain body of real knowledge . . . does indeed exist." [1]

Huxley and Haddon consider that the term "race" as applied to existing human groups has no significance:

> In most cases it is impossible to speak of the existing population of any region as belonging to a definite *race,* since as a result of migration and crossing it includes many types and their various combinations. For existing populations, the word *race* should be banished, and the descriptive and non-committal term *ethnic group* should be substituted.[2]

The principal conclusion of "We Europeans" is that cultural factors are of more importance than biological factors in human groups.

> To disentangle the genetically unimportant effects of environment from the genetically essential action of genes is difficult in all organisms and especially so in man, where the social and cultural environment—unique characters of the human species—play predominant parts. Until we have invented a method for distinguishing the effects of social environment from those of genetic constitution, we shall be wholly unable to say anything of the least scientific value on such vital topics as the possible genetic differences in intelligence, initiative and aptitude which may distinguish different human groups.[3]

From these opinions it may be inferred that the varying experiences of differing ethnic groups of tropical whites are due to differing degrees of culture or to differing factors in the environment. A number of leading authorities believe, however, that various races differ in mental, physiological, and other equipment, and it is necessary to state their views. The negro, for example, is so successful in the tropics, and the northern white so unsuccessful, that many writers speak of the negro as the child of the tropics and describe the tropical white man as a wilting plant that has been carried beyond its natural habitat. It is not known, however, whether the greater success of the negro has been due to physiological qualities (such as pigmentation and the power to resist tropical diseases), to mental and psychological qualities (such as cheerfulness, docility and the willingness to accept a low social and living standard), or to the vast ethnic transplantations effected by white nations in colonizing the tropics with enslaved or exploited negroid peoples.

Aleš Hrdlička considers that human races are distinguished by different characters, "morphological, physiological, chemical, psychological and even pathological." Whatever characteristics are considered—color,

cranial capacity, cephalic or nasal indices, hair, stature, and so on—
varieties exist. Mental differences between races, although numerous
and in some cases important, have so far eluded direct and precise
specification or determination. Pathological variations, mainly "pre-
dispositions" and "immunities," appear to be largely environmental and
local rather than racial in character, but their indirect effects range
among the basic characters in human evolution. Among these fall the
so-called neurasthenias.[4]

Mental Variations

H. S. Jennings believes that the existence of mental differences among
races is definitely established, although it is uncertain whether this is
due to heredity or to environment. This, he thinks, is proved by the
different roles played by various peoples in history and by their varied
cultural achievements.[5] We must note, however, A. J. Toynbee's point
that the negro race is the only one of the primary races that has not
made a creative contribution to at least one of the twenty-one great
civilizations.[6] Jennings considers that mental differences are in perfect
agreement with the results of experimental studies in psychology and
race mentality. The more perfect the technique of study becomes, the
more clear and unquestionable become the mental differences among
different peoples. P. Sorokin states that all studies of the comparative
intelligence of the contemporary negro and white peoples (the Caspian,
Mediterranean, Alpine, and even their blends with yellow peoples) have
invariably shown that the intelligence quotient of the blacks, and even
of the American Indians, is lower than that of the yellow or the white.[7]
Some authorities believe that the studies of G. O. Ferguson, E. B. Reuter,
and others have demonstrated that the greater the infusion of white
blood with the negro, the higher is his intelligence quotient. Mental
tests, the number of geniuses produced, cultural achievements, and the
superiority of halfbreed Indians over Indians of full blood, all indicate
that the red race makes a somewhat better showing than the negro
but that it is inferior to the white. On the other hand, Chinese, Japanese, and high-class Hindus seem little inferior to the whites of European
origin.[8] If this variation in intelligence exists, it might partly account
for the varying degrees of development attained by differing ethnic
groups in tropical environments. We have seen, for example, the remarkable fact that standards of progress and culture in the Central
American republics appear to vary according to the proportion of white
blood and that many observers believe the same to be true of South
America.[9]

In Chapter VII we discussed one of the few scientific studies of a
comparative nature that has been made in the tropics, the examination
conducted by C. B. Davenport and M. Steggerda of the northern whites,
negroes, and browns who have inhabited the Cayman Islands and parts

of Jamaica under the same geographical, social, and economic conditions for periods of from one to three centuries.[10] According to these investigations, the blacks showed superiority to the whites in matters pertaining to musical talent—discrimination of pitch, tone intensity, and rhythm. They also showed superiority in simple mental arithmetic and in carrying out complicated directions for doing things. On the other hand, the whites showed a distinct superiority in the tests of intellectual ability. They were superior in copying geometric figures, in making without pattern a drawing of a man, in criticism of absurd subjects, and in the forming of practical judgments.

In Chapter VII it was shown that the school teachers in mixed schools for whites and negroes in Saba consider that the children of north European families resident in these moderate tropics for more than two centuries have greater intellectual capacity than negro children occupying much the same social, economic, and educational environment. Unfortunately, however, the results obtained by Davenport and Steggerda on racial intelligence conflict with the views of other scientists who wholly discount the value of intelligence tests. E. A. Hooton, for example, writes:

Anthropologists have not yet reached the point of an agreement upon criteria of race which will enable psychologists to isolate with any degree of facility the racial types which are to be studied. Psychologists have not yet been able to develop mental tests which anthropologists are willing to trust as fair gauges of mental capacity. Neither group has yet perfected its technique of measurement. Until we know exactly how to distinguish a race, and exactly what intelligence tests test, we shall have to hold in suspension the problem of racial mental differences.[11]

Pigmentation

Mental ability, however, is only one factor in determining the superiority or inferiority of any race or individual in the tropics. Slight as is our knowledge, there are indications that many "racial" and individual differences may exist regardless of the environment and that physical, psychological, and other traits may go far in counterbalancing any superiority in intelligence.[12] We may take, for instance, one phenomenon that has been partly investigated—pigmentation.

Sir Aldo Castellani has summed up the evidence on the subject of pigmentation.[13] It is common knowledge that races inhabiting regions of intense sunlight are in general strongly pigmented, although exceptions occur. Castellani says "there is no doubt that the European living in the tropics becomes darker, a fact which specially applies to descendants of the settlers," although he draws attention to the fact that "a certain number of Europeans do not become sunburnt in the tropics." [14] As noted of the communities in Saba, St. Thomas, and Barbados (Chapter VII) the skin of many whites in tropical localities takes on "a peculiar whitish colour, even in cases in which blood examination does not reveal any sensible decrease in haemoglobin." W. P. Chamberlain examined healthy young American soldiers of an average age of twenty-six years who had spent some twenty months near sea level in the Philippines. He reported that the red cell counts were the same as for healthy young men in the temperate zone and, while the percentage of hemoglobin and the color index were a little low, they were not sufficient to indicate a definite anemia.[15]

Loewy provided explanations for the increased tolerance that accompanies pigmentation.[16] Chalmers and Castellani showed that dark pigmentation was useful in cases of leucoderma, and, according to the latter, it has been experimentally proved that pigment has a protective action against long-wave radiation (visible rays) in cases of photodynamic sensitization, such as "buckwheat sickness" of cattle.[17] On the whole, it seems probable that pigmentation and the relatively greater number of sweat glands in dark skins are protective and bestow advantages on colored races over white.[18]

[The skin consists of an outer horny *corneum,* beneath which are successively the *malpighian layer,* the *corium,* and the *subcutaneous layers.* The solar-radiation spectrum, for these purposes, is conventionally divided into the following bands in order from short to long wave lengths: *extreme ultra-violet, far ultra-violet, near ultra-violet, visible* (violet, green, yellow, orange, red), *near infra-red,* and *far infra-red.* Each layer of skin behaves quite differently with respect to the absorption and transmission of each of these bands. Pigment, hair, and blood also greatly affect the absorption, but they have a varying distribution in the skin. Pigment, we know, increases and hair decreases absorption. The more blood in the capillaries the more shorter-wave radiation will be absorbed and carried into the system as added heat, and the more the long-wave radiation will penetrate to deeper layers.

In general the extreme ultra-violet rays are all absorbed by the corneum; the far and near ultra-violet are likewise largely absorbed by the corneum but some of them reach the corium, the near ultra-violet being taken up by the malpighian layer to a somewhat greater extent than are the longer ultra-violet rays. The visible radiation suffers least absorption in the corneum and most in the corium; the near infra-red penetrates to all layers but more is absorbed by the corium and corneum than by the others. Whereas no ultra-violet rays reach the subcutaneous layers, from 1 to 20 per cent of the visible and near infra-red are absorbed there. The far infra-red rays hardly penetrate the skin at all.

The outer skin pigment, or *melanin,* is formed mostly in the basal cells of the epidermis, or *malpighi,* but appears also in the corneum to a considerable extent when pigmentation is extreme. Negroes have more pigment than whites, in both layers.

The old view, first stated by Finsen,[19] that the pigment is a protection against excessive damage by ultra-violet rays, is no longer precisely tenable: since the shorter rays are so largely absorbed in the corneum that few reach the epidermis, the pigment cannot be credited with such a protective effect. Some of the longer ultra-violet rays, however, reach the blood in the capillaries of the corium, the overlying malpighian pigment, which increases after irradiation, regulating the amount of such penetration. Thus the pigment is a screen only for the corium, or "true skin," against the longer ultra-violet rays.

It is common belief that the pigment, by virtue of its better absorption of visible-red and infra-red rays, also functions to localize the heating effect of solar radiation near the skin surface, whence heat is more readily lost to the environment, and that the pigment thus protects the body from overheating. It is plausible to assume, therefore, that in a hot climate the negro enjoys an advantage over the white man by reaching the sweating point sooner and by sweating more abundantly owing to the higher skin temperature. Unfortunately, careful experiments to demonstrate such effects have failed, and the supposed advantages, if any, of the negro skin may have to be sought in some other mechanism. When clothing is worn the reflection, absorption, and transmission of radiation and heat by the fabrics become of as great if not of greater importance than the pigmentation.

Some of the effects claimed for pigmentation are undoubtedly due to vascular training (of the capillary dilatation), to the thickness and character of the outer horny layer of the skin, and to nervous or psychic factors.

The different degrees of absorption of various rays according to the amount of pigment, however, may still be of great adaptive importance, because the ultra-violet and red rays which reach the corium produce chemical and vascular responses that become less or nearly absent in proportion as the pigment screens out those rays. Reduction of blood sugar and of blood pH, for example, has been observed to result from irradiation to the corium; also carbohydrate foods (common in the tropics) seem to affect the permeability of skin to infra-red radiation. Possibly by such mechanisms various irregular chemical changes or modifications of regular changes unfavorable to heat acclimatization are set up, from which the negro would be protected by his melanin. If they reach the capillaries intensely, infra-red rays can raise the body temperature and thus speed up biological processes so as to increase metabolism—a disadvantage in a hot climate; however, this may be somewhat counteracted by the reduction of blood sugar mentioned above, which tends to reduce metabolism.

Thus we see that the visible and infra-red rays are of great significance in the tropics regardless of pigment, and also that pigment is probably important in relation to racial and individual acclimatization in the tropics, although not in the manner generally believed in the past. Nor are the ultra-violet rays unimportant. Pigment or no pigment, they may produce pronounced toxic as well as certain therapeutic effects. Intense pigment prevents erythemal "burn" and may thus be of some conceivable advantage in the tropics in view of the fairly rich ultra-violet climate there, even though it may decrease the possible therapeutic effects of the ultra-violet rays.

Those who cannot tan may be, but are not necessarily, unsuited for the tropics.—
R. G. S.] [20]

Manual Labor and the Northern Whites

It is a truism that any people who colonize the tropics permanently and as genuine settlers must engage in all types of work. The regional section of this book has indicated that the southern European peoples may be able to colonize the moderate tropics. Mediterranean peoples, such as Spaniards and Italians, have gained a firm footing as settlers in Florida, northern Queensland, and parts of Central and South America. Although they are likely to be absorbed by colored peoples over most of tropical America, they are increasing in Cuba and Puerto Rico and are absorbing the blacks. In the low, humid tropics of Panama groups of Spanish origin have proved efficient in the hardest types of manual labor, and a working force of Spaniards remains on the canal today. It is generally thought that the southern European white is less capable of rugged labor under tropical conditions than is the negro, and he is certainly less immune to tropical sickness. There is no doubt, however, that, when safeguarded from tropical diseases and when prepared to accept the economic and social standards of a tropical peasantry, the southern Europeans can survive and maintain themselves indefinitely over a large part of the tropics. Unfortunately, there is no means of ascertaining the underlying causes of the southern European success—for example, how far it may be due to racial experience of comparatively hot climates, or to the African, Moorish, and other colored blood in peoples like the Spaniards and Portuguese.[21]

The problem of the northern white is more complex. The whites in the marginal regions of Florida and Queensland and in the wet-dry lands of northern Australia are genuine working settlers and seem capable of carrying out practically all types of manual work, although we must make allowance for the fact that these communities are very recent and in some cases possess peculiar economic advantages.[22] In trade-wind islands, such as the Caymans, Barbados, Saba, and Jamaica, northern whites have survived as a peasantry for many generations, although in most cases isolation, economic factors, and possibly climatic degeneration have reduced these groups to the level of their negro competitors and in some cases below it.[23] In Panama in the low, humid tropics northern whites engage in many activities. Nevertheless, this community is recent; it rests on a substratum of negro labor, and it enjoys a standard of living, diet, vacations, and other privileges that are probably unequalled in the tropics.[24] On the African plateaus the northern whites again depend on colored labor, and the settlements are newly established.[25]

On the whole, we must suspend judgment on the suitability of northern whites for tropical settlement, but we can accept two highly important facts as beyond dispute: first, northern Europeans can survive and breed for generations in the moderate tropics despite grave handicaps of racial competition and tropical disease; second, northern Europeans are making definite and encouraging progress in parts of the marginal tropics.

Some biologists believe that races survive if they possess one or more traits that particularly suit their environment or enable the possessors to find a new environment where such traits have special advantages. This opinion may not hold much hope for northern whites in the tropics if they do not happen to possess characteristics peculiarly suited to the environment. On the other hand, it is possible that the growing control of tropical diseases will enable the northern whites to adjust themselves permanently in parts of the moderate tropics. This raises the very important question of racial alterations in tropical environments. Historical evidence from the West Indies and statistics and observations in Queensland and northern Australia may perhaps indicate that changes do take place. Scientists such as Sir Raphael Cilento and Dr. H. C. Clark differ as to whether the changes denote degeneracy or improvement, and we shall discuss the opposing views in the following chapters.

In short, it must be admitted that, except for the results of researches on a few subjects such as pigmentation, our knowledge of racial suita-

13

bility or adaptability to tropical conditions remains vague. Sir Aldo Castellani summarizes what he terms "the well known racial peculiarities with regard to climatic resistance" in half a page. He states:

African negroes do not thrive in cold climates, while they stand well the torrid climate of tropical Africa and tropical America. The average Caucasian finds difficulties in becoming acclimatized in most tropical countries, although the Latin races seem to be capable of living in the tropics more easily than the Anglo-Saxon. People of the Jewish race seem to stand different climates better than other races. Certain authorities, including Sir Arthur Keith, hold the view that the endocrine organs play an important part in the evolution of racial characteristics, and thus it appears probable that climate, through its influence on the thyroid, adrenal and other endocrine glands, is involved to a considerable extent in the process of evolution.[26]

Unfortunately, much of the above statement is based on history and general observation rather than on scientific facts and is contested by some authorities. Carr-Saunders points out that the recent northward movement of the negro in the United States may be disproving the theory of direct climatic influence, although the vital statistics are "difficult to interpret." "The chances of life or death," he writes, "depend largely upon access to health services, housing conditions and occupational circumstances." However, there does not seem to be any reason for supposing that negroes in these northern regions "are less well able to survive . . . than the Europeans." [27]

RACIAL MIXTURE IN THE TROPICS

Another important but little-known aspect of white settlement in the tropics is the mixture of ethnic groups. This, as we have seen in the cases of South Africa and the southern United States, is not a purely tropical problem, for mixture always occurs when two or more peoples occupy the same environment. No ethnic group, however pure or however filled with pride of blood, can avoid this. Degenerate members of the more advanced people will always mingle with their belated neighbors. We have shown, for example, that in tropical Australia the lower grades of northern whites cohabit freely with the primitive aborigines. For a small population persons of mixed blood are increasing at a considerable rate, although it is stated authoritatively that the interbreeding of the half-castes among themselves is the chief cause of the increase. In other tropical countries such as Brazil the problem is of far greater importance than in Australia, where the number of aborigines is and always has been comparatively insignificant. We have already seen that in most parts of the tropics the colored peoples, with their lower standards of living and culture, are absorbing the whites. Hence, it is vital to ascertain whether these biological changes are advantageous to humanity and whether the white peoples should continue to send colonists to tropical regions in which absorption is almost certain to take place.

Unfortunately, as indicated above, the scientific aspect of the question is often clouded by racial prejudices and by differences in social and economic status. Only too often the "superior" and the "belated" peoples occupy the same geographical environment but are bitterly hostile, owing to the legacy of history and to variations of social structure and economics. Only too often the inevitable but unhappy crossbreds are objects of scorn to both parent peoples. Their status is less settled and their family environment and traditions less favorable than those of the offspring of either parent group.

Fortunately, the biologist now possesses much accurate information on the mixing of diverse types of organism and on the manner in which the chromosomes and genes act. H. S. Jennings [28] states that, if the organisms from which come two sets of genes are very diverse, fertilization may not take place. If the organisms are diverse but less distant, the eggs begin to develop, but the young organisms die. Sometimes two sets of chromosomes work perfectly together in producing offspring, but, as in the case of the mule, the product of the horse and ass, the new combination of chromosomes produces no further offspring. Sometimes, again, hybrid individuals may produce relatively few offspring. There is every grade of complete or partial sterility in different hybrids. In a large class of crosses the chromosomes of two parents will combine normally, yet the individuals produced are imperfect or abnormal, because the two different sets of chromosomes tend to cause development in different directions and the mixed individuals are less efficient physiological machines than are pure ones. The structures and functions resulting from the union of two different germ cells form a combination that does not work harmoniously. There are a great number of cases of this sort, in which the characteristics coming from the two parents are unharmonious. The consequences range in different cases from early death, through conditions of abnormality and deficiency, up to mere awkwardness and stupidity of behavior. In organisms that reproduce through two parents, as do man and the higher animals and plants, practically every individual differs in some of its genes from every other, yet reproduction continues with success. The union is a sort of insurance, a device by which the probability of getting at least one good gene to each pair is greatly increased. In plant and animal breeding the phenomenon of "hybrid vigor" is widely utilized, and the mating of two slightly diverse ethnic groups may sometimes produce offspring that are superior to either group.

In the case of man, we may ask whether there is incompatibility between the genes or between the chromosomes, whether the combination of two ethnic groups is inharmonious, and whether combinations are supplementary, so that some or all the offspring of a cross may be superior to the parent group. According to H. S. Jennings the answer is that no incompatibility of chromosomes can be observed among the different human races. The germ cells of the negro and of the white man have 24 chromosomes each, and these unite and work perfectly together in forming vigorous offspring and in forming functional germ cells in those offspring. The same is true of crosses between all peoples of mankind. Despite popular misconceptions on the subject, there is no sign of abnormal structure or function, or of the partial or complete sterility of the offspring of crosses. With respect to the main features of physical structure and of physiology, the offspring of parents of different race are as perfect and vigorous as the offspring of parents of the same race.[29] Hrdlička holds the same views as Jennings. Human races are without exception freely miscible. Barring cases due to individual causes, there is no evidence of sterility, weakness of offspring, or intellectual extinction among mixed bloods. It is a complete fallacy, for example, that the negro-white will not breed beyond the quadroon or octaroon. Hrdlička also states that there is no incompatibility in the chief features of the later structures and physiological functions. At least with respect to the great biological functions such as nutrition, respiration, nervous action, and reproduction, the two sets of structures and functions can be united in a single individual who is an efficient machine. Frequently the union of diverse sets of genes will produce individuals who are more vigorous than either of the parents and hybrid vigor will result.[30] The data included in Table XVI illustrate, for example, very marked hybrid vigor as measured by fertility for the interracial crosses examined (p. 184, below).

Some authorities believe that racial mixtures produce many cases of disharmony as regards structure, function, mentality, and behavior. C. B. Davenport considers that the physique of different stocks in the United States varies greatly and that the union of individuals with widely diverse organs may have serious ill-effects. For example, defective teeth are less common in nations of comparatively pure race. In "Race Crossing in Jamaica" Davenport also demonstrates that some of the mulattoes have unexpected combinations of long legs and short bodies, or long bodies and short legs. Other individuals have the long legs of the negro and the short arms of the white, which would put them at a disadvantage in picking up things from the ground.[31]

Even more serious is the fact that mental and psychological disharmonies appear in mixed peoples. In the words of Jennings:

Both the genetic situation and the state of the present evidence indicate that there are characteristic differences in mentality between diverse races. Crossing between two races should therefore give rise to diverse combinations of mental characteristics, some of which will be inharmonious, others harmonious.[32]

On the whole, it appears that no single rule applies to all ethnic crosses. Some, like the Chinese-Hawaiians, show hybrid vigor, others enfeeblement. Such crosses as the Dutch-Javanese produce beauty. Others are devoid of form or grace. In some cases there appears to be a lack of resistance to disease—a liability to tuberculosis, for example.

Davenport also notes the bad behavior of Filipino-white and negro-white crosses, a phenomenon apparently due to conflicting instincts.[33] The Eurasians of India are better able to endure the climate than are Europeans, but they lack industry and perseverance and suffer serious temperamental conflicts in their emotional life.[34] The Caucasian-Amerind crosses of the American tropics have more ambition on the average than the pure Indian and are better acclimatized to extreme tropical conditions than are Europeans. On the other hand, peoples such as the Metis (the Portuguese-negro cross in Brazil) are not in general characterized by hybrid vigor. Tuberculosis is common. Agriculture is distasteful to them; they are fond of display and are unreliable. Some, on the other hand, are extremely intelligent, and as there are few social barriers over most of the American tropics, they attain to high political office.[35]

Jennings thus summarizes his view of the question:

A population derived from a mixture of races having diverse characteristics will be much more heterogeneous than a population from a single race. There may be better combinations, and worse combinations, than are found in the single races. There will certainly be many individuals showing combinations of characteristics not found in the original races. In the long run there is selective elimination of the inefficient combinations, so that, finally, a race emerges that is again relatively homogeneous, combining characteristics from all the original races. This process has been gone through many times in the past; through it have arisen the races of the present day.

If the selective elimination that occurs is based on efficiency, it may be hoped that the race finally emerging will be superior to any one of those entering into the combination. But such a consummation will require a long period of time. And in the interval, while the poorer combinations are still present and in process of elimination, the mixed race may expect a lively and varied history. A nation composed of races in process of mixture will not be among those happy peoples whose annals are vacant.[36]

If Jennings is correct, it appears that hybridization may be dangerous between extreme racial types such as those which so frequently make contact in the tropics. Although scientific proof may still be lacking, ideals, such as the "White Australia" policy, may have a sound biological basis.[37]

In direct contradiction to Jennings' views are the opinions of Huxley and Haddon. These authorities state that it is extremely difficult to come to any firm conclusion on the biological results of wide crosses. Disregarding sweeping assertions on the alleged biological inferiority of half-castes, they admit that

. . . we are however confronted with the possibility that very wide crosses may give biologically "disharmonic" results in later generations, by producing ill-assorted combinations of characters. . . . If the primary sub-species of man were really developed in comparative isolation, each adapted to a different main type of environment, it may be argued that to upset the adjustment brought about by thousands of years of selection is bound to produce some disharmony. Further, if it be true that some ethnic groups possess a low average level of innate intelligence, to allow crosses between them and more intelligent types is a retrograde step.[38]

Huxley and Haddon consider that these arguments have some validity, but they point out that the great variability induced by wide crosses may be expected to throw up some exceptionally well-endowed types, while new types may be better adapted than old ones to the wholly new environment that man is ever creating for himself. In the opinion of these writers "race mixture" turns out to be not primarily a matter of race at all but a matter of nationality, class, or social status. It may well be that in many cases the discouragement of "racial crossing" may be the correct policy—for example, if unrestricted Asiatic immigration seems likely to upset the general type of culture in large-scale segregated areas such as the United States or Australia. But, say Huxley and Haddon, "Do not let us in such cases make it a question of 'race,' or become mystical on the subject, or justify ourselves on false biological grounds." [39]

Ethnic Groups in Tropical Jamaica

Unfortunately, scientists have made few comparative studies of tropical peoples, and there is little information in this field to throw light on the conflicting scientific views, but reference should perhaps be made to the work of Davenport and Steggerda in Jamaica and of Porteus and Dunn on the highly mixed peoples of Hawaii. As shown above, Davenport and Steggerda believe that the whites of Jamaica are superior to the blacks in mental ability. They also consider that the browns, who result from the white-black crosses, show unharmonious combinations more frequently than do the parent groups and that these disharmonies are more common in the brown adults. In Davenport's words, "One gains the general impression that, though on the average the Browns did not do so badly, there was among them a greater number of persons than in either Blacks or Whites who were muddled and wuzzle-headed." [40] There appeared to be an excess per cent over random expectation who seemed unable to utilize their native endowment. On the other hand, some individuals among the browns were superior in certain respects to both blacks and whites. "In four of the eight Army Alpha tests the browns seem to be inferior to both the blacks and whites. These are all important tests of mentality and lead to the conclusion that, on the average, the browns are frequently inferior in mental tests, while they show more extremes of excellent and poor performance than the other groups." [41] School teachers in northeastern Queensland and in Saba hold similar opinions about white and colored children reared in the same geographical, social, and economic environment. The whites are superior to the aborigines or negroes in mentality. On the average the browns are inferior to both blacks and whites, but they vary greatly, and some are as good or better than any members of the white, aboriginal, or negro groups.[42]

Ethnic Groups in Tropical Hawaii

The trade-wind islands of Hawaii have witnessed a great flood of Portuguese, Spanish, Chinese, Filipino, Puerto Rican, and Japanese immigrants, but there is more equality of opportunity and less racial prejudice than in most tropical countries, and some of the mixtures seem fairly good. L. Symes has summed up the position as follows:

With the exception of the "Japanese menace" no aspect of the Hawaiian situation has been discussed so widely or so unscientifically . . . as that of its "mixed-breeds," mixed-breeding being synonymous with degeneration in the minds of many editorial writers. There are, as the census figures have shown, over 28,000 Hawaiian-Orientals and Hawaiian-Caucasians in the territory—the Hawaiians having no race prejudices. The part-Hawaiian is increasing more rapidly than the pure-Hawaiian is dying off. (As a matter of fact, the latter is now almost holding his own, numerically.) There has been a gain of 125 per cent in the part-Hawaiian population in the past twenty years, and the part-Hawaiian is much more resistant to disease than his pure-bred brother. The Chinese-Hawaiian combination is usually admitted, even by the race purists, to be a fortunate one, but there is nothing to indicate that the inter-breeding of the Hawaiians with other groups has, in itself, resulted in physical or moral degeneration. When this has occurred, it has been due largely to the bad social conditions which frequently surround the children of such marriages. This fact has been forcibly emphasized by a man who knows the Hawaiian and part-Hawaiian intimately, Dr. Frank E. Midkiff, President of the famous Kamehameha schools, in a report for the Seth Richardson Investigation. . . . Dr. Midkiff says:

"Concerning the statement that the weak qualities of both races are inherited and the strong characteristics lost, I would say that this is purely a social matter . . . Ethnologists and anthropologists of the Bishop Museum find clear evidences of racial improvement due to crossing . . . Moral qualities are not inherited. They are the results of culture, especially of the early impressions of children in the home environment. . . .

"A new race is growing up here in the Pacific, which may be known as a new Pacific race; it will have the characteristics of many races. The Hawaiians are, in origin, Caucasian-Mongolian, and there is biologically no reason for the Hawaiian not mating happily with Chinese or whites. The physical characteristics of this new race are excellent and the mental and social characteristics are excellent also when the early home environment is fortunate and proper. . . . One thing that hinders progress toward desirable results is the fact that many of the fathers of these children are globe-trotters, ne'er-do-wells, and persons of low character qualifications." [48]

Porteus and Dunn, too, are fairly optimistic, although they are not very complimentary to the white-Hawaiian cross. In their opinion the Chinese coolies are thrifty and frugal and have a strong sense of family duty and responsibility, but they are individualistic and secretive and show a marked tendency to violence. The Chinese-Hawaiian hybrids stand first among all of the hybrids in industry and independence and are sought for positions of responsibility. The docile temperament of the Hawaiian and the intellectual proclivities of the Chinese are combined. The excellent home training of the Chinese fathers is largely responsible for the high ideals of their offspring. In the Hawaiian-white union the restless, ambitious, individualistic temperament of the white appears to be dominant. As regards physical features, Dunn found that the hybrids inherit the shorter head of the Hawaiians as a dominant characteristic. They also show the broader noses of the Hawaiians. The darker hair color, the wave of the hair, the dark eye and skin of the Hawaiians are partially dominant in the offspring. The second and later generations of hybrids show much variability.

As far as vitality is concerned the statistics in Table XVI indicate considerable hybrid vigor in some of the mixed Hawaiian peoples.

On the whole the vital statistics for the Caucasian-Hawaiian and Asiatic-Hawaiian blends indicate hybrid vigor, and the general opinion

TABLE XVI—HAWAII: SELECTED VITAL STATISTICS BY RACES*

RACE	BIRTHS PER 1000 1929	DEATHS PER 1000 1929	EXCESS BIRTHS PER 1000, 1929	INFANT MORTALITY per 1000†
American, British, German, and Russian..........	12.48	8.00	4.48	36.73
Chinese............	27.47	13.10	14.37	51.87
Filipino............	22.77	13.18	9.59	190.17
Hawaiian..........	21.60	33.30	−11.7	206.16
Japanese...........	38.12	8.76	29.36	52.50
Korean............	27.06	13.06	14.0	42.11
Asiatic............. Hawaiian	73.08	18.61	54.47	131.58
Caucasian.......... Hawaiian	62.57	17.28	45.29	102.31
Portuguese........	32.43	10.13	22.30	69.95
Puerto Rican.......	45.10	16.76	28.34	83.37
Spanish............	26.23	3.28	22.05	....
All others..........	66.29	70.08	−3.59	....

*Data from Annual Report, Governor of Hawaii, June, 1930. As this table does not indicate the proportion of males and females in each group listed, the conclusions must be treated with caution.
†Date not given—presumably 1929.

of observers is that these crosses show fairly satisfactory characteristics. It is quite clear, on the other hand, that the rapid increase of cross-breds in Hawaii is likely to absorb the other elements of population, with the exception of the Japanese, who maintain a high standard of racial purity. The result will be a Caucasian-Hawaiian-Asiatic race of unknown character, although Americans in Hawaii appeared to me to be hopeful that the educational process called "Americanization" will tend to produce good results. But the future is doubtful, and Hawaii presents some warnings to the white nations that set a high value on ethnic purity, while the economic trends present serious aspects for the whites. Writers such as Moe and Lind point out that Hawaii has seen a succession of invasions by various white and colored peoples, most of whom have begun as plantation laborers and have risen in the social scale until they are no longer attracted by plantation work. The whites are still holding their own in the professions, though other groups are beginning to compete in this field. The Japanese and Chinese are securing the bakery, tailoring, dressmaking, building, and carpentry trades and are getting a grip upon the building and contracting business. Almost all the Americans encountered in Hawaii are convinced that the process of "Americanization" will build up a satisfactory Hawaiian nation and solve the racial and economic problems, but they recognize that the difficulties are great.[44]

An interesting study has also been made by H. L. Shapiro of the Caucasian-Polynesian peoples of Pitcairn and Norfolk Islands—the descendants of the mutineers of the *Bounty*, who have been located for several generations slightly outside the tropics.[45] Shapiro concludes that the people of Norfolk Island have hybrid vigor to a marked degree. There is a decided increase in stature and in the size of the family in the first generation, and, although this vitality diminishes after five generations, it remains stronger than in either of the parent stocks. Inbreeding seems to have produced no harmful effects.[46]

After examining the evidence on the subject as a whole, we can only conclude that some ethnic mixtures seem satisfactory and others unsatisfactory in the tropics, for reasons that have as yet defeated satisfactory analysis. Huxley and Haddon correctly stress our scientific ignorance on the subject of ethnic groups. In this field there is pressing need for further research.

CHAPTER XIII

SOME ENVIRONMENTAL FACTORS

ISOLATION

With "race" ranks "place." The fundamental bases of white settlement in the tropics are the characteristics of the invaders and of their location. It was made evident in the regional part of this book that one of the most important phenomena affecting white settlers is isolation. Two main circumstances give rise to isolation. The first is spatial, as for instance in parts of northern Australia, where the white settlements are isolated even though the aboriginal population is very sparse. The second is racial and may operate through either racial prejudice or economic competition. Isolation from racial prejudice is evident in the small aristocratic groups of Spanish descent in some of the South American republics. Competition has isolated white groups in numerous cases where, for instance, whites are in contact with dense negro populations. Generally, however, the factors both of location and race are at work. Racial pride and negro competition drove the so-called poor whites of the southern United States into highland regions, where, under hard economic conditions and bad diets, they have developed certain unfavorable psychological and physical traits. Similarly geographical, racial, and economic isolation has retarded the progress of scattered white groups in areas such as tropical Australia and South America.

It was formerly believed that isolation worked its evil effects largely through inbreeding, but this is denied by recent writers such as Pitt-Rivers. According to this anthropologist, "the old view that close inbreeding must necessarily be conducive to degeneracy or decline, although increasingly discredited by scientific and empirical facts, still receives a measure of popular support." There are, however, abundant facts to show that the closest inbreeding is compatible with the continued and even increased vigor of a stock. Pitt-Rivers believes that marriage between near relatives cannot be proved to affect the offspring adversely [1] wholly by reason of their consanguinity and regardless of the inheritance received. This dictum does not deny the facts evident, for instance, in the Bahamas, that mental weakness and disease, or the liability to disease, have developed in small consanguinous groups. Nevertheless, it complicates our problem by lessening the weight generally attributed to inbreeding in creating degeneracy in small isolated communities.

One highly important point is clear, however, from the facts set out in this book. As noted in Chapter IX, the phenomenon of geographical and racial isolation is so weighty that it behooves the governments of white nations in the temperate zones to consider seriously whether they should continue to permit their nationals to conduct small-scale efforts at establishing settlements in isolated tropical regions,[2] particularly where these regions already contain other ethnic groups in a lower stage of development.

TROPICAL SOILS

The nature of tropical soils in relation to white settlement is of profound importance. The problem is one for experts, and a vast field awaits scientific research. Certain points, however, are already evident. The old theory that the hot, wet tropics with their dense vegetation are almost wholly of great fertility is incorrect, for it is clear that the tropics include many sterile soils.

Most notorious of tropical soils are the much debated laterites, usually red in color and thoroughly leached. Under the influence of heavy rainfall and high temperatures the mineral matter of the original parent material has been largely broken down. Iron and aluminum are concentrated in the subsoil, but the critical soluble plant foods have been dissolved by internal drainage waters and carried out of the *solum*. In spite of the heavy forest cover, the organic matter or humus content is slight.[3] These soils are very low in lime and acid in reaction. They are also deficient in potash and phosphates. Thus they are poor soils. Even in the virgin state the laterites are not suitable to farming—particularly to commercial agriculture. As a result, the abandonment of land, new clearings, and nomadic agriculture are frequent, and dense agricultural populations evolve only on young unleached soils or on the flood plains of river valleys.

When cleared, the soil is in early, if not immediate, need of fertilization and will not endure continuous cropping without the most careful and persistent attention. Both lime and organic matter are required, since the forest mold and the soil structure are subject to rapid disappearance under cultivation.[4]

Even the "rederths" and red lateritic loams of the tropics are not highly productive under natural conditions, although these soils are not as greatly leached as the true laterites.[5]

In his brilliant study of Australian soils Professor J. A. Prescott, Director of the Waite Agricultural Research Institute, University of Adelaide, states that the laterite formations of Australia are fossil in character and must be classified by geology rather than by climate. He notes that the most striking feature of these soils, which probably cover vast areas of northern Australia, is their low fertility—in some cases an absolute infertility. So far they have given no response to normal fertilizer treatment. This low fertility is reflected in the dwarfed character of the natural vegetation, which is lamentably evident to any traveler in the Australian tropical regions other than those on the

Queensland coast. The so-called wodgil soils of Western Australia have become so notorious for their infertility that they have now been withdrawn from selection. Prescott notes:

It would be of interest to discuss how far the disappointing agricultural development of such climatically promising areas as Esperance and Kangaroo Island, and possibly also of North Australia, is due to the local predominance of these soils with a past.[6]

In the Macrossan Lectures of 1930 as well as in Chapter VIII of this present work I have emphasized the role played by the soils of the Northern Territory in the failure of white settlement.[7] The history of that unfortunate region is a striking proof of the general principles enunciated by Prescott and other soil scientists.

A leading American authority, the late C. F. Marbut, considered it a mistake to classify all red tropical soils as laterites. True laterites are much less widely distributed in the tropics than was formerly thought.[8] They have not been thoroughly investigated, however, even in Cuba, where considerable soil research has taken place.

Soils of the types mentioned by these experts explain why the level interfluves in many tropical regions support only grass or scanty forest, while the younger and more fertile soils on the slopes are cultivated. Many other tropical soils are poor because the abundant rain causes them to be waterlogged, as in the flood plains of the Amazon or in New Guinea. Huntington suggests that many poor tropical soils can support magnificent forests, owing to the fact that the trees have become adjusted to a watery environment and require a very small supply of minerals. Also, trees of the same kind rarely grow together in large numbers, so that no one kind of tree exhausts its own particular plant food. This poverty of soil does much to explain the sparse and backward populations of many tropical regions. The people have to cultivate the poor soils laboriously. They must rest them frequently, and they face grave difficulties in the wetter regions where vegetation grows with unbelievable rapidity and the land must be cleared of hardwood trees.[9]

Fortunately the tropics contain many soils of far better quality than the laterites. The famous chernozems, for example, which are found between the semiarid and the humid regions in both the middle and low latitudes, are a fine type. These soils are black earths—dark brown to black in the cooler middle latitudes, with lighter colors prevailing in the tropics. Prescott notes that in Australia black earths develop only in heavy soils. Black soils would be much more frequent in tropical Australia but for the sandstone tableland and desert sandstone country of lateritic character that dominate the surface features of the Cape York Peninsula, the Northern Territory, and the Kimberleys. Prescott classifies the soils of the Barkly Tableland and of the Victoria, Ord, and Fitzroy river areas not as black soils, but as soils belonging to the more arid brown and gray group.[10] Figure 52 shows the parts of northern Australia in which "black earths" akin to those of India, North America and Russia may be expected to occur. Wolfanger notes that the "gray-erths," which are the typical soils of the tropical deserts, are characteristically pebbly, sandy, or rocky. The natural vegetation is scattered, harsh, and scanty. There are few animals, and such as do exist produce meat of low quality. The people are scattered pastoralists. In such lands dense populations occur only where the rivers are responsible for fresher soils that may be irrigated.[11]

The soil potentialities of most other tropical regions appear to be greater than those of northern Australia. We have noted in previous chapters the productivity of the volcanic soils of areas such as the West Indies and of the humus soils of Florida. C. F. Marbut thought that there was much hope for parts of the Amazon basin. He believed that 70 per cent of this region of a million square miles was capable of "some form of agricultural development" and could support a very dense population living on tropical products. The Antilles and Central America had, in his opinion, even greater potentialities.

Unfortunately, as Marbut himself recognized, the great centers of white population can supply most of their needs from regions closer at hand than the tropics. Moreover, the white man has not yet found it possible to be an original producer of high efficiency in tropical areas, and, although the last few years have shown that with precautions he can live out his natural life span in these regions, he has not yet evinced any ability for engaging in production other than as an organizer or overseer.[12]

The scanty researches on tropical soils tend to one conclusion: the vital necessity of soil surveys. Little has been done as yet in Africa, northern Australia, or South America, although United States scientists began the pioneering with some fine work in the Virgin Islands and Cuba.[13]

Bennett and Allison wrote their classic work on the soils of Cuba "with the hope that as a pioneer effort it might be the forerunner of such studies in the tropics as may . . . be helpful in showing the great need for basic studies of this kind in this vast region, as a preliminary to the development of a more systematic and efficient agriculture, based upon correct systems of land utilization."[14] These scientists more than proved their case, for their work classified the soils of the island, explained why the sugar industry flourished in some areas and languished or retreated in others, and showed why agricultural methods, which proved valuable in some localities, were totally unsatisfactory in others. It is essential that this scientific work should be extended. Until the governments of such tropical countries as northern Australia cease making haphazard attempts at settlement and utilize more fully the remarkable achievements of the soil scientist, no adequate estimate can be made of the potentialities for white settlement even in those parts of the tropics that appear to offer some hope.

Tropical Climates

To white settlers in the tropics the most powerful, complex, and mysterious of all environmental factors are those relating to climate.[15] Climate has been defined as the average of weather conditions, together with the variation from that average, and this variation or changeability is of particular importance in the tropics, where the climate is frequently monotonous. For many years scientists have been analyzing climate and amassing data, but the methods of collecting these data are by no means uniform, and the information is still insufficient. To take for example the factor of wind, the idea of measuring the cooling power and "sensible temperature" goes back to Heberden (1826); and Van Bebber, Ward, and other prominent climatologists were advocating the importance of sensible temperature and wind to comfort as long ago as three or four decades. Later, from 1913 to 1923, Sir Leonard Hill, in a brilliant series of studies, gave a practical demonstration of the importance of wind in comfort and health. Yet, in spite of this and the obvious influence of wind upon human settlement, it is still very difficult to obtain adequate wind statistics for important tropical regions and impossible for most local areas. On this point the well known geographer, Professor Griffith Taylor, states that "it is a counsel of perfection to advise the meteorologist to allow for wind velocities in his study of comfort as controlled by climate." [16]

For a long time many atmospheric (and some geophysical and astrophysical elements) have been suggested as of probable or possible importance in health, disease, or death, but it is only in the last two decades that any very extensive investigations have been given to them, notably by German and Swiss clinicians and physicists. The development of the air-conditioning industry and the broadening of public health research has of late provided much of the impetus to more careful study in environmental physiology and medicine. Needless to say, there has been discouragement in this work owing to the inherent difficulty of the problem and a somewhat conservative attitude on the part of many pathologists.

The solution of the general problem of climate and health requires extensive studies of the effects of many elements—among them atmospheric ionization, sunshine, barometric pressure, perhaps other unknown factors—all of which have an important bearing upon health.[17]

Difficult as is the analysis of climate, of far greater complexity is the analysis of its effects upon man. It is necessary not only to estimate the weight of the various climatic factors acting both separately and in conjunction, but to disentangle them from other phenomena—racial characteristics, parasitic diseases, cultural level, isolation, diet, unhygienic surroundings or habits, and changing social tastes. Some of these phenomena depend partly upon climate and are often called secondary climatic factors. Many, however, lie entirely outside the climatic sphere. Even eliminating these non-climatic factors, we see the truth of Sir Andrew Balfour's statement that knowledge of the effects of climate, particularly of tropical climates, is still limited and inexact.[18]

Classification of Climates [19]

We have accepted the definition of the tropics as a zone that possesses an annual average temperature of not less than 70° F. According to variations in temperature, wind, and moisture, this zone has been further subdivided into the marginal, trade-wind, wet-dry, desert, highland, and low equatorial tropics. Differences between these types are insufficiently appreciated. Many white communities, for example, fail to realize how varied are the types of housing required in the widely different kinds of tropics.

Dr. C. Warren Thornthwaite has recently published a map that classifies world climates on the basis of "precipitation effectiveness" and "temperature efficiency," his climatic regions thus corresponding generally to vegetation regions.[20] In Australia, Professor J. A. Prescott and James Davidson have studied the ratio of precipitation to atmospheric saturation deficit for purposes of agriculture and animal and plant ecology,[21] and W. Wynne Williams has mapped the effects of the monthly rainfall on tropical industry. Little work, however, has yet been done in applying quantitative classifications of climate to the problem of white settlement in the tropics. I have attempted to use Thornthwaite's classification for this purpose, but with inconclusive results, although it appears that white settlers have survived or succeeded only in the lower ranges of Thornthwaite's tropical scale of "precipitation effectiveness" and "temperature efficiency" and that in general high humidities were more deleterious than high temperatures.

As regards the effects of heat and moisture upon human beings, Dr. Ellsworth Huntington and Professor Griffith Taylor have published suggestive researches, which are outlined in the next chapter. Henry Barkley, following the crude empirical methods of Taylor, has considered the factor of relative physical comfort as a guide to man's effective occupation in Australia. He develops the idea of an index of comfort based on atmospheric vapor pressure.[22] [But the notion that vapor pressure alone is any adequate index of comfort has long ago been shown to be invalid. The use of wet-bulb temperature, Knoche's desiccating-power (*Austrocknungswert*), the equivalent temperature, the physiological saturation deficit, physiological relative humidity, etc.,[23] would be somewhat better, but these also suffer from more or less serious inherent limitations that discourage climatologists and medical men from attempting the labor of evaluating them in practice.—R. G. S.]

Huntington has produced maps correlating climatic data with human energy and civilization, with conclusions unfavorable to the future

prospects of white settlement in the tropics.[24] At present our knowledge and methods appear inadequate for sweeping generalizations,
particularly as these must ignore local and micro-climates and non-
climatic factors.

Local Climates

The frequency of unfavorable types of weather at given stations and the frequency
of interruptions in the sequence by a more favorable type will become significant in a
greater degree, since the development of the vast resources of the Tropics depends upon
the ability of progressive peoples to live and work in the climatic conditions found
there. Thus it seems that a study of the weather conditions to be encountered from
day to day is appropriate.[25]

This quotation is from a study by J. Elmer Switzer of the frequency
of weather types in the climate of certain cities in Mexico, the Canal
Zone, and Cuba. Switzer attempted to give a conception of the weather
by the use of statistics covering daily temperature, rainfall, and velocity
and direction of the wind; but interesting as his idea was, his data and
method were inadequate. However, such analyses as we can make
emphasize the importance of the climatic environment as a prelude
to the study of any white group. We have seen, for example, that on
the tiny island of Saba (Chapter VII) a significant majority of the
whites live at high elevations on the windward side of the island. In
coastal towns of tropical lowlands such as Ancon (Panama) or Darwin
(Australia), the position of the residential quarters illustrates the importance of local climatic factors, as also do the elevated sites of country
villages and dwellings in Puerto Rico. A practical recognition of the
thesis is seen in the business of the New York Life Insurance Company,
which states, for example, that "rates of extra premium should depend
on part of country, occupation, and whether the applicant is acclimatized or not." [26]

Some Possible Effects of Regional Climates

The equatorial climates are marked by high temperatures, high humidities, and considerable monotony, and as a result the equatorial
regions present the most difficult field for the control of parasitic diseases and of pests. Thus while parts of this zone offer high economic
potentialities, the difficulties resulting from the climate are great, and
it is doubtful if the white races will ever gain sufficient control of tropical
diseases to establish extensive and permanent settlements. In this zone
no large white settlements of long duration are found, and, although
groups of Portuguese, Spanish, and Dutch seem to have kept their blood
pure in some settlements of the East Indies and northern South America,
these groups are small. A little settlement of Dutch origin at Kisar in
the East Indies is cited as an illustration. This community of Dutch-
Malays dates back for about a hundred and sixty years, and its mem-

bers still show Dutch characteristics, such as fair hair, but none of the evidence indicates the survival of any pure-white blood.[27]

The wet-dry lands and deserts appear to possess better climates for white settlement than the equatorial regions, for, in spite of high summer temperatures, they have cooler winters, lower humidities, and greater and more frequent changes of weather than the equatorial climates. Ward considers that these wet-dry or arid regions are better for the whites than the moist tropics, but he points out that the heat, dust, and brilliant sunshine are trying and that the deficient rainfall usually makes the difficulties of white settlement very great.[28] The truth of this statement is illustrated in the chapter on northern Australia (Chapter VIII).

The trade-wind islands and coasts and the marginal regions seem more suited to white settlement than the equatorial, wet-dry, or desert areas, for they possess in general somewhat lower mean annual temperatures, their humidities are usually lower than those of the equatorial regions, and many of the islands and coasts in the trade-wind regions are swept by constant winds.

Opinions vary greatly as to the tropical highlands. These regions possess lower temperatures, clearer air, lower pressures, higher winds, and sometimes lower rainfall than the equatorial lowlands and at the same time have more equable climates than those of the wet-dry lands. Hence, many consider that in such areas the whites can create permanent working settlements. Ward points out that India has been ruled from a height of 7000 feet and states that the climate of many tropical plateaus has been designated as "perpetual spring." [29] Yet Balfour and others draw attention to conditions that are possibly deleterious. Even at considerable altitudes the tropical climate is still monotonous, and Europeans living continually on high plateaus, like those of Colombia or Costa Rica, often complain after a time of nervous symptoms and find a temporary change to the low country beneficial.[30]

14

CHAPTER XIV

ACCLIMATIZATION AND HEALTH: I. CLIMATOLOGICAL AND STATISTICAL STUDIES

Can the white man become acclimatized and preserve his vitality, energy, and health in any of the tropical climates?[1] This is a basic problem of white settlement. In the past, history and observation have answered in the negative. Some medical scientists now reply affirmatively, but others are still pessimistic. Unfortunately all types of evidence remain contradictory and complex.

As indicated in Chapter VI, doctors and educationists in the marginal tropics of northeastern Queensland are in two camps. One group points to satisfactory but very recent statistics of health and vitality, and can see no signs of mental or physical degeneracy. The other group is cautious in criticizing the communities among which it makes its living but sees signs of degeneration as evidenced by lack of vitality and energy, loss of tone, dehydration of the tissues, bad teeth, and a low comparative standard of intellect after the age of sixteen. In Florida authoritative observers believe that on the whole there is no mental or physical failing. They consider that the results of statistical research on the whites of the warm southern states are capable of favorable interpretation and that disease and the presence of low-standard negroes fully account for any alleged decadence. The "backwardness" of the South has usually been attributed to historical factors.[2] In trade-wind islands, such as Saba, the Caymans, and Hawaii, opinions are again varied. Here, as on the tropical plateaus, many non-climatic factors must be taken into account, and certainly the whites of the plateaus of northeastern Queensland, where Australian national policies and a high living standard offer unusual protection, appear to become acclimatized and keep their vigor and health.[3] As to the wet-dry lands of northern Australia statistics and opinions also vary, but many of the whites—men, women, and children—show no decline.[4] In the low tropics of Panama opinions likewise differ. According to the statistics the physical and intellectual condition of the children of the select group of Americans is excellent, but some doctors see signs of adult decay.[5] In the hot, humid equatorial tropics the views of almost all medical scientists are pessimistic, as instanced by those of Professor Kenneth Black of Singapore. Professor Black writes:

In the tropics, flowers bloom early but wither quickly, and similarly the majority of the local inhabitants reach old age when Europeans have barely attained middle age. For example, presbyopia is a progressive weakening of the internal eye muscles, which have to do with accommodation (focussing) of a normal eye for near work; glasses have, therefore, to be worn for near work for its correction. In England, presbyopia becomes manifest at the age of forty-five and even later, whereas among the tropical races it comes on at about the age of thirty-five and even earlier. Dr. Dexter Allen, D. O. Oxon., who has been engaged for the past thirty years in eye work in the tropics, has informed me that she observes among Europeans, who have lived long in tropical countries, that presbyopia comes on early and sometimes as early as thirty-eight. Her observations on Europeans have been confirmed by Dr. Harston, who was Ophthalmologist, Hong Kong University. This is direct evidence that residence in the tropics produces physical deterioration. The same is true of senile cataract; this is a degenerative change in the lens of the eye causing opacity, and occurs more frequently and develops earlier in those peoples who inhabit hot countries.

When people go from a country with a superior to one with an inferior climate, their power of sustained work deteriorates sooner or later, although sometimes at first it is stimulated by the change, especially if the change is to a "bracing" climate. Dr. G. H. Garlick states that the officer in charge of the Colonial Survey Section making a topographical survey of Johore, reported: "It is worthy of note that the graph showing the area produced per (white) man per month, after rising steeply at the commencement as each man became accustomed to his work, maintained a steady level of about three to four square miles a month, depending on the type of country, until the man had been working for two-and-a-half years, after which it showed a steady drop, until the completion of three years, when the men were relieved and returned to England. This drop was unquestionably due to the strain of working in a climate in which the shade temperature was seldom below 80° F. day or night, winter or summer." This is evidence of importance proving a deterioration in efficiency of the European topographical men after a certain period of service in Malaya.

What is true of physical is likely, on investigation, to be found true of mental deterioration. But here the subject, from the scientific aspect, bristles with difficulties as our knowledge of the physiology and pathology of the mind is so meagre, so full of theory and with so few proved facts, that science plays a game of skittles. As fast as theories and explanations are forthcoming to explain the processes of the mind, they are knocked down only for others to be set up. It seems, however, the experience of almost all observers that residence in the tropics, and indeed in any inferior climate causes mental deterioration. It is indisputable that good mental health is as important as good physical health. Sir Havelock Charles not only stoutly supporter Cuvier's axiom "that the nervous system is at bottom the whole animal and other systems are only there to serve it," but declared that "tropical residence damages the nervous system even though it produces no physical disease." [6]

I have met only one medical scientist with experience of the equatorial tropics who is optimistic as regards white settlement in these regions, Dr. G. J. P. Barger, an American medical missionary, who had spent many years in the Congo, where he had brought up a healthy family of four children. It is to be noted, however, that they had taken strict and continuous health precautions and had secured several periods of "leave." [7]

No effort will be made in this work to trace in detail the many medical investigations of tropical acclimatization with their unsatisfactory and conflicting results. We shall attempt, rather, to outline some of the most important problems of acclimatization, health, and disease, and to explain the existing state of statistical and experimental research. Up to the present most of the researches have been conducted in the field of physiology, but beyond this lie vital problems of psychology and neurology still almost untouched. So closely are these complex problems interwoven that the sections which follow must constantly overlap.

STATISTICAL RESEARCH ON THE EFFECTS OF CLIMATE

Working from statistics, climatologists have attempted to discover how far human life and activity are controlled by climatic factors and laws. They have constructed climograms (or graphical correlations of climatic factors with one another and with health) and maps illustrating the relationships of climate to health, energy, and civilization. They have drawn up climatic scales of comfort and discomfort. Although many of the conclusions of these investigations must be distrusted on grounds both of data and of method, it is important to examine them.

As early as 1839, L. Moser attempted to find a correlation between temperatures and death rates, and later J. L. Casper, E. G. Dexter, Cleveland Abbe, Griffith Taylor, Ellsworth Huntington, and others have engaged in similar types of research. Investigators in several biological fields now consider that there are climatic limits and optima for all types of life. Abbe wrote:

Everyone must recognise the general fact that certain atmospheric conditions, such as the dryness of the air, stimulate, while other conditions such as moist air relax the human system. As with man, so with other animals and plants. Each family and species, each type of animal and plant has its optimum pressure, temperature, and moisture; and any considerable departure from this means a corresponding amount of change in the direction of the degeneracy in the individual.[8]

Sir Aldo Castellani holds similar views. "There cannot be any doubt in our opinion," he writes, "that there is a distinct optimum condition of climate for man, just as for plants and animals. Any departure from the optimum for a given race or individual seems to render people not only less efficient, but also more susceptible to disease."[9] The same opinion is held by Professor Kenneth Black.[10]

CLIMATIC THEORIES OF TAYLOR AND HUNTINGTON

Prominent in the field of climatic influences on human life are the statistical researches of two geographers, Griffith Taylor and Ellsworth Huntington. Taylor uses statistics of wet-bulb temperatures and relative humidities to construct regional climographs, which indicate the average wet-bulb temperature and humidity for every month of the year. He also presents a "comfort" and "discomfort" scale, which place the ideal climate for northern whites at 45° to 55° F. wet-bulb temperature with humidities of 70 to 80 per cent. Working from the leading centers of northern white population, Taylor constructs a "type white climograph," in which the wet-bulb monthly temperatures range from 37° to 62° F. and the humidities from 68.5 to 87 per cent. In presenting a "tentative scale of discomfort," he notes that wet-bulb temperatures of 65° to 70° F. are often and temperatures above 70° F. are usually "uncomfortable."[11] If Taylor's estimate of discomfort is correct, the equatorial lowlands are always uncomfortable for whites and the monsoonal regions, the trade-wind areas, and the margins are uncomfortable for much of the year.

Taylor's claims for his climograph are modest. He states that he has made an attempt to elucidate by correlation the limits of comfortable settlement for the Anglo-Saxon branch of the white race. He believes that he has obtained a useful criterion in the "type white climograph" and that the discomfort scale indicates the difficulty of peopling the Australian tropics. Although more research is needed, we may accept these conclusions as approximately correct. The collection of data on temperature and humidity had advanced sufficiently for Taylor to express with fair accuracy the temperature and humidity of certain tropical spots by means of his climograph. The listing of places with wet-bulb temperatures of more than 70° as "usually uncomfortable" is supported by the history and experience of white settlers in the tropics. Taylor's scale of "discomfort" justly emphasizes the oppressive high average humidity and heat that lead to the breakdown of many white settlers, particularly women, and create considerable natural selection among immigrants to the tropics.

Griffith Taylor's conclusions are supported by the researches of Dr. Ellsworth Huntington.[12] Huntington postulates the laws that every environmental factor, such as temperature, sunlight, humidity, or wind, can be and sometimes is sufficiently excessive or deficient to destroy any particular organism and that every organism, whether an individual or a species, has an optimum climate. Man can survive a wide range of environmental conditions; nevertheless, people who live under the least favorable climatic conditions will be at a disadvantage as compared with those who live near the climatic optima and hence are more healthy, energetic, and progressive. From a large mass of statistical data, supported in a few cases by laboratory experiments, Huntington then attempts to lay down optima for physical energy, mental efficiency, civilization, and health.

It must be strongly emphasized that Huntington clearly recognizes the dynamic influence of the human race upon its environment. The climatic optimum, in his opinion, "varies according to a people's stage of progress." The temperature control, for example, "changes with the growth of clothes, heating methods and the like. . . . This tendency in itself is enough to account for a considerable part of the shift in the centers of civilization." [13]

Huntington presents curves which, in his opinion, illustrate the effect of mean temperatures on the vital processes of certain living organisms and on human physical and mental efficiency and health. From various statistics, particularly the death rate, he calculates that the optimum temperatures for white people, living under present-day conditions of housing and diet, are 38° F. for mental energy and 65° F. for physical energy and health. Weather variations are important and changes of temperature should be about 3° F. from day to day.[14] The optimum humidity under these conditions is about 80 per cent. This "ideal climate" is approximately that of the British Isles and corresponds fairly well with Taylor's "type white climograph." Although some of Huntington's optima extend over fair ranges, it is obvious that the tropics lie well outside the ideal limits that he depicts.

Criticisms of Huntington's Theories

Huntington's views have been attacked by sociologists such as P. Sorokin and R. B. Vance, by medical scientists such as W. A. Murray in South Africa and Sir Raphael Cilento in Australia, and by statisticians such as the Australian C. H. Wickens.[15] These critics appreciate Huntington's brilliant theories and stimulating generalizations, but they maintain that he exaggerates the correlation between climate and human progress, vitality, energy, health, birth and death rates, social organization, religion, art, and the like. They consider that he reaches inaccurate conclusions from insufficient data and that he misinterprets statistics, overemphasizes the importance of the death-rate data as indicative of health, and confuses the primary factors of climate with secondary controls such as disease and diet. They point out that other investigations of a similar nature have produced very different results. To take mental energy as an example, Dexter found that the temperature at which the minimum clerical errors occurred was 58° F. and that no marked increase occurred until 77° F.[16] So again, Hines's experiments on school children showed that the optimum temperature for intellectual activity was 65°-70° F., and that temperatures below 60° F. had bad effects upon mental work.[17]

Despite these criticisms, many eminent authorities have adopted Huntington's methods and make use of his researches. While C. P. Yaglou points out that "both statistical and experimental studies indicate that there can be no ideal climate to suit every purpose," he believes in climatic optima and holds that the optimum climate for infants under one year is about 63° F., some 8° F. above Huntington's figure and approximately the same as Huntington's value for persons of more than five years of age.[18] It is unnecessary for us to enter the controversy on the constituents of the ideal climates for white mentality, energy, and health. We must, however, examine some of the implications of Huntington's theories.

So violent have been Huntington's critics that they have ignored the hope he offers for white settlement in the tropics. In the first place, he believes that the climatic optima for whites, for negroes, and for Asiatics (such as the Javanese and Japanese) are not very dissimilar, the difference in temperature being only 4° or 5° F.[19] If future research confirms this opinion, it may well follow that the varying experiences of races in the tropics are due less to climate per se than to factors such as diseases, diets, and living standards, which can, in some cases, be controlled.

Second, Huntington emphasizes, as we have seen, the dynamic progress of human civilization. Of great importance is the stress that he also lays on human adaptability. "If mankind," he writes, "is derived from one primitive stock, and can yet live comfortably in so great a variety of climates, there is every reason to believe that the white man might become acclimated to the tropics, provided he subject himself to a sufficiently rigid process of selection." [20] Here, Huntington thinks, lies the main hope for white settlement in the tropics. The whites who today inhabit these regions are in all probability highly selected. By means of such selection for generation after generation a strain of white people could probably be produced that would be able to stand the climate quite as well as the present tropical races. "If the specific tropical diseases like malaria and hook-worm could be eliminated, the chances are that such people could live in comparative health and comfort. They might also maintain their present stage of civilization and go on to a higher stage provided they could overcome the tremendous handicap of contact with tropical races of lower standards." [21]

These statements show Huntington, if anything, overoptimistic. Perhaps he reads evolution backward too readily, and can we be sure that we can do in a few centuries what Nature took many thousands of years to accomplish? As far as they can be accepted, however, his climatic and social statistics tend to support the evidence of history, which indicates that tropical conditions make human settlement and the evolution of a high standard of civilization extremely difficult.

We can say with safety only that Huntington and his school have propounded theories that statistical and laboratory research tend to confirm, but that more research is needed before these theories can be accepted as scientific truth. To take one difficulty among many: "In the present state of our knowledge it is impossible to say whether man is a critical mechanism in regard to climate, or whether there is a fairly broad band of conditions to which he is indifferently tolerant." [22] [However, the tolerance of an individual must not be confused with that of a large population, and furthermore, the concept of a purely physiological tolerance apart from culture can only be regarded as academic and unreal.—R. G. S.]

Statistical Researches in Queensland

As we have seen, Sir Raphael Cilento has examined the expectation of life, the annual average death rate, the birth rate, infant mortality, and other statistics relating to Queensland whites.[23] He finds that the Queensland death rate (1906-1917), the infant mortality (1906-1917), and the male and female expectation of life are better than the average of the Australian Commonwealth. From the point of view of tropical research these statistics must be largely discounted owing to the fact that the great majority of Queenslanders live in the subtropics. Of more importance are Cilento's statements that the infant mortality rate in northern Queensland and the death rate in hospitals are lower than in subtropical Queensland and that the birth rate in the northern coastal districts is as good as that in the south. The Census of 1933 gives remarkably good figures for tropical Queensland, and other data support Cilento's views. In 1920, for example, the Australian Medical Congress in Brisbane declared that "the opinion of the medical practitioners present was overwhelmingly in favour of the suitability of North Queensland for the successful implantation of a white working race." [24]

Yet there is clearly much truth in Huntington's contention that Cilento's views are too optimistic. The Queensland experiment is very recent. Much of the heavy labor in the sugar industry is still drawn from the south, and it is noteworthy that in the northern sugar areas the Italian is rapidly ousting the Anglo-Saxon white. Huntington's statement that the north Queensland population is highly selected is important, for many Australians certainly avoid residing in the Queensland tropics. As an American critic has pointed out:

Although his [Cilento's] argument is cleverly constructed, it flies in the face of a mass of testimony that can have but one meaning. It is not enough to demonstrate the health of the inhabitants and their physical capacity to stand the high temperatures and humidities. . . . A far more important question, which is overlooked by Dr. Cilento, is the matter of comfort and tolerability.[25]

Professor Griffith Taylor emphasizes the importance of comfort and tolerability in the development of northern Australia. In his opinion there is little likelihood of white Australians attempting to settle their tropics while "there are larger areas of cooler country which will long await settlement." [26]

The material that I collected when visiting Queensland in 1936 includes some evidence in support of the statistical data favoring white settlement. On the other hand, doctors, educationists, and other authorities differ so greatly as to the future of the experiment that the Queensland figures must be used with care (Chapter VI).

STATISTICAL RESEARCHES IN FLORIDA AND PANAMA

Statistics also indicate that white settlement is making good progress in the marginal zone of Florida (Chapter V). Here health and diet campaigns and favorable conditions for the citrus fruit, truck vegetable, and tourist industries promote development despite the handicap imposed by the presence of the negro. One can find no statistics to show how far the population is "selected," but allowance must certainly be made for the fact that the growth is recent and includes a large proportion of immigrants from the northern and cooler parts of the United States.

In Panama the researches made by Columbia University on school children showed no deterioration and indicated a slightly higher intellectual level than for similar groups in the United States. Once again, however, the northern whites of Panama are highly selected.[27] In contradiction to these results Ellsworth Huntington has found that the health, energy, and civilization of whites in the Bahamas are at a very low ebb. These white groups are, however, small, isolated, inbred, diseased, outnumbered by negroes, and situated in surroundings where soil and other factors are difficult.[28]

INSURANCE COMPANY STATISTICS

An examination of governmental publications and the literature issued by important private organizations, such as the missionary societies and insurance companies, throws further light upon the improvement of health in the tropics, the existing difficulties, and the possibilities of future progress. Both the official and private publications lay great stress on many important aspects of white settlement, for example, the general improvement in health and the importance of regional variations within the tropical zone.

Arthur Hunter, actuary of the New York Life Insurance Company, New York, has published some valuable papers on the experiences of this important company, which does a great deal of business in the tropics. He points out that mortality varies widely among foreigners resident in different countries and indicates that it is better in the Orient than in the Occident. He notes that the mortality rate is showing a marked improvement in some tropical countries. This is probably due not only to improved conditions of health but to the fact that the old type of adventurer is being replaced to a large extent by picked men sent out by great business organizations, which maintain a close watch over their employees' methods of living and keep them under strict control.[29] Basing his conclusions upon the mortality experience of the company, the changing conditions, the type of man going to the tropics, the climatic and hygienic factors, and the opinions formed from personal visits, Hunter divides tropical countries into five classes. Class I includes countries in which insurance companies can safely charge the northern or domestic rate of premium. Classes A, B, C, and D, include those in which the companies should charge an extra premium of $2.50, $5, $10, and $20 respectively per $1000 on the ordinary life plan. He places in Class I the whole of the subtropical United States (including the tropical parts of Florida), the southern section of Rhodesia, the southern sections of South West Africa, and the Bahama and Hawaiian islands. In Class A he includes no tropical regions. In Class B ($5 per $1000) he places the more favorable parts of Kenya, Uganda, and Tanganyika, the northern sections of Rhodesia and South West Africa, the Panama Canal Zone (for Americans and Canadians only), parts of Mexico, Peru, the better sections of Brazil (such as the highlands of Minas Geraes, Rio de Janeiro, São Paulo, Paraná, Santa Catharina, and Rio Grande do Sul), the northern section of Australia, the islands of Fiji, Tonga, New Caledonia, the New Hebrides, Samoa and the Society Islands in the South Seas, and Antigua, Barbados, Cuba, Dominica, Jamaica, Puerto Rico, St. Lucia, St. Vincent and the Virgin Islands in the West Indies. Class C ($10 per $1000) includes the chief towns of Abyssinia, the less favorable sections of Kenya, especially the coastal and lake regions, Madagascar, Mauritius, Nyasaland, Portuguese East Africa (north of the Tropic of Capricorn), Annam, Cambodia, and Cochin China (French Indo-China), Borneo, Burma, Celebes, Ceylon, Formosa, Guam, India, Java, the Malay Peninsula, the Philippines, Siam, Sumatra, British Honduras, Costa Rica, Guatemala, Honduras, Nicaragua, Panama (except the Canal Zone), Salvador, the more unfavorable parts of Mexico, Bolivia, Colombia, Ecuador, British, Dutch, and French Guiana, Venezuela, Brazilian states (such as Bahia, Minas Geraes, other than the mountainous sections, and Pernambuco), Pará city, South Sea islands (such as the Bismarck Archipelago, New Guinea, the Solomons, and Timor), the Dutch West Indies, Grenada, Guadeloupe, Haiti, Martinique, Santo Domingo, Tobago, and Trinidad. Class D (unhealthful places, which carry an extra premium of $20 per $1000) contains Abyssinia outside the chief towns, Angola, Eritrea, the Somalilands, the Sudan south of Khartum, the more unhealthful parts of Tanganyika and Uganda, and Zanzibar. Hunter considers that still greater extra premiums should be charged for some regions, according to the part of country, the occupation of the applicant, and whether he is acclimatized or not. In some regions $20 might be sufficient; in others, such as the upper parts of the Amazon basin, $50 would not be excessive. Hunter thinks that the companies should exact $30 extra for Belgian Congo, Cameroons, Dahomey, French Equatorial Africa, French Sudan, Gambia, Gold Coast, Guinea, the Ivory Coast, Liberia, Nigeria, Senegal, Sierra Leone, Toga, Amazonas, Matto Grosso, and Pará (outside the city).

Hunter himself notes as a fundamental aspect of his classification the vital importance of variation in geographical regions "from swampy lands to high tablelands," but he also perceives the great changes that occur over comparatively small areas and the complexity of the controls. He writes: "To have attempted to differentiate between different parts of all these countries would have been impossible, especially in view of the changing conditions in many of them." [30] He believes that insurance companies are unwise to grant liberal rates to applicants on high tablelands. Many of the plateau regions have malarial fever and, in Africa, the tsetse fly. Some of the tablelands are comparatively healthful, but the conditions of life are unsatisfactory. There may be a lack of available medical attention, and social isolation "may result in a poor mortality through a lessening of the moral fiber." Again, while conditions regarding alcohol have improved, there is still a considerable amount of drinking among foreigners resident in tropical and semitropical countries, not only in isolated posts, but in the large cities. "It cannot be gainsaid that there is a larger consumption than at home among men of the same class and in the same occupation." [31]

Hunter thinks that Africa is the most difficult continent for which to decide on an extra scale of premiums, owing to the wide diversities in climate, population, and administration. Spasmodic outbreaks of yellow fever still present a hazard. It was "largely on account of this scourge that acclimatization extras were charged." It seems, however, that length of residence decreases the danger and that a "decreasing acclimatization extra might suitably be charged."

It is interesting to see that the insurance expert, like the geographer, is bewildered by the "difference of opinion between men resident in these countries concerning the effect of the climate on health or the difference between their opinions and the available statistics." The mortality in the West Indies, for example, was 147 per cent of the Hunter mortality tables, yet a former director of the Barbados Insurance Company expressed the opinion that "Barbados was the most healthy place in the world" and that it was odd that an extra premium was charged for "a place that he knew was more healthy even than England." [32] To take another example, in Rio de Janeiro sojourners told Hunter that they felt in excellent health for two or three years, yet after ten years, notwithstanding frequent vacations, they were compelled to return to the United States "on account of the debilitating effect of the climate." A company in South America, working at an elevation of nearly 5000 feet found it necessary to send their men away for some weeks every few months and give them a three months' vacation at the end of the second year. Otherwise they were unable to stand the climate and the conditions. Such instances, says Hunter, could be multiplied again and again to emphasize the point that "with few exceptions residence in a semi-tropical or tropical climate with the necessary change in living conditions results in a higher mortality than in the United States or Canada." [33] Unfortunately, the experience of the New York Life Insurance Company lies more with sojourners than with settlers.

In analyzing the causes of the higher mortality in tropical and subtropical countries, Hunter lays the chief blame at the doors of climate and of racial or cultural contacts. Both in his writings and in conversation he admits a steady improvement due to advances in transportation, communications, medicine, sanitation, and the like. He feels, however, that we still have much to learn about tropical disease. This highly experienced actuary reaches the conclusion that the white does not become thoroughly acclimated to the tropics. He does not have the vitality of the white man in the temperate zone and does not adapt himself to heights over 6000 feet. "Even under the best conditions there is a point beyond which the improvement in tropical mortality cannot go and it can never . . . equal that in Northern climes under similar conditions."

EVIDENCE FROM GOVERNMENT SERVICES

Governmental publications make the same points as Hunter: the general improvement in health, but the great diversity consequent upon the wide variations in climatic and social conditions in the tropics. The memorandum outlining the conditions of medical appointments in the

British Colonial Service notes, for example, the great difference between the climates of the trade-wind islands and coasts and those of more severely tropical lands.

The British West Indies, Honduras, and Guiana are subject to "the cooling influence of the north east trade winds" during at least three quarters of the year.

Consequently, Europeans, both men and women, find no difficulty in remaining healthy, even after long residence there, but for those who are not brought up in the tropics an occasional change to a temperate climate is advisable and it is not desirable to keep European children there permanently after the age of nine or ten.[34]

Again, the memorandum states that

The climate of Fiji is of the "ocean" type and experience shows that Europeans maintain their physical and mental vigour unimpaired over long periods of time. The climate is excellent for young children, though it is probably best for girls and boys to seek a cooler climate from the age of fourteen upward.[35]

These trade-wind regions of the tropics are contrasted with Somaliland. The memorandum notes that, even in this small protectorate, climatic conditions vary widely, but a "short tour of service is necessitated by the nervous strain produced by various causes such as the continuous high winds over prolonged periods and life amongst a highly excitable and unstable race." [36] Again, in Gambia, the climate is not unpleasant, but it is not suitable to European children.[37] The memorandum pays a striking tribute to the progress of medical science by the comment that "the general health of European women on the Gold Coast is good." In this respect D. B. Blacklock stated in 1930 that from 1881 to 1897 the death rates of the Gold Coast and Lagos were 75.8 and 53.6 respectively, but by 1928 for 3894 officers in Gambia, Sierra Leone, the Gold Coast, and Nigeria, the death rate was only 6.7 and the invalid rate 11.7 per thousand.[38] Nevertheless, some of the old difficulties remain. The statement that "in individual cases it may be desirable for a Medical Officer to decide for himself as to the probable effect of the climate and country upon his wife's well-being" strongly emphasizes the importance of psychological factors. The memorandum notes that in Malaya the climate is "for the tropics not unhealthy." "People who lead regular active lives have no difficulty in keeping in good health." European children do well, but only up to the age of six. "Women probably feel the effects of the climate more than men." [39]

The conditions of leave in the medical service again indicate the variations in environment. Long leave is granted in West Africa after 24 months, in East Africa after 20 to 30 months, in the West Indies after three years, and in the western Pacific after three years, a period temporarily extended to four.[40]

CHAPTER XV

ACCLIMATIZATION AND HEALTH: II. PATHOLOGICAL, PSYCHOLOGICAL, AND PHYSIOLOGICAL STUDIES

TROPICAL DISEASES

In Chapter IV we traced the advance of scientific medicine and sanitation in the tropics and the improvements wrought in white health. Epoch-making discoveries have paved the way for the formulation of certain fundamental generalizations on the so-called tropical diseases.[1] We now realize that there is a geography of disease.[2] We know that diseases are more numerous in hot, humid regions, which favor the multiplication of microörganisms. We also know that many diseases are due to parasites whose distribution is governed by geographical controls.[3] And at last we appreciate that many types of tropical sickness reflect the incidence of the social and economic, as well as of the geographical, environment.

Hookworm and Malaria

Of the many diseases that seriously impede white settlement in the tropics we shall consider as examples hookworm and malaria. Both are of immense range and importance. Both rank among the greatest scourges of humanity. There is, however, one fundamental difference between them. While the medical scientist is defeating hookworm, malaria remains in the broad sense largely beyond control.

For centuries both hookworm and malaria were "concealed diseases," not only in the sense that their true causes were unknown, but because though they were rarely fatal they weakened the system against other and more killing forms of disease. Even more serious was their effect upon economic development because of the impairment of the health of their victims. The International Health Board of the Rockefeller Foundation has stated that hookworm and malaria "constitute what is probably the most serious obstacle to the development of civilization in the regions where they prevail."[4] Of hookworm A. S. Chandler writes: "There is probably no widespread human infection of equal significance to the human race which is less self-assertive than the hookworm infestation."[5]

Hookworm disease is never spectacular like yellow fever or pernicious malaria. And for this very reason it is the greater menace. Acute diseases sometimes tend to strengthen the race by killing off the weak; but hookworm disease, working so insidiously as frequently to escape the attention even of its victims, tends rather to debilitate the race by attacking the strong as well as the weak. The cumulative effects of the disease on the race—physical, economic, intellectual, and moral—which are handed down from generation to generation through long periods of time, are even more important than its contribution to the death roll among individuals. This one disease, where the infection is practically universal, may go far towards explaining the retardation of backward peoples.[6]

Hookworm

The geography of hookworm and the biosocial factors that influence it are now well known. To reach optimum development and an infective stage, the hookworm larvae require a constant temperature of not less than 70° F. for a minimum of five days, and the rainfall must also be considerable. The soil temperature kills the larvae if it falls below 40° F. at night. Hence, hot, moist regions such as the humid tropics are particularly subject to hookworm, although it ranges from 36° N. to 30° S. of the equator and covers regions which embrace some 900,000,000 people—about half the inhabitants of the world.

While hookworm is primarily controlled by climate, other factors, such as soil types, drainage, and social development, have great influence. Hookworm is strongly affected by the density of the population, by race, sex, age, sanitary habits, nutrition, and general standards of life. Racial differences seem to be important, and it is generally believed that the white races are more susceptible than some of the dark-skinned peoples, particularly the negro.[7] The negro of the United States, for example, has a greater immunity than the white man and is less severely infected. Similar facts have been noted in the parts of this book on Florida, Barbados, Costa Rica, and Puerto Rico (Chapters V and VII). It is significant, for example, that in Puerto Rico, in the mountainous regions of the interior, which are largely inhabited by whites, the eggs number from 5000 to 8000 per gram of stool, while on the northeastern coastal plain, where the proportion of colored people is higher, the average of eggs is only 2000 to 4000 per gram.

The elucidation of the hookworm problem is an excellent example of the way in which medical science has thoroughly explored and acquired the knowledge to defeat one of the worst of the so-called tropical diseases. Recent investigations have shown, for instance, that the intensity and the incidence of infestation are more limited than was formerly suspected. Dry spells of weather and the drying up of the soil are harmful to the larvae, and any locality with less than 40 inches of rain a year is not likely to have a heavy infestation, although, if the habits of the people favor the disease, a high incidence of light infestation may occur. Where the ground remains almost continuously dry for six months or more, there will be only light infestation, even if the annual rainfall is high. In Burma and India only very small areas are seriously infested. Regions of particularly heavy infestation include a few localities in the southeastern United States, the southern shores of the Gulf of Mexico, Central America, northern South America, the Brazilian coast and tableland, most of the West Indies, equatorial Africa, parts of the Malay Peninsula and Siam, some of the South Sea islands, and a few limited areas in

China. In Australia hookworm is confined to small areas on the north-east coast, where there is a rainfall of more than 60 inches. The east coast of the Cape York Peninsula is the most heavily infested region. Here, however, the incidence among the whites is low, and the number of worms per person small. The aborigines in the endemic areas are said to have a much higher infestation and have the hookworm disease fairly frequently.[8]

Research has shown that great importance must be attached to the soils. Heavy clays and very light porous or sandy soils are unfavorable to the disease, while sandy loams are the most favorable. The importance of this soil control is clearly shown by the distribution of hookworm in Barbados (Chapter VII) and probably helps to account for the fact that the Cayman Islands are only lightly infested (Chapter VII). In Little Cayman there is no infestation at all.

Social conditions are also of great importance. The people of lower Burma, for example, suffer little, owing to their habit of using primitive latrines, while the people of the Shan States protect themselves by wearing shoes. The whites of Simson's Bay, St. Martin, in the Dutch West Indies (Chapter VII), are an example of the improvement that can be wrought by the introduction of unpolluted water, shoes, and latrines. Occupation is also important as influencing sanitary habits. Chandler considers that fishing peoples are almost immune; yet the whites of St. Martin show that even the occupation of fishing is less important than is sanitation. Malnutrition and other devitalizing factors are of primary significance, as is evident from the unhappy example of the whites of Puerto Rico.

The hookworm was first recognized as a human parasite by an Italian physician, Angelo Dupino, in 1838, but the great fight against the disease opened in the era of medical discovery at the close of the century. In 1878 the Italians discovered the ova count, and in the period 1896-1902 Dr. Charles Waddell Stiles, zoologist of the United States Bureau of Animal Industry, announced the discovery of the *Necator americanus* and attributed the state of the poor Southern whites to the disease. Despite ribald gibes from the northern states and the angry resentment of Southerners, Stiles won adherents to his views. Soon the correctness of his opinion was demonstrated by the work of Dr. Bailey K. Ashford in Puerto Rico, where two-thirds of the people were treated in seven years and the principal planters testified that the efficiency of their laborers was increased by 67 per cent. In October, 1909, a gift of a million dollars by John D. Rockefeller led to the establishment of the Rockefeller Commission for the Extermination of the Hookworm Disease. Working in the United States, the Commission conducted surveys to show the extent and ravages of hookworm, and opened campaigns to cure sufferers and to stop soil pollution. In spite of ridicule and abuse, the Commission converted the nation. Hundreds of counties in the

South helped with funds and adopted the dispensary methods of combating hookworm. By 1914 the Commission had examined 548,992 school children and had shown that no less than 39 per cent were infected. In August, 1914, Rockefeller founded the International Health Board to conduct similar or allied work throughout the world, with such striking results as those described in the chapters on Queensland and Costa Rica. In its annual report for 1926 the International Health Board summarized its conquest of this terrible disease.

At the present time it is fair so say that hookworm disease has almost disappeared from the United States, and is rapidly coming under control in many parts of the world. But the great achievement is not the social and economic rehabilitation of the more than six or seven million people who have been treated for the disease during the past ten or fifteen years; it is the development of administrative measures that will prevent millions yet unborn from ever suffering from its ravages.[9]

In reviewing the problem of hookworm in the tropics, one cannot estimate the degree to which the disease has been responsible for the white failures, but unquestionably it has gravely retarded progress in such countries as Costa Rica and was possibly a main cause of the decline of the whites in certain regions, such as Barbados. The work of medical scientists has now made hookworm controllable among peoples of fair living standard and education in tropical regions, such as northeastern Queensland, and scientists are now able to examine the factors that will control the future of white settlement without having to allow for any effects from the disease.

Malaria

A far more serious problem than hookworm is malaria, which is, as we shall show, in the broad sense, an uncontrollable disease. It is carried by several species of anopheles—wide roaming swamp mosquitoes—which cannot be destroyed as easily as the *Aëdes* (*Stegomyia*) *aegypti*, a "house" mosquito, the vector of yellow fever.[10]

The ravages of malaria have been, and still are, terrible.[11] Dr. Woods Hutchinson stated that malaria has probably killed more people than war.[12] Dr. Andrew Balfour estimated that malaria killed 2,000,000 people a year and annually cost the British Empire $300,000,000 in deaths and sickness.[13] Dr. H. R. Carter believed that malaria was the only disease capable of rendering a region uninhabitable.[14] How appalling is the strength of the disease, despite the advance of medical science, is shown by the reports of that great organization, the United Fruit Company,[15] which has spent vast sums and has made some progress in fighting malaria in Central and South America. These show that, as at Panama, the disease can be controlled in a limited area by the draining of land and the establishment of water supplies on modern scientific lines. Nevertheless, the company states that the disease causes 90 per cent of the sickness in their camps and that it is contracted by every laborer who is on the tropical coast for a year or more. Similar facts are evident in Panama, where the American settlements remain small camps heavily fortified against malaria (Chapter XI).

As in the case of hookworm, the factors that control malaria are primarily geographical in character. High temperatures and rainfall are essential, and the disease is particularly prevalent in tropical and sub-tropical areas, although people have contracted it in the cool-temperate zones from mosquitoes carried by ships.[16] Local geographical conditions are also important. Interesting researches in the United States have shown a close relation between physiographical features and malaria. A study carried out at the station for malarial research, in collaboration with the Florida State Geological Survey, indicates that the area of intense malaria in the southeast closely coincides with the outcrop of certain Tertiary limestones. These form a "solution topography," with many shallow basin-shaped depressions devoid of outlets, in which surface water is retained in the wet summer, providing breeding places for the anopheles in temporary water.[17] On the same subject Boyd and Ponton note that "but few communicable diseases are as peculiarly diseases of places as is malaria" and state that the malarial regions of the southeastern United States are regions characterized by "solution topography." [18]

Social factors and the living standard also exercise an important influence upon malaria. Medical officers of the United Fruit Company emphasize the importance of adequate housing, diet, and nutrition in the South American tropics. In Australia Sir Raphael Cilento attaches great importance to the standard of living enjoyed by most workers in tropical Australia, a condition that he feels is a happy augury for the future and one that bids fair to guard Australia from a menace that has crippled many another country.[19] The battle against malaria has met with success in some parts of Australia, although the disease still presents a serious problem in remote areas such as the Northern Territory. In the American stations at Panama and in other small areas the whites have been successful, but they have made little progress throughout the greater part of the tropics. Vance's summary of the situation in the southern United States is applicable to most of the tropical zone. "The battle is slow and long. There still awaits a method, cheap, common-sense, and convincing. It may not be found." [20]

When one adds to malaria other diseases, such as sleeping sickness,[21] it is quite clear that, although the white man has made remarkable advances, the battle is far from won, except in regions where very favorable economic conditions cover the high costs of sanitation. Vast areas of the tropics still remain beyond control, and the optimistic argument that, because the white man has succeeded in certain localities, under certain geographical and social conditions, and against certain diseases, he must inevitably be victorious throughout the tropics, can hardly be regarded as logical or scientific. The ultimate result of the conflict only time can demonstrate.

15

Some Psychological and Neurological Problems

One of the greatest obstacles to white settlement in the tropics is the lack of adequate knowledge concerning possible mental, psychological, and neural reactions to climate. These reactions are possibly of great importance. R. DeC. Ward believed that the non-measurable nervous results of tropical climate were critical and fundamental.[22] Sir Havelock Charles, as noted above,[23] declared that "tropical residence damages the nervous system even though it produces no physical disease." Professor Kenneth Black, of Singapore, admits that the problem "bristles with difficulties as our knowledge of the physiology and pathology of the mind is so meagre." He states, that "it seems, however, the experience of almost all observers that residence in the tropics, and indeed in any inferior climate, causes mental deterioration." [24] Professor Gordon Harrower of Singapore and other authorities have noted "tropical amnesia," or loss of memory,[25] which grows more severe throughout the period of tropical sojourn but lessens and disappears during "leave" in the cool-temperate zone.[26]

Psychological Disturbances

It is far easier to point to the existence of these signs of deterioration than to determine their causes, particularly as the views of recent authorities throw considerable doubt upon the old theories, which attributed all such phenomena solely to tropical climates. Thus M. Carthew notes that psychic disturbances in the tropics are usually attributed to such climatic factors as temperature, humidity, winds, ultraviolet rays, and electric disturbances, or to toxemias, deficiency of the endocrines, or unsuitable diet and clothing, and that few scientists have stressed the factors of psychological or sociological etiology, which may be the most pregnant causes.[27]

Carthew strongly emphasizes the fact that in the tropics the white man is usually sojourning among a host of native peoples and living a life of more or less mental antagonism to his surroundings. A mental conflict is thus created with no corresponding outlet of emotion. This, as psychologists recognize, produces an emotional excitement, resulting in bodily and physical fatigue through which the will, the intellectual control, and the power to reason become deficient. Hence the need for high pay, frequent leaves, and other ameliorations of tropical service. Carthew further divides the tropical whites into three classes: the adventurers (sojourners such as officials and traders), the missionaries, and the beachcombers or poor whites. Very significant is the emphasis that he justly lays on the cheerfulness, equilibrium of temper, and philosophical outlook of the missionaries as opposed to the other classes. Although less strictly selected than the adventurers [28] and granted far less indulgence or leave, missionaries frequently labor in the tropics up to the ages of sixty and seventy years. Despite this, they show fewer symptoms of minor psychoses and rarely have acute breakdowns. The reason, says Carthew, is psychological. The missioner has been trained to control his emotions, and to canalize those instincts which are at variance with his social environment. Carthew believes that it is along this line that a solution will be found for prophylaxes and the treatment of minor disturbances.[29]

The truth of this dictum is clearly evident in the West Indies. The attitude of the missionaries in some of these islands is most impressive, particularly that of the Catholic priests and nuns, who have given up all wordly hopes and rarely, if ever, return to Europe. Surrounded by negroes and in many cases almost entirely isolated from Europeans and European culture, they retain a serenity and cheerfulness that seems reflected in their health.

R. L. Buell provides important evidence from a different and unexpected angle. In his opinion negro troops conscripted to France suffer more severely from cold and exposure than natives from Morocco, Tunis, Algeria, or Indo-China. Owing to the climate of eastern France the negro lives "in a state of very unstable psychological equilibrium and has, as a result, a high morbidity." Social factors are important, however, as the negro is thrown into contact with the lowest class of French people and acquires a love of drink and a contempt for white women. Thus the organic weakening is partly the result of psychic weakening and suffering. Repercussions, as the French would say, of a sexual and psychic order often terrorize the negro into neurotic manifestations, and he becomes supersensitive to disease.[30] From this it appears that exile from their native "herd" may affect deleteriously people of any color who seek a strange environment.

Tropical Neurasthenia

In discussing tropical neurasthenia, Professor Millais Culpin states that the nineteenth century conception of neurasthenia is giving way to a psychological etiology and classification, that the maladjustment is sociological rather than physiological, that there is no neurasthenia peculiar to the tropics, and that use of the term "tropical neurasthenia" should be discontinued.[31] Culpin quotes the views expressed in the *British Medical Journal* (mostly of 1926) by various correspondents who attributed tropical neurasthenia to a great variety of climatic and other factors. The extracts, says Culpin, show that the authorities quoted hold fundamentally different conceptions of neurasthenia, while none seem aware that the problem is the concern of psychopathology.

Dr. Stannus gives a graphic summary of the "undeniably noxious stimuli" that, associated with fear and anxiety, afflict the sojourner in the tropics. The sojourner, he writes,

. . . is exiled from home; often separated from his family, generally unable to make ends meet for some reason or other; suffering in many cases loneliness and lack of congenial society; envious of others; disappointed over promotion; with ambition thwarted. Living amidst a native population causes him annoyance at every turn, because he has never troubled to understand its language and its psychology. From early morn till dewy eve he is in a state of unrest—ants at breakfast, flies at lunch, and termites for dinner, with a new species of moth every evening in his coffee. Beset all day by a sodden heat, whence there is no escape, and the unceasing attentions of the voracious insect world, he is driven to bed by his lamp being extinguished by the hordes which fly by night, only to be kept awake by the reiterated cry of the brain-fever bird or the local chorus of frogs. Never at rest! Always an on-guardedness.[32]

Anyone who has traveled much in the tropics and who has seen the constant need of "on-guardedness"—the precautions against disease, the boiling of all water, the care of diet, and the tireless supervision of child-ish native servants—must appreciate the weight of these arguments. The following notes, made in 1930, when I was spending some weeks with friends in Mandalay, further illustrate this point.

There is no doubt that life in Burma takes it out of men severely and that they must go very steadily and take many precautions. One is inoculated against a variety of diseases—smallpox, cholera, plague, and the ever-present enteric. The precautions are extraordinary: inoculation, the boiling of all drinking water, no eating of fresh vegetables, the constant need for footwear (as hookworm and leprosy are rife), no bathing in the rivers through fear of enteric (a B. B. T. C. man has just been brought in with it), and, on tour, the invariable use of soda water, even for cleaning the teeth. Then again, the snakes. No one goes on the grass after dark without taking a lantern, and no one enters a dark room. This week we have not been able to shop in the bazaars, as the Burmese and Chinese are dying from plague at the rate of 130 a week. Our hosts asked us to miss our Communion on Christmas Day, as the cup is said to be most unsafe. The hot season, the conditions of life, and the constant battle with irresponsible native servants play havoc with the women, few of whom can manage stretches of more than four years.

From personal experience Culpin pictures the differences between the healthy manual workers of Laura in tropical Queensland and the "nervy" community of white sojourners in Shanghai, a warm-temperate location outside the tropics. In his opinion people in the tropics have nervous troubles, just as do people elsewhere. In the tropics, however, these troubles are increased by the difficulty of emotional adjustment to harmful stimuli of which some are peculiar to the tropics and some dependent on an attitude to life rather than on climate. When such conditions arise, they should be handled in accordance with modern knowledge of the minor psychoses and not with the idea that they are peculiar to the tropics. Unfortunately, the tropical disabilities that fall within the scope of psychological medicine have been disowned by tropical and neglected by general medicine, with the result that a doctor can go out to the tropics well qualified to deal with everything but the conditions that are more prolific in causing chronic ill-health and in-validism among Europeans than all the tropical diseases put together. The prophylaxis, says Culpin, lies in the examination of would-be tropi-cal residents.

Here again are statements the truth of which will be admitted by most scientific workers who have experience of the tropics. One finds remarkable examples supporting Culpin's views in the Northern Territory of the Australian Commonwealth. Some of the native-born and immigrant white women are happy, hard-working, abstemious, and thoroughly contented with their lot. Others are discontented, sickly addicts to various unhealthy stimuli, and obviously unfit for tropical residence. Observations in the West Indies and in the American colony at Panama give similar results, while even in northeastern Queensland the women vary greatly in their psychological reactions to the hot climate.

Figures of health and invalidism for the official services in tropical places, such as British East and West Africa, emphasize the great importance of mental, psychological, and neural conditions. Culpin shows that of 353 cases of invalidism 28 per cent were for various forms of psychoneurosis and 45 per cent for psychological reasons. Whereas in foreign service 43 per cent of the psychoneurotic cases were invalided home in the first four years, the same percentage was spread over twenty-five years of home service. Dr. Squires points out that in the etiology of tropical neurasthenia the important point is not so much the action of abnormally severe stresses on an average individual as the action of stresses of a more ordinary severity, although possibly of an unaccustomed nature, on individuals of a special constitution. While admitting the possible harmful effects of temperature, humidity, hot winds, light rays, and the like, he believes that the emotional factors are more harmful than the physical agencies. The agents of infection in these neurasthenics obviously lie far deeper than the microscope can reveal. A mental dissecting of the future administrator of the tropics is every bit as important as a physical examination. Sir David Forsyth has pointed out that many young men select tropical service because they are negative to life, antagonistic, or quarrelsome, or because they possess inferiority complexes, such as shyness—especially towards women. Thus the individual takes a neurotic disability to the tropics, and the neurotic percentage is increased.[33]

SOME PHYSIOLOGICAL INVESTIGATIONS

Of all methods of attacking the problems of acclimatization and resistance to disease the most promising is that of experimental research. Yet up to the present the results have been inconclusive and must, in many cases, be regarded with suspicion, particularly where they have been obtained in cool-temperate countries and with non-acclimatized subjects. Dr. G. C. Shattuck, Assistant Professor of Tropical Medicine at Harvard, writes:

Although much progress has been made in the prevention of the infectious diseases in the tropics, knowledge of the effects of climate upon health has been practically at a standstill for years. On the other hand, the future of the tropics may be very largely dependent upon increased knowledge of climatic influences, and the precautions against them which the northern races should take in order to maintain good health in the tropics.[34]

An examination of any summary of recent researches—for example, that of Sir Aldo Castellani in "Climate and Acclimatization"—confirms the opinions of Shattuck and Drinker that, up to the present, work in this field has produced extremely conflicting and confusing results.[35]

A recent memorandum by Dr. Cecil K. Drinker summarizes in some detail the position as regards physiological research.[36] Drinker thinks that three facts emerge from the study of the literature on the physiology and biochemistry of tropical whites. First, the volume of research already done is large and, although full of disagreement, offers a fair foundation upon which to commence work. Second, the general character of this work is in the form of simple statements of facts obtained by the application of standard laboratory procedures. For example, it is generally agreed that the basal metabolism of northern whites living in the tropics is reduced, but even in regard to this straightforward fact we lack adequate descriptions of how rapidly this physiological change occurs in the individuals under observation, the degree to which the adaptation varies with age or sex, and whether individuals who show rapid deterioration in the tropics have overmade or failed to make adjustments. Hitherto work on both the physiology and biochemistry of life in the tropics has not displayed the versatility and resourcefulness necessary for substantial progress. This is due to the fact that most of the workers in the field have been medical men, who have been untrained in experimentation and who, for the most part, have limited their activities to the collection of data through the application of standard methods: in other words, the field has been in the hands of collectors and cataloguers of data. The third fact that emerges from examination of what has been done is that a most promising opportunity to go further exists.

With due regard for these strictures, we may outline some of the findings of "foundational" value as compiled by Castellani and other authorities.[37]

The incidence of climate on human activity was better understood after Sir Leonard Hill invented the "katathermometer." This instrument measures the net rate at which heat is taken away from it under the environmental conditions to which it is exposed and thus gives some quantitative idea of the rate of heat loss from the human body under similar conditions. Although innumerable later modifications of the katathermometer have been made, it has not yet been possible to construct a simple instrument that imitates the complex energy exchange of the human body with its environment.[38] Hill found that the effect of wind on this loss of heat was often the chief factor in comfort. Body heat is produced by oxidation regulated by types of food, by muscular activity, and by autonomic reactions to external stimuli (cold, heat, emotion, etc.). It is lost by convection, evaporation, and radiation. High temperatures may be made tolerable by low humidities or high winds (or both), which increase the evaporation of perspiration.[39]

The early experiments of Lining (1738), Ellis (1758), and Blagden and Fordyce (1775) established the fact that a normal man, suitably clothed, can regulate his temperature so that with high air temperatures it still remains within normal limits if the atmospheric humidity is low. Castellani adds that "these experiments have been well borne out by life in the tropics."[40] It is quite otherwise, however, when the atmospheric humidity is high. Haldane observed that there was no abnormal rise of the body temperature until the wet-bulb thermometer indicated 88° F., provided that the experimenters were stripped to the waist or clothed in light flannel.[41] If, however, the wet bulb exceeded this by even one degree, the body temperature rose hour by hour in proportion to the rise of the wet-bulb thermometer above 88° F., but the body temperature increased more rapidly when high wet-bulb temperatures were reached than when they were relatively low. With the abnormal rise of body temperatures was associated increase of the pulse rate by about twenty beats per minute for each degree Fahrenheit. When the rectal temperature reached 102° F. hyperpnea was observed, while other symptoms associated with the rise of the body temperature were profuse sweating and a general feeling of discomfort and exhaustion.[42]

Experiments of Dill and Associates

D. B. Dill, H. T. Edwards, P. S. Bauer and E. J. Levenson have recently conducted important experiments at the Fatigue Laboratory, Morgan Hall, Harvard, and the Barro Colorado Island Biological Laboratory, Canal Zone. These writers express the problem as follows: [43]

Man's response to an increase in external temperature is familiar enough in certain respects. In rest, the heat control mechanism together with voluntary actions may maintain a constant internal temperature. If external temperature and humidity are sufficiently high, body temperature increases and then physiological responses may be quantitatively or even qualitatively different; eventually the phenomena of heat stroke are observed. In exercise, the increased rate of heat production calls for a corresponding increase in rate of heat dissipation; if these rates are not equal body temperature changes. The rate of heat dissipation depends on various internal conditions, such as the rate of heat production and the rate of blood movement from active muscles to the periphery, as well as on such external conditions as temperature, relative humidity and velocity of air movement. The problem of temperature control in exercise is so complex that relatively few studies have yielded useful quantitative results.

The numerous precautions which must be taken if one is to establish a precise relation between temperature and various physiological functions have been worked out for various species of animals by Crozier and associates. Reference may be made, for example, to Crozier and Stier.[44] It is impossible when man is the subject to attain such constancy of conditions. What we have done consists of a study of performance with approximately constant humidity (50 per cent), with almost no air movement and with the room temperature either at $12 \pm 1°$ C. or at $34 \pm 1°$ C. Internal conditions could not be controlled so precisely. Each of the 5 subjects worked in the hot room at a rate which brought on exhaustion in from 37 minutes to an hour and at the same rate in the cold room.

The following were the results of the experiment:

Each subject did the same work on the bicycle ergometer with (a) an external temperature of $12 \pm 1°$ C. and (b) an external temperature of $34 \pm 1°$ C. and a relative humidity of about 50 per cent in each case. The work done involved an oxygen consumption of 1.9 ± 0.5 liters per minute and a moderate or small oxygen debt. Rectal temperature was observed frequently, using a thermocouple, and heart rate was recorded continuously with a cardiotachometer. Observations on the metabolism indicated that work is carried on with the same mechanical efficiency and with the same fuels under these extreme conditions.

For a given rate of work the rate of increase of body temperature as work is carried on is nearly constant for the first few minutes. Then a constant temperature may be reached if conditions for heat dissipation are favorable; otherwise body temperature rises until exhaustion intervenes.

The heart rate increases with external temperature even when internal temperature is the same. Its output per unit time may remain constant or increase slightly. Consequently its output per beat must diminish with increasing external temperature. Blood supply to the skin and inactive muscles increases and to active muscles probably diminishes with increasing external temperature.

In our experiments 4 of the 5 subjects became exhausted at the high temperature when doing work which they carried on easily at a low temperature. Yet there was no considerable lactic acid accumulation in the body as a whole, no exhaustion of fuel reserves, and a large unused reserve of pulmonary ventilation. The most probable hypothesis for explaining these data is that the heart muscle itself had reached the limit of its capacity, for it had attained its maximum rate while no other part of the organism was working at capacity.

The implications of these experiments are many, for physical activity is often carried on under conditions unfavorable to heat dissipation. The leisurely habits of those who live in the tropics have a sound basis in physiological necessity.

Dill's experiments are not conclusive. His work is simply an early step in the researches necessary, for, even in the limited range of his experiments, he has not yet dealt with factors such as humidity or air movements, nor is it clear how far he has applied his methods to acclimatized whites. Nevertheless, his results agree with the findings of other experimenters, such as Houghten, and possibly explain the underlying causes of the phenomenon noted by Cilento that the north Queenslander "moves slowly and conserves his heat producing energy in every way." Dill's concluding remark that "the leisurely habits of those who live in the tropics have a sound basis in physiological necessity" is of profound significance. Laboratory researches may yet dispel the clouds that overshadow the evidence of history, observation, and statistics and may give conclusive proof that the tropical settler faces physiological, neurological, and psychological handicaps.

CHAPTER XVI

DIET, CLOTHING, EXERCISE

DIET

The scientific invasion of the tropics is not only grappling with disease but is revealing and exploring other major scientific problems, one of the chief of which is diet. Nutrition is a comparatively new field of research,[1] for the analysis of regional diets and their influence on health and efficiency perforce awaited the development of biochemistry. Scientists, however, have now grasped the importance of the question. Thus, E. V. McCollum writes:

Students of mankind have hitherto failed to realise the importance of the selection of food supply as an agency in the improvement of a race. . . . As a result of my many experimental observations I have come to hold the view that animal experimentation, human geography and history all point in an all but conclusive manner to diet as the principal cause of our health troubles, insofar as these are not brought about by any communicable disease.[2]

In recent years the biochemistry of nutrition has made considerable progress. Knowledge of the subject grew with the chemical analysis of foods and made rapid progress with the discovery of the essential vitamins. It is not believed that all primitive peoples who have survived have succeeded in balancing their diet. McCollum and others hold, for example, that many meat-eating races have done this by consuming the protective glandular organs. The Chinese peasant, again, has obtained a balanced diet of rice and green vegetables despite the absence of milk. The Mexican peasant has balanced his high intake of protein in corn and beans by drinking pulque, a liquor intoxicating but rich in vitamins. It is obvious that this question of a balanced diet is of fundamental importance to white settlement in the tropics.[3]

As regards the geography of diet, McCollum and Simmonds consider that successful human dietaries are found in three types of geographical environment, two of which include parts of the tropics. They write:

In the warmest regions of the world, which are also characterized in general by excess of wetness, live the rice-eating peoples. Their diet is in the main vegetarian and consists of rice as the principal cereal, with additions of soy beans, various tubers and root vegetables, and large amounts of leafy vegetables of many kinds. . . . The leaf of the plant is superior to the seed, tuber, root or fruit in its dietary properties. In fact, the edible leaf is in itself complete from the standpoint of its dietary principles. . . . The importance of the leafy type of vegetable in the diet of the rice-eating peoples cannot be overestimated. Because of the density of population, milk-producing animals are not kept in the rice-eating regions. . . [The] only food of animal origin is eggs, poultry and pork, . . . but in some places considerable amounts of fish are available. People on such a dietary regimen, are very successful in their physical development and compare . . . with the best specimens of the human race.[4]

217

We may note how seldom this diet is adopted by the white man who colonizes the hot, wet tropics.

Another successful type of diet is found in the hot, dry tropics, where the inhabitants subsist through the conversion of pasturage into human food through the agency of flocks and herds. Here the only article fit for abundant human consumption is milk, which is usually sour. Yet upon this diet, supplemented by small amounts of such foodstuffs as barley, bread, dates, and meat, the peoples of the hot, dry tropics "maintain surprising vitality." [5] In tropical pasturing countries like northern Australia the few white settlers probably approach this pastoral diet more nearly than the whites of the hot, wet tropics approach the native vegetarian diet of those regions.

The shortest residence in a tropical country and the briefest examination of tropical literature bring home to the student the importance of diet. Ellsworth Huntington puts the matter from a pessimistic point of view in supporting the thesis that "the less stimulating the climate, the less favorable is its type of diet." [6] We cannot, perhaps, go so far as to accept in full Huntington's generalization but we can agree that much of the so-called tropical degeneracy is due to the primary factor of climate creating an unfavorable secondary control in poor nutrition. Whether in all cases the climatic factor is more important than the dietetic is by no means certain. For example, McCollum, unlike Huntington, believes that the American loyalists who went to the Bahama Islands declined not through the climate but through poor diet.[7]

The difficulties surrounding tropical diets are evident in the regions we have surveyed.[8] In the warm-temperate and tropical areas of what is now the southeastern United States the white colonists evolved a shocking diet. Pork, or bacon, with bitter coffee, became the staples. The cooking was appalling, and digestions were ruined by the British cultural inheritance of distilled liquors, which were wholly inapplicable in an almost tropical summer climate.[9]

Fortunately, over much of the South the diet has improved greatly. Vance, for example, states that the trucking areas enjoy a healthful varied diet. In Florida, where the southern regions possess a moderate tropical climate, the trucking areas enjoy such a diet even during the off seasons. From October until June most rural people eat citrus fruits, as nearly every home possesses fruit trees. From December until June or July there is an abundance of one or more vegetables. Education, too, is assisting matters. Food habits are being reformed under persuasion and demonstration, and demonstration clubs of farmers' wives are bringing about improvements. It is significant that many workers in the field believe that adequate diet is not so much a matter of economic class as of the mother's training.

Nevertheless, the situation in many parts of the South is far from satisfactory. The basic diet of pork, fats, starches, and sweets still reigns supreme in the cotton and tobacco belts. Corn is the mainstay in the mountains, and the southeast coast is generally lacking in milk. Thus the representative Southern dietaries deviate from the best standards of nutrition more than other sections of the United States.

The deficiency disease of pellagra appears to be one of many evils resulting from these bad adjustments of diet. Discovered in 1907-1908, its "universal recognition made it seem like the outbreak of an epidemic." Unfortunately, as in the case of hookworm, the South has bitterly resented publicity in this respect.[10]

Where the peoples of hot countries are relatively inefficient, diet causes much of the inefficiency. We saw from Chapter III how appalling was the diet adopted by various white communities in the Caribbean. Even today in islands such as Puerto Rico the low standard of the great mass of the population is largely caused by malnutrition and under-nutrition. This is due partly to the fact that a large part of the rural population is said to be living on the verge of starvation and partly to the growth of a poor diet of imported foods following upon the development of the one-crop sugar industry.[11] This problem of malnutrition demands close regional study, for it is desperately urgent both in the West Indies and in other tropical lands. We were much impressed by the diversified crops and higher standards in Jamaica as compared with certain other islands of the Caribbean.

It is also clear that poverty and a low standard of living render the people more prone to the ravages of diseases such as hookworm and malaria. Doctors of the United Fruit Company, for example, maintain that a high standard of living is almost as important as medicine and sanitation in dealing with tropical disease. There is also the question of seasonal variations in the living standard, and there are intermittent calamities such as hurricanes and swarms of locusts. These terrible visitations destroy crops and greatly affect health in the islands of the West Indies. Education in dietetics is also essential. As indicated in Chapter VII, Saban people who have lived in the United States appreciate the value of milk, fruit, and green vegetables, but the majority of the white population suffers greatly from dyspepsia, owing to a diet of biscuits, bread, and tea. In many West Indian islands the schools might well teach elementary knowledge of diet and hygiene. Under the guidance of doctors of the Rockefeller Foundation, Jamaican educationists are conducting a splendid dietetic campaign.

Another method of attacking the problem lies with the employers, particularly those who are in charge of one-crop industries. Where the land of native populations has been absorbed in great plantations, it is essential that the laborers should receive workers' blocks for home gardens and should be educated and encouraged to use this land for the betterment of their nutrition. This is the policy of such organizations as the United Fruit Company and is very different from that of some of the rubber companies that operated in South America during the boom days. The latter often enforced the rule that workers should buy all their food from them, and supplied a diet "almost invariably of the dried variety, with perhaps a few cans of salmon or sardines thrown in." [12] In Hawaii, too, the large sugar and pineapple plantations find their efficiency greatly improved by attention to diet.

From his journeys in the Amazon basin, Earl Hanson throws some extremely illuminating light on the diet problem. On the Orinoco River, above the Maipure Rapids, the white survivors of the rubber boom have been forced to support themselves by farming, hunting, and fishing. "They grumble about their isolation," says Hanson, "but put a certain amount of gusto into their grumbling. They seem comparatively healthy, do a great deal of laughing and joking, and are on the whole much more lively than any similar group I found anywhere else on the jungle rivers and away from the cities." [13] On crossing the Brazilian border, Hanson expected to find that the Brazilians would consider themselves much better off than their Venezuelan neighbors. Instead of that "they did little but whine about their hard lot and about the unhealthfulness of the Rio Negro." The reason appeared to be that these whites were able to ship rubber and other products to Manaos and to import foodstuffs. "The result was obviously malnutrition."

Continuing his observations on the South American tropics, Hanson notes that the Salesian fathers on the Rio Negro and the Benedictines on the Rio Branco plant and eat fresh vegetables. The Englishmen of Manaos buy and eat fresh meat and vegetables. In eastern Bolivia, near the mouth of the Beni River, the Bolivians and Swiss, who make Cachuela Esperanza and Riberalta such delightful places, buy a steady supply of fresh vegetables from the Japanese colonists, who are not prevented from working because of racial pride. The healthy cattle ranchers on Marajo Island live on a well-balanced diet of vegetables, meat, milk, and cheese.

Hanson regards the Salesian fathers at Barcellos and São Gabriel as of particular interest in relation to tropical problems. A number are Europeans—Austrians and Spaniards—and they have been years in the tropics. They have generally suffered from every illness the region affords. Yet they are distinguishable from the rest of the whites in that they have maintained their mental alertness and carry out an amount of hard, physical labor that would be remarkable even in the temperate zone. Undoubtedly one reason for this is the fact that they plant gardens and so obtain fresh foods.[14] In Hanson's words:

To a man who travels in the Amazon Basin it becomes apparent that the same race prejudice that keeps white men from doing any work also tends to keep them from eating any vitamins. . . . The mark of the white man as a civilized being is his commerce; the more he disdains local products in his own daily life, the more he depends on commercial products brought in from outside, the more civilized he is and the more enervated he becomes.[15]

In the cases of Panama and northeastern Australia we have white communities of greater wealth and higher living standards. As indicated in Chapter XI on Panama, the diet is now "adequate and of wide range." We did hear some complaints that canned foods were too common and that milk was scarce, but we found that milk and a splendid variety of fruit and fresh vegetables were offered in the restaurants at comparatively moderate rates. Unfortunately, Panama is an economic freak, and the white colony enjoys a high living standard for the tropics and a diet of a kind only available on one of the greatest highways of the world.

Turning to the vast region of the Australian tropics, one enters a zone marked by a variety of diet. In the past the scattered pastoralists of the outback stations perforce relied on cattle products. The camel trains frequently came up at intervals as great as six months, and for months the whites were compelled to subsist on weevily flour. Modern transport has improved matters, but the white ant remains a constant menace to vegetables. In such coastal towns as Darwin the difficulty of obtaining milk is serious, while the supply of vegetables has been curtailed since the "White Australia" policy reduced the number of Chinese gardeners. Also the bad old English food traditions prevail: the hotels, for example, serve the heavy meals of temperate Australia and of Britain.

Cilento sums up the problem on the advancing frontiers of Australia:

In so far as food deficiencies are concerned, we have not learnt yet to organise our supplies adequately to our necessities, and so in north and western Queensland, and, indeed, on all the borders of our advancing frontiers, the problems of food supply range from trachoma and "barcoo rot" to scurvy, beri-beri, and many less obvious results of food-deficiency, just as they did during the early days of Sydney, when the advancing edge of colonization extended no farther than Parramatta. These dietary deficiencies are found as corollaries to that conservatism which impels our people to cling to traditions of diet (as also to traditional methods of thinking, clothing, housing, hours of labour, and other factors in environment) quite unsuited to the country.[16]

In Chapter VI it was indicated that the situation is better in eastern Queensland, although campaigns for greater dietetic knowledge are required. The heavy rainfall, some of which occurs at all seasons, permits the growing of various kinds of vegetables and fruits. Also dairying is possible in the highlands, and milk is available, although the population of the coastal plains should secure larger quantities from the plateaus. Above all, the "White Australia" policy, the tariff, and government agreements with the important sugar industry assure to the white worker sufficient means to secure, if he wishes, a fairly satisfactory diet and to maintain an adequate standard of life.

Alcohol is an unmitigated curse throughout the tropics. The student of white settlement in the tropics may have no teetotal leanings or sympathies, but he cannot stay for any length of time in almost any tropical region without seeing grave alcoholic excesses and hearing from trustworthy authorities that the abuse of alcohol is a menace. In this respect there seems little to choose between the English, Australians, Americans, or Dutch, for large quantities of liquor are everywhere in evidence. All leading medical authorities agree that alcohol should be avoided in the tropics. Castellani, for example, writes:

Alcohol should never be taken before the sun goes down, for it unfits the individual for work and is the most important predisposing cause of sunstroke. . . . This accounts for the difference in mortality of expeditions in which soldiers are allowed to drink alcoholic beverages and those in which they are not.[17]

Yet it is very seldom that the whites realize the importance of this. In every British station one hears both settlers and sojourners put forward the old fallacious theory that whisky is essential to the health of the white man in the tropics. In many parts of the tropics matters have improved since the days of heavy and chronic drinking mentioned in Chapter III, but the situation still remains serious in most tropical lands. The dictum of the Rice expedition does not apply to the Amazon basin only. "If we selected the one disease of the region to which the greatest degree of physical degeneration is due and which indirectly furnishes the underlying cause of many infections, it is alcoholism." [18]

It is easy to discover the reasons for alcoholism among white people of the tropics. The heat demands the frequent imbibing of liquids. Under the humidity and monotony both sexes feel that they require some stimulus. There are also other factors. In the words of Roy Nash:

Men of the highest grade do not always gravitate to the most isolated posts; social restraint is less, salaries and leisure generally more than at home. The result is that Europeans and Americans become—well, cocktails gradually take the place of exercise. Until this factor is eliminated, it is not wise to generalize too glibly about the impossibility of the white man ever getting along there.[19]

Exaggerated, perhaps! Yet, these frank sentences contain much truth.

[The diet problem in the tropics is not a matter of the choice of foods alone. It is by no means certain that standards of nutrition of the temperate zone apply directly to the tropics. The body and stomach behave somewhat differently in the tropics, the energy needs are less, and the nutritive qualities of given foods may vary with soil and climate.

The almost unconscious tendency of people in warm climates to choose diets lower in protein and fat and higher in carbohydrates than in cooler climates has been regarded by some as an adaptation. The proteins have a high specific-dynamic action, turning into body heat sooner than do the carbohydrates. Fats are unpalatable in hot weather; they supply a large heat value in small bulk and are therefore less adapted for giving a normal stomach distension when a low caloric intake is desired. Carbohydrates have more bulk per calory, and give a higher standard of muscular efficiency than proteins and fats. The mechanism by which the body adjusts its diet in view of these facts is unknown, but possibly some effect of ultra-violet or infra-red radiation (see pp. 175-176, above) may be involved. However, Radsma has shown that the reduction of basal metabolism commonly observed in the tropics is not due to the removal of protein from the diet, for the body temperature averages higher! Avoidance of protein is probably rather more a help in keeping the actual metabolism low and on an even keel, and represents a lack of acclimatability in many cases. Endocrine regulation of metabolism is claimed to be important in adaptation to heat; if so, the relation of diet to the thyroid and adrenals must be considered.

Where natural sources of vitamins have to be relied upon, a certain amount of protein food is necessary, and in many places is the easiest source of several essential diet elements—some of the most successful white colonies have thrived on an abundance of it. But various observers find reason to question the quality of many raw protein food materials, since the eating of them is not always a protection against deficiency ailments in the way it should be. Without minimizing the well-known fact that deficiency diseases from eating too little protein foods are very widespread and a major cause of low vitality in the tropics, we have to reckon also with the possibility of poor soil and unfavorable solar radiation conditions as a cause of poor-quality plant foods. Thus, Dumont [20] ascribes the poor health in the Belgian Congo to calcium-deficient soils, plants, and foods, and Keil suggests [21] that the hypovitaminotic condition of well-fed children in Dutch Guiana results from deficiency of the plant foods owing to lack of the proper chemical energy in the sunlight; in warm climates rich in sunshine tuberculosis and other diseases which yield to heliotherapy are sometimes common.

The disturbing effects of heat on digestion, appetite, and gastro-enteric tone are well known. There are more weak stomachs in the tropics, more enteric infections, and the diminished appetite has to be stimulated with spices. All this is partly related to diet either as cause or effect.

Too much fruit can cause "intoxications," just as too much fat, canned meat, or warm canned milk, and many tropical fermentation dyspepsias are improved by a rich carbohydrate intake with omission of fats.—R. G. S.]

CLOTHING AND HOUSING

In the previous chapters it has been shown that in many parts of the tropics white settlers suffer from poverty and its resulting evils, the whole process forming a vicious circle of distress. This is very evident as regards the comfort and the housing of white workers. Moreover, in many parts of the tropics the upper-class whites add to their difficulties by absurd conventions in dress. Even today scientific authorities differ upon some of these questions. British experts, for example, advocate sun helmets, spine pads, dark glasses, and dark houses as protection against the tropical sun. They advise the use of cholera belts and blankets to prevent chills. They maintain in all seriousness that the evening dress of England, with its starched shirts and collars so pernicious in the tropics, is essential for the maintenance of racial superiority and self-respect. The Americans and Australians are beginning to learn from experience that such precautions are unnecessary. In northern Australia and Panama men and women wear the lightest of headgear with impunity, and some of the whites, particularly children, even go outdoors bare-headed. An American medical missionary, Dr. G. J. P. Barger, who spent many years with his wife and family on the Congo, told me that they were all more healthy when they decided to abandon the conventional tropical helmet in favor of light, well-ventilated hats.[22] One government official, for many years resident in Darwin, never wears headgear, and frequent examples of the practice are seen in northeastern Queensland. Of course the climatic conditions in the Asiatic tropics may differ from those of tropical America or Australia in ways not yet ascertained.[23] Despite the work of Shattuck and others, the causes of the distribution of sunstroke remain a mystery,[24] while many conclusions, such as those of Woodruff on the effects of tropical light, are the subject of scientific dispute.[25]

No attempt will be made to examine the various views on the most suitable materials and colors for tropical dress,[26] but it is important to note Yaglou's statement that laboratory investigations show that normal clothing reduces the cooling effect of wind by about 50 per cent, as compared with that which obtains when light work trousers, socks, and shoes are worn. The importance of stripping to the waist in hot industries is, therefore, apparent, provided the temperature conditions do not exceed the limits at which air movement no longer cools the body, but heats it. In certain instances clothing is particularly advantageous, especially where the air is not mechanically cooled by "saturation," as is sometimes done in hot factories.[27]

On the whole, one can say that the dress of white settlers in the tropics has improved greatly since the days when the British murdered their soldiers in India and the white women of the West Indies committed suicide by slavishly following European customs in dress. Yet certain peoples, including the British, can still make improvements. It must be noted, on the other hand, that thin, flimsy dresses expose women who live in unprotected areas to the bites of insects, such as the anopheles mosquito.

Throughout most of the tropics poverty has resulted in wretched housing. Competition in the sugar and other industries makes it difficult to provide screening, detached kitchens, or the flooring and privies that are so essential for the combating of disease. Even in the Queensland tropics in the choice of sites and designs of towns and houses only too frequently slight attention has been paid to such vital questions as the direction of the prevailing winds. Some of the best housing in the tropics is that enjoyed by the American whites in Panama. Judged by this standard the white housing in tropical Australia, in Florida, and in Rhodesia is poor, and that in Costa Rica, Cuba, Puerto Rico, or St. Thomas scandalous. The sections of Part II of this book that deal with northeastern Queensland, Panama, the African plateaus, and other regions, describe the conditions and needs. The publications of Sir Raphael Cilento, Dr. D. B. Blacklock, the United Fruit Company, and many other authorities deal with this important problem in detail and should be consulted, as there is general agreement that local conditions and requirements vary greatly.[28]

One of the greatest hopes for white settlement in the tropics lies in the development of air conditioning, which is now being introduced on a commercial scale. We may shortly see the time when whole communities of white workers will live in air-conditioned villages and labor in air-conditioned factories and mills, so that field work alone will remain outside the influence of the improved conditions it introduces. At present the expense is a deterrent, but the system is spreading rapidly, and the success of central heating in cold countries, such as the United States, indicates what engineering science may achieve in hot countries. There are, of course, disadvantages and difficulties. It is unwise, for example, to lower house temperatures too much below the external temperatures. A reduction of 10° is in general considered the best and affords great relief.[29]

There remains a wider aspect of the question of comfort than the points considered above. White people, particularly white women, are prone to dislike the tropics because they regard tropical temperatures and humidities as uncomfortable, and in many cases they flatly refuse to settle in uncomfortable habitats. Others retire to colder climates after a time, when they discover that they are unsuited to the tropics. Hence there follows what Huntington rightly terms a natural selection of tropical settlers. This may or may not produce good results, according to the types of people who are still prepared to emigrate. The truth, which Griffith Taylor teaches as regards Australia, applies to many tropical regions.[30] The white races will not overrun the tropics while they can still find homes in more comfortable places.

Exercise

The scientific invasion of the tropics is exposing many fallacies. No question is more important than the truth or falsity of the popular belief that the white man, and still more the white woman, must avoid manual labor in the tropics.

This theory, which undoubtedly originated in the earliest days of the prescientific invasion, may have been due to conditions of climate, to health, to laziness, or to pride of race. Whatever its origin, it fed on conquest, enslavement, and exploitation until it became a creed, which, however false, had tragic effects upon many groups of whites.

If we consider the history of the white invaders of Asia or of the New World, we find that they would toil prodigiously in the operations of war but quickly came to regard any manual labor as contrary to their creed. In almost all tropical countries the whites could secure colored slaves and servants cheaply and easily. The factors of climate and disease were important, but the dominating factor seems to have been the plantation with its enslavements. As has been shown in the chapter on the West Indies,[31] the whites themselves employed colored workers to undercut white labor, so that few white working communities remained.

The tangled evidence from the West Indies does not prove that the whites could not settle the islands and engage in all types of labor. On the contrary it is significant that the planters long continued their demands for white workers. Moreover, in regions such as Costa Rica, Cuba, Puerto Rico, and Saba white working communities have managed to survive. The southern United States offers evidence from a different

16

angle. The negro, the plantation system, and disease forced the whites to emigrate, or produced white degeneracy in environments which, with the growth of science, have proved suitable for white labor.

Authorities still disagree on the question of labor and exercise in the tropics. As Earl Hanson says, "On the one hand they tell us that exercise is essential to health, and on the other hand they tell us that it must be indulged in very carefully in the tropics, because there it is apt to be dangerous." [32] Thus Sir Raphael Cilento, long a resident in the Australian tropics, attaches the greatest importance to the value of manual labor, whereas Sir Aldo Castellani writes, "If possible, travelling and muscular exertion should be done in the early morning or late afternoon, and avoided in the middle of the day, when a siesta, where possible, is beneficial." [33]

We found in Burma that British military officers were prepared to tramp a score of miles through mud or dense jungle and during the hottest part of the day if good shooting offered.

Experience in the tropics makes one agree with E. R. Stitt, who considers that women in general stand the tropics less well than men, because, as a rule, they have no serious employment and considerably less domestic work than at home.[34] In many cases this dictum is undoubtedly correct. Almost every tropical settlement has its quota of lazy, bored, card-playing, spirit-drinking women, who would be far healthier and happier if financial circumstances forced them to do their own housework, if not some labor out of doors. There are many healthy and happy women in the white working communities of northern Queensland and the Northern Territory of Australia.

Hanson notes an interesting case from the Amazon. The white ranchers of Marajo Island, at the mouth of the river, are "strapping, big, active people, as fine examples of good mental and physical health as one could find anywhere." They are totally different from other white men on the Amazon, probably because they lead active, outdoor lives in all weathers, whereas the other whites are planters or traders, who live by peon labor and hence believe firmly that the climate prevents the white man from undertaking manual work. Hanson suggests that a careful study should be made of Marajo Island. The white ranchers are not newcomers. They are descendants of colonizers who established themselves three centuries ago and handed down the unusual tradition that it was not necessary for the native to make every physical effort for them.[35]

This point is indeed of fundamental importance. Only too often a white man goes to the tropics with the fixed idea that he will die if he works. He hires native labor cheaply and he drills the same views into his son. The son too "will be quite honest in thinking that the white man cannot work in that region, and the fact that he has to keep dosing himself with patent medicines all his life will prove to him that the tropics are essentially unhealthy." [36]

The most important evidence, which is vital in its bearing upon north European settlers, comes from those regions of scientific penetration where disease is under control. In Florida we were told that the white man could manage all types of field labor except cane cutting and that negro labor was no longer essential. In Panama we saw white artisans who had toiled strenuously in machine shops for upwards of a quarter of a century and white prisoners whose health improved under labor on the roads.[37] The United Fruit Company—the great banana organization—reports similar circumstances in the low tropics. In the Queensland tropics, where the Australians have established a white working population of more than 300,000 persons, the white man and white woman not only perform all their own domestic work but fill every type of employment. From the records of the sugar plantations and mills in tropical Queensland it appears that the British gangs (tropical Australians or immigrant Britishers) head the list for physical fitness and endurance. Breinl presents similar evidence from the shipping companies of north Queensland: in the arduous employment of wharf lumping only in a few of the very hottest months of the year (and in these only on certain extremely dry, hot days with northerly winds) was the summer efficiency lower than the winter efficiency, and then only to the extent of 11 per cent.[38] Cilento notes that it would be interesting to compare the figures with the "time lost" records of any European or North American country.

These statements and statistics are impressive, but many scientists view them with suspicion, and there are evidences both in northern Queensland and the Northern Territory that the tropical climates affect the efficiency of labor and that it is less satisfactory than in the temperate zones.[39] Again, although we must hold experimental work in cool-temperate laboratories and factories as suspect owing to problems of acclimatization and of reproducing outdoor conditions, great weight must be given to the statement of C. P. Yaglou that

. . . it has been proven by recent laboratory experiments and verified in actual practice that the highest effective temperature under which a man can perform muscular work and maintain his efficiency is about 80°. . . . Continuous exposure to excessive heat lowers the stamina of man and destroys much of his economic usefulness. He becomes susceptible to disease, and suffers from anemia and muscular and joint pains, which eventually induce premature old age.[40]

On the whole, it appears that the vexed question of manual labor by white races in the tropics is not yet answered satisfactorily. It seems that exercise is essential [41] and that even the northern whites can perform manual labor of all kinds in the moderate tropics, if their health and economic conditions are satisfactory, but the conquest of disease is too recent and the regional environments are too varied for dogmatic conclusions on the subject.

CHAPTER XVII
SOME ADMINISTRATIVE AND ECONOMIC
PROBLEMS

In an outline such as this it is impossible to do more than set down a few general reflections on the immense subject of tropical economics and government. Economic and administrative difficulties have not caused all the white failures, but they are by no means of secondary and minor importance, as some authorities state.

Few white peoples of the tropics are politically or economically independent and few have established really satisfactory governments. Some writers have used these facts to support the superficially attractive thesis of climatic degeneration. Why, it is asked, have the white nations of the temperate lands established free, wealthy, and powerful offshoots in the United States, Canada, South Africa, temperate Australia, and the southern republics of South America and yet in general failed to plant similar branches in the tropics? An answer is found partly in the fact that in the United States, Canada, Australia, and parts of South America and Africa the whites encountered sparse and weak aboriginal peoples, whereas they met dense colored populations or introduced prolific colored races in India, Java, Jamaica, and other tropical lands, with the result that all the troubles of racial absorption, intermixture, and instability eventuated. Furthermore, the whites undoubtedly faced difficult and unhealthful environments over most of the tropics, but it is uncertain whether their troubles were due mainly to the primary factor of climate or to secondary factors, such as parasitic diseases. Sorokin points out that the backwardness of tropical peoples is not necessarily an argument in support of the theory of tropical degeneracy, for backward peoples are found in the temperate zone as well.

In certain parts of the tropics, such as Cuba, Costa Rica, Florida, and northern Queensland, where the whites have controlled disease by scientific methods, they are absorbing various colored races, and self-governing or partly self-governing communities have taken shape. Thus the white working peoples of Florida and northern Queensland have shown their capacity to share in the self-government of the United States and Australia; and Puerto Rico, in the hands of the rising generation, may similarly prove its capacity (Chapter VII). In spite of many obstacles, the white republics of Costa Rica and Cuba are making political progress, and the same may be said of other self-governing republics of the American tropics where the ruling classes are mostly white or mixed-white. In such tropical regions as India, Java, and Africa, however, where comparatively small numbers of whites settle or sojourn among dense colored populations of low social and economic development, the difficulties of administration are greater. The government is almost always external in character and is conducted by relays of administrators from the temperate zone.

From the conquistadors to Kipling the great colonial powers have felt that they must secure "dominion over palm and pine" and take up "the white man's burden," and as recently as 1916 S. L. Parrish put before the Congress of the United States the thesis that the tropics were becoming of more and more economic importance to the temperate countries, that the whites could never undertake tropical colonization, and that the indigenous peoples of the tropics could never govern themselves except under white control.[1]

It appears, nevertheless, that the political ambitions and abilities of the colored peoples are increasing, and that the whites already see the writing on the wall. Typical of the Filipino is the remark that "he would prefer to go to hell with a government of his own, than to Heaven under the Americans." [2] But in most tropical countries, the time for white withdrawal has not yet arrived:

All the experience acquired in the Dutch East Indies proves that if the contact between the Dutch administration and the population is too speedily relaxed, the population, contrary to the opinion of many people, will certainly reap no benefit.[3]

Ignorant and untraveled philanthropists have directed much criticism against white administration in the tropics, but the more one journeys in these regions the more one appreciates how vital it is that the whites should continue for the time being to govern the native peoples and how elevating have been the administrative, social, and scientific labors there of such peoples as the Americans, Dutch, and British.

Turning to the economic field, we find that in some tropical regions fertile soils, satisfactory rainfalls, and easy communications offer great productive facilities but that elsewhere deserts, swamps, dense forests, and other natural obstacles create almost insuperable difficulties. Regions of white success—northern Queensland, Florida, Cuba, Costa Rica—not only possess moderate tropical climates but offer particular advantages for sugar, coffee, truck farming, citrus fruits, and other agricultural industries, and moreover, with the exception of Costa Rica, are relatively near important markets. Up to the present no community of white settlers in the tropics has developed extensive manufactures, except, perhaps, such processes as sugar crushing and the Cuban and Florida tobacco industries. Here lies a large potentiality for development, for some parts of the tropics offer great possibilities for water power.

Over much of the tropics the main causes of retardation are natural conditions that impoverish the people. Hence evolves a vicious circle. Wealth is needed to raise the standards of health, energy, diet, and culture, but the people have insufficient resources, health, energy, diet, or culture to produce the requisite wealth. In some areas the ability and capital of northern nations are creating progress, but in others advance is slow and self-government seems very far off.

A leading feature in the history of most tropical peoples has been some form of merciless exploitation by the strong white nations of the temperate zones. Recent historians have made valiant efforts to whitewash the southern Europeans—the Portuguese and Spanish—and to attribute the chief blame to the northern Protestants.[4] It seems, however, that almost all the white races have used systems of forced labor. The technique of British, French, American, and Dutch slavery, of Queensland blackbirding, or of modern South American peonage, has varied only in the degree of its severity. Nor have these white peoples confined their exploitation merely to colored races. The British in the West Indies have treated their own kinsmen of the poor or the criminal classes as slaves.

In recent times there have been several sweeping changes. The cash nexus, with its greater freedom, has in most countries replaced the slave systems. Many employers have become aware of the cash value of health and sanitation, and have begun to care for their employees. Under modern science the use of free white labor has increased. Unfortunately, however, exploitation remains, and the tropical settler suffers only too often from selfish nationalistic or industrial policies, or even from exploitation by his own government or countrymen.

In the chapter on Costa Rica several methods were noted by which whites of the tropics have been exploited. The loaning of money on outrageous conditions, the furthering of one-crop industries, and the introduction of negro labor under conditions and with promises that the fruit companies fail to honor are examples in modern times. If the temperate nations have brought great advances in health, culture, and industry in the tropics, they have also created a multitude of troubles.

A fundamental cause of many recent difficulties is the one-crop industry, which strong external influences have frequently enforced upon weak white communities, such as those in Costa Rica and Puerto Rico. We have already examined some of the unfortunate results that have followed the introduction of this system, which exposes the unhappy settlers to exploitation, malnutrition, and the vagaries of the policies, demands, and markets of the temperate lands. The situation is particularly cruel when the temperate nations create industries and then raise tariff barriers against them, as the British and Americans have done in regard to the West Indian sugar industry. Certain American writers hold the United States largely responsible for the political and economic difficulties of Cuba. The Americans built up the Cuban one-crop sugar industry. Then they placed the industry under disabilities that caused ruin and revolution. Then they sent in the marines.[5]

Sometimes, however, national policies have favored the tropics. The white settlers of northern Queensland, for example, depend, like most

Australians, upon tariffs, bounties, or subsidies, and the industries of Florida are protected by the tariff policy of the United States. Yet even in the Australian tropics national policies can be deleterious to the white settler. It has been shown that, apart from the difficulties of soils, climate, and isolation, the Australian tariff and Navigation Acts impose hopeless burdens on the development of white settlement in the northern and northwestern parts of the continent. The chief hope for white settlement in the Australian tropics lies in northeastern Queensland, where the pressing requirements are greater diversification and the development of manufacturing industries.

C. L. Jones in his examination of Costa Rica clearly sums up the main economic needs of many white communities in the tropics. He believes that these communities must modify the conditions of life, allow more sustained efforts by the laboring classes, evolve new desires, and kindle dissatisfaction with low living standards, which now create a vicious circle of poverty and disease. They must broaden their economic life by a diversification of export products and markets, particularly as competition between tropical countries keeps costs almost on a slave basis.

At home, says Jones, the tropical communities must provide subsistence crops of greater variety for local consumption. They must establish new industries, even if only the lighter industries, for this will lead to a more nearly self-sufficient national economy. Many of these improvements will require new capital. Although some of the white communities appear to be passing out of the stage of economic exploitation under which Canada and the United States once suffered, the transition from dependence on foreign to dependence on local capital will be slow, even if scientific progress eliminates those effects of climate and disease that have so far "stepped down" the energy of tropical whites. Aided by science and humanitarianism, some of the largest white communities have at last an opportunity to work out their own salvation. "Their future," writes Jones, "economic, social, political, turns in all but slight degree on what their peoples can do for themselves, not on influences from outside the national borders." [6]

CHAPTER XVIII
SUMMARY AND CONCLUSION

We return to our original questions. Why have white settlers in general failed in the tropics? Are they beginning to make progress? Can they hope for ultimate success? It is easy to give superficial replies: that obstacles, particularly disease, impeded white progress, that the situation is improving with scientific advance, and that with further scientific discoveries white settlers may achieve widespread success. Unfortunately, such answers are too simple. The preceding chapters have indicated the number and the complexity of the human, environmental, and cultural factors of the problem and the profound difficulty of basal analysis. As Lucien Febvre says in "A Geographical Introduction to History," "We have only reached that stage of the Genesis when the light begins to be distinct from the darkness." [1] The growth of scientific knowledge is continually exposing new forms of interaction between man and his surroundings, and, until all interactions are discovered and elucidated, there is grave danger that generalizations may be premature. Moreover, neither man nor his environment is static. Human effort ebbs and flows. Environmental factors appear and disappear. There is also the element of chance. There are not only causal but casual factors as well.

Yet, although we must emphasize the profound difficulty of the problem and the slight extent of existing knowledge, we may admit that history, observation, and laboratory and statistical researches have secured some definite facts concerning the various types of tropical environment and the interaction between those environments and certain white groups. [2] Mankind has acquired proved data upon geographical locations, soils, climates, flora, fauna, parasitic diseases, and other phenomena in the tropics. There is also some definite information as to the responses of white men, women, and children to these phenomena, with respect to such matters as pigmentation, resistance to disease, diet, and standards of living. Very important are certain proved facts of racial contact—for example, population density or weight of numbers, the invariable presence of crossbreeding, the undercutting of advanced groups by groups who will accept lower living standards, and the political and economic pressures exerted by external peoples on the tropical whites.

Beyond these proved facts of white settlement lies a vast mass of uncertain data and unproved theory. Under this heading we may place debatable subjects such as variations in racial intelligence, the relative capabilities of people and individuals to adjust themselves psychologically or physiologically to tropical climates by the process known as acclimatization, the results of crossbreeding, and theories of climatic optima, of climate and civilization, and of climate and race. Bearing in mind the limits and uncertainty of existing knowledge, we shall now summarize the outstanding facts, problems, and conclusions set forth in the earlier chapters of this book.

Environmental Factors

Tropical regions differ in their accessibility. In any country accessibility has both external and internal results. On the external side are such questions as the pressure of external peoples or the proximity of external markets; on the internal, such problems as internal communication and transport. Accessibility may be either advantageous or disadvantageous to white communities. The isolation of the Costa Ricans on the Central American plateaus is probably the principal factor that has saved them from absorption by indigenous Indian peoples or negro exotics. On the other hand, "The eastern Andean valleys would be ideal for colonization if they were on a seaboard, any seaboard. As matters stand, there can be no development of them short of a time when a world demand for their products has come into being through the denser peopling of the earth." [3]

As regards soils the known data are increasing, and the old fallacy of the immense and widespread fertility of the tropics has been disproved. Nevertheless, the tropics contain large areas of high fertility, whose potentialities may be disclosed by careful soil studies.

No aspect of the tropical environment has been so closely studied as that of climate. Although there are many minor regions and "local" climates, it is sufficient for our purpose to distinguish six main regional types: the trade-wind coast lands, the trade-wind islands, the plateaus, the deserts, the equatorial regions, and the wet-dry lands. It further appears that these types differ in their suitability for white settlement. Unfortunately, however, the constituent factors of climate, the variation of these factors in the different regions, and their effects upon white settlers are still obscure. The whites have been more successful in the moderate tropics, such as the plateaus and trade-wind margins and islands, than in the wet-dry or in the hot, low tropics, and this fact, together with statistics and laboratory tests, suggests that the higher temperatures are deleterious. The evidence on air movements varies. High winds may be trying, but it appears from observations in Florida, Jamaica, Saba, Queensland, and other places, and from many laboratory experiments that in general air movements are highly beneficial. The effects of humidity are uncertain, but most whites appear to detest hot, humid areas, and one finds few white working settlers in the equatorial lowlands. It must be remembered, however, that in these regions parasitic diseases have been a controlling factor in the past. Little is known as to the effects of weather variations, but observation shows that monotony is likely to be injurious and that variations assist white settlement, as Huntington's statistical researches would appear to indicate. It is believed that monotony is the chief fault in the climate of tropical plateaus, although very high altitudes have other evil effects. Some studies have been conducted upon other climatic factors, such as sunlight, ionization, and atmospheric electricity, but the results are uncertain, and other unknown climatic factors may exist. Despite their great labors, even the climatologists have not yet provided sufficient data for the elucidation of the climatic factor in white settlement in the tropics.

Tropical flora and fauna and their effects on social standards and economic policies have been examined incidentally in this book. Here again science is helping white settlers to make progress. Plants and animals have been improved and transported from region to region on a prodigious scale, and the development of immense areas (for example parts of the wet-dry regions of northern Australia) undoubtedly depends upon scientific progress. Every aspect of the problem presents the same feature. Although we possess considerable knowledge of the environmental factors that affect white settlers in the tropics, there is great need of further research.

THE REACTIONS OF WHITE PEOPLES TO TROPICAL ENVIRONMENTS

History shows that during the last four centuries many white groups invaded the tropics. In most cases they failed to establish communities that engaged in general activities, including manual labor. In most cases, moreover, they retreated or were absorbed by indigenous colored peoples or by exotic colored peoples of white introduction prepared to accept lower standards of life. Occasionally, however, white groups survived, and in some instances, several of which are comparatively new to the tropics, they are meeting with apparent success.

The invaders may be divided into two classes, the northern Europeans and the Mediterranean whites. The latter—Spaniards, Italians, and Portuguese—react more favorably to tropical conditions than do the former, and have to a greater extent survived. The incoming whites found superior advantages for settlement in the western hemisphere and in Australia than in the Old World tropics. In areas such as Cuba, Puerto Rico, Costa Rica, Florida, and northern Queensland, where they have been most successful, the tropical climates were moderate and the indigenous populations were, in general, sparse.

The white invasions of the tropics seem to have proved the following facts: (1) The majority of white groups, whether northern or Mediterranean in origin, can inhabit the moderate tropics and reproduce for many generations. (2) In these moderate tropics white settlers can engage in all types of labor, even manual work, and contrary to early opinions labor or exercise in the tropics is essential to health. (3) Almost all white settlers in the tropics breed freely with peoples of lower cultural development and tend to be absorbed if the peoples of lower development are sufficiently numerous. (4) Peoples who are prepared to work harder and to accept lower standards of living tend to drive out groups that demand easier conditions of life. (5) White peoples have been greatly affected in the tropics by such factors as disease and diet, by economic phenomena, and by political and economic policies, whether their own or those set up by an administration outside the tropics.

The above facts seem clear. Very different is the outlook when we attempt to examine the causes of these human responses to tropical environments. The whole problem of racial and individual reactions to the tropics is full of doubt. Certain colored peoples, such as the negroes and Chinese, are more cheerful and docile than are white peoples in tropical environments and are prepared to accept lower living standards. Similarly certain white groups of Mediterranean origin fare better in the tropics than the northern whites. It is, however, impossible to say whether this "superiority" is due to ethnic characteristics, to differences in cultural development, or to variations in the tropical environments occupied by the invading groups. The most we can say is that for unknown reasons certain colored peoples seem superior in the tropics to certain white peoples and that similar variations appear to exist among the white groups. This phenomenon, however, is not confined to the tropics. The United States, for example, shows many instances of the negro supplanting the white, or of whites of lower cultural development supplanting whites of higher development in various types of manual work.[4]

The same difficulty occurs with respect to individual reactions. Some authorities hold that blonde individuals are less suited to the tropics than are the darker types, but this again is a surmise not yet capable of proof. It also appears that population density or weight of numbers has an important influence on white settlement, but this phenomenon, too, is not confined to the tropics. The failure of the whites to settle permanently in certain temperate regions of dense colored population shows that the problem exists in cooler lands. Nevertheless, the small number of retarded colored people in such lands as northern Queensland or Costa Rica clearly facilitated the white penetration of these areas, and it is quite clear that European and American governments are inviting disappointment and suffering when they permit and even encourage small groups of white settlers to invade areas inhabited by retarded peoples whose numbers are dense or expanding. Here the history of most of the American tropics may be taken as exemplifying a fairly general principle.

Allied to this question is the problem of crossbreeding, which is almost universal when two or more peoples settle in the same locality. Here again the existing scientific knowledge is slight. The results of the researches of Davenport and Steggerda on the intellectual ability of whites, negroes, and their crosses in Jamaica, agree in general with the results of similar studies in the United States and with the observations of West Indian school teachers who handle white, negro, and crossbred groups of similar social status. Some authorities, however, emphatically deny the value of studies of this type based on intelligence tests. All we can say is that over short periods of time it appears that the crossing of members of widely different ethnic groups may create mental and physical disharmonies but that after a number of generations these disharmonies tend to disappear. The matter demands further research, for, although the existing results are slight and are open to criticism, they tend to show that highly important national policies, such as the "White Australia" policy, may have a biological as well as a social basis.

It appears from history, observation, and laboratory experiments that very high temperatures may damage the intellect and memory of adults. Experience in Queensland and Panama seems to indicate that children are not affected up to puberty and that adult deterioration may be due to social phenomena, but the controls present great difficulty in analysis. Observers differ as to whether psychical reactions and psychoneuroses are attributable to climate or to social factors, such as life among native populations, dependence upon native servants, and "kitchen neurasthènia," but again little is clear. It is fairly certain, however, that the tropical climate produces some decline in energy.

Similar difficulties exist in elucidating other reactions of white settlers to the tropical environment. White groups can live and reproduce for generations in the moderate tropics, and it appears from the statistics of Florida, Cuba, Puerto Rico, and Queensland that the moderate tropics do not affect the birth rate. Again, where sanitation, the control of parasitic diseases, diet, and the living standard are satisfactory, the whites do not suffer an unduly high percentage of deaths. Indeed, the death rates in Panama and northern Queensland are exceptionally low, although allowance must be made for the fact that the whites in Panama are certainly, and in Queensland probably, a select group.

The fine results achieved by the whites in Queensland and Panama have unfortunately misled a number of medical men. If modern science and high living standards have enabled white groups to live safely in a particularly favored region such as Queensland or in medically fortified camps in unhealthful places like Panama, malaria and other diseases remain unconquered over large parts of the tropics. As in Florida, colored peoples or other peoples of low standard may remain as reservoirs of disease and contaminate the whites. All we can say at present is that science has made remarkable improvements in tropical health, but the fight is only just beginning and as yet there is no certainty that scientific medicine will conquer, particularly in the hot, wet tropics.

Another pressing problem is that of diet. The knowledge gained in Florida and Panama indicates the importance of the subject, and progress in this field may help substantially to break the vicious circle of poverty, poor diet, and sickness, although some of the dietetic deficiencies suffered by tropical whites may be due to the tropical environment.

Among other subjects awaiting investigation is that of racial and individual attitudes to manual work and comfort and particularly to the discomforts caused by life and labor in tropical climates. Apart from all questions of disease, the evidence from history, observation, statistics, and the laboratory indicates that the majority of the white and some of the colored peoples have an aversion for hot, humid climates and that many whites dislike all types of tropical climate. It is useless for the critics of Ellsworth Huntington to deny that this dislike of certain tropical climates creates a natural selection. As Griffith Taylor has pointed out, this factor, apart from any other consideration, will keep such areas as northern Australia almost empty until the temperate regions are densely occupied. How far scientific advance will remove these obstacles is uncertain. Air conditioning offers hopes for the future, but economic factors would seem to confine it to particularly favored communities and lands.

Distaste for tropical climates influences white settlers not only through the discomfort of living factors, such as housing, but in the all-important questions of exercise and work. It seems clear that the early ideas were fallacious and that physical exercise is essential in hot climates. Moreover, recent experience in such regions as Florida and Queensland, as well as centuries-old experience in Costa Rica and the West Indies, indicates that both northern and Mediterranean whites can carry on even manual labor in the moderate tropics and that, far from being deleterious, this physical exertion is essential to health. It is clear, nevertheless, that many white groups and individuals abhor heavy labor in tropical climates and that this fact greatly impedes white settlement.

Finally, we must refer to human reactions to the tropics as manifest in administrative and economic policies, both internal and external to the tropics. Scientific research has not yet solved the vital problem of the vicious circle: whether the climate so debilitates the whites that they cannot avoid low living standards, poor diets, and weak administrative and economic policies or whether, if lifted above these difficulties, the whites would no longer suffer from the climate. In this respect the future of Florida, northern Queensland, and Costa Rica will be of great interest. On the external side, while the white nations of the temperate zone have done much to elevate the white peoples of the tropics, they have also, only too often, mercilessly converted tropical industries to their own purposes, destroyed balanced economies, and then left the unhappy tropical peoples in the lurch. It is apparent that the white groups in regions like Queensland, Cuba, and Costa Rica must work out their own salvation by diversifying their industries and by creating higher living standards through their own efforts.

The Future

To the racial purist the future that lies before the white settler in most parts of the tropics is far from promising apart from the fact that the increase of the white population in many countries, and in consequence white emigration, seem certain to decline. Throughout much of tropical America, the West Indies, and Africa the white peoples are likely to undergo absorption or be driven out. In northern Queensland the outlook is more hopeful. In the short view, the probable merging of the white and colored peoples may create grave social difficulties and possibly some biological disharmonies. Whether the ultimate result will be the production of new ethnic groups adjusted to the various tropical environments only time can show.

At present much can be done to assist white sojourners and settlers by further scientific investigations and by administrative and economic policies based on the results of those investigations. The early history of white settlement in the tropics was a story of wasted lives, wasted efforts, and wasted resources, but the recent years glow with achievement. The scientific world has at last glimpsed the vastness and complexity of the problem. In the hands of scientific workers lies the solution.

NOTES

NOTES

The numbers at the top of the inner margin of each page indicate the pages of the text to which the notes refer.

Data in brackets with the initials "R. G. S." have been contributed by Mr. Robert G. Stone, Blue Hill Meteorological Observatory, Harvard University.

CHAPTER I

THE PROBLEM OF WHITE SETTLEMENT IN THE TROPICS

[1] The word "race," which is retained by many leading British and American authorities, is used throughout this work, but it is rendered suspect by the criticisms of J. S. Huxley and A. C. Haddon set forth in Chapter XII.

[2] Works such as "We Europeans" by J. S. Huxley and A. C. Haddon (New York, 1936) illustrate the difficulty of discovering any satisfactory terminology or classification.

[3] See Alexander Supan: Grundzüge der physischen Erdkunde, 7th edit., Vol. 1, Berlin and Leipzig, 1927, p. 141; also A. A. Miller: Climatology, London, 1931, pp. 53 and 54.

[4] W. Köppen: Versuch einer Klassifikation der Klimate vorzugsweise nach ihren Beziehungen zur Pflanzenwelt, Geogr. Zeitschr., Vol. 6, 1900, pp. 593-611 and 657-679.

[5] Miller, op. cit., p. 57.

[6] J. W. Gregory: The Menace of Colour, 2nd edit., London, 1925, p. 17; and Helmer Key: The New Colonial Policy, London, 1927, p. 41. See also A. N. Carr-Saunders: Population, London, 1925, pp. 67-71.

[7] Gregory, op. cit., p. 17.

[8] G. T. Trewartha: Recent Thought on the Problem of White Acclimatization in the Wet Tropics, Geogr. Rev., Vol. 16, 1926, pp. 467-478; reference on p. 467.

[9] R. DeC. Ward: The Acclimatization of the White Race in the Tropics, Ann. Report, Smithsonian Instn. for 1930, Washington, 1931, pp. 557-576; reference on p. 558 (reprinted from New England Journ. of Medicine, Vol. 201, 1929, pp. 617-627); idem: Can the White Race Become Acclimatized in the Tropics? Gerlands Beiträge zur Geophysik, Vol. 32 (Köppen-Band I), 1931, pp. 149-157.

[10] R. R. Kuczynski: The World's Future Population, in Corrado Gini and others: Population (Lectures on the Harriss Foundation, 1929), Chicago, 1930, pp. 281-302; reference on p. 302.

[11] Recent information on the growth of population is published in the Annals of the American Academy of Political and Social Science, November, 1936. W. L. Holland considers that the population of India is increasing by 3,400,000 per annum; that the Japanese working population is increasing by 500,000 a year, but that the total population "will be stabilized around 1950 at about 80 millions"; and that China has shown "considerable regular increase of population in modern times" (Population Problems and Policies in the Far East, pp. 307-317). According to W. S. Thompson and P. K. Whelpton (Population Policies of European Countries, pp. 297-306), Germany presents since 1933 "the largest increase on record in any nation (except as an immediate postwar reaction); in Italy, however, Fascist efforts have failed to check the decline in the birth rate, although this decline is "at a slower pace than in many other countries."

[12] C. B. Fawcett: The Question of Colonies, Geogr. Rev., Vol. 28, 1938, pp. 306-309.

[13] Cf. T. H. Thomas: Modern Abyssinia: A Selected Bibliography, Geogr. Rev., Vol. 27, 1937, pp. 120-128, especially pp. 125-126.

[14] [It was generally thought up to a few decades ago that tropical diseases were almost insurmountable, because they were held in some way to be caused by the climate. It is interesting to read now in an article written in 1885 that "much of the disease which is usually attributed to the effects of tropical climate may be avoided" (C. V. Poore: Climate in Its Relation to Health, Journ. Royal Soc. of Arts, Vol. 33, 1885, pp. 916 ff.; reference on p. 916). See also R. W. Boyce: Mosquito or Man? The Conquest of the Tropical World, 2nd edit., New York, 1910.—R. G. S.]

[15] Dr. Huntington's chief works on the subject are: The Adaptability of the White Man to Tropical America, in G. H. Blakeslee, edit.: Clark University Addresses, New York, 1914, pp. 360-386; Civilization and Climate, New Haven, 1915, 3rd rev. edit., 1924; World Power and Evolution, New Haven, 1919; Temperature and Mortality in New York City, Statistical Bull. Metropolitan Life Ins. Co., Vol. 4, Feb., 1923, pp. 4-7; The Character of Races, New York, 1924; West of the Pacific,

New York, 1925; Climate and the Evolution of Civilization, *in* G. A. Baitsell, edit.: The Evolution of Earth and Man, New Haven, 1929, pp. 330-383; Natural Selection and Climate in Northern Australia, *Econ. Record*, Vol. 5, 1929, pp. 185-201; Weather and Health, *Bull. National Research Council, No. 75*, 1930; The Effect of Climate and Weather, *in* E. V. Cowdry, edit.: Human Biology and Racial Welfare, New York, 1930, pp. 295-330; Climatic Pulsations, *in* Hyllningsskrift tillägnad Sven Hedin på hans 70-årsdag den 19 febr. 1935, pp. 571-608, *Geografiska Annaler*, Vol. 17, 1935 [special number]; Season of Birth, New York, 1938.

[16] Sir Aldo Castellani: Climate and Acclimatization, London, 1938, p. 150.

[17] Ward, The Acclimatization of the White Race, p. 575.

[18] Quoted in Ward, The Acclimatization of the White Race, p. 574.

[19] Castellani, *op. cit.*, pp. 146-147.

[20] Quoted by H. J. Spinden: Civilization and the Wet Tropics, *World's Work*, Vol. 45, 1923, pp. 438-448; reference on p. 444.

[21] Castellani, *op. cit.*, p. 147.

[22] R. B. Vance: Human Geography of the South, Chapel Hill, N. C., 1932.

[23] See the following publications of Sir R. W. Cilento: The White Man in the Tropics, *Commonwealth of Australia, Dept. of Health, Service Publ. (Tropical Division) No. 7*, [1925] pp. 38-39; The White Settlement of Tropical Australia, *in* P. D. Phillips and G. L. Wood, edits.: The Peopling of Australia, (*Pacific Relations Ser., No. 1*), Melbourne, 1928; Rejoinder to Professor Huntington, *Econ. Record*, Vol. 6, 1930, pp. 127-132; Australia's Problems in the Tropics, *Rept. 21st Meeting, Australian and New Zealand Assn. for the Advancement of Sci., Sydney Meeting, 1932*, Sydney, 1933, pp. 216-233; Some Medical Aspects of Racial Resistance, *Medical Journ. of Australia*, Oct. 14, 1933; Australia's Orientation, State of Victoria, *Dept. of Public Health, Health Bull. 35-36*, Melbourne, 1933, pp. 1039-1066. R. H. Cohen criticizes Cilento in: Het Blankenvragstuk in tropisch Queensland, *Mensch en Maatschappij*, 1931, pp. 217-235.

[24] J. Russell Smith: Memorandum to Rockefeller Foundation, manuscript in Rockefeller Foundation Library, New York. See also below, p. 268, note 29.

[25] Quoted by Helmer Key: The New Colonial Policy, London, 1927, p. 192.

[26] See also P. Sorokin: Contemporary Sociological Theories, New York, 1928; A. D. A. de Kat Angelino: Colonial Policy, 2 vols., The Hague, 1931.

[27] Ward, The Acclimatization of the White Race, gives an excellent summary of the advantages and disadvantages of each type.

[28] Gregory's "The Menace of Colour" is a valuable work in spite of its unfortunate title.

[29] See, for example, Spinden, *op. cit.*

[30] A. G. Keller: Colonization, Boston, New York, etc., 1908; H. R. Carter: Yellow Fever: An Epidemiological and Historical Study of Its Place of Origin, Baltimore, 1931; Victor Heiser: An American Doctor's Odyssey, New York, 1936.

[31] For Huntington's works see note 15 above.

[32] Sorokin, *op. cit.*, pp. 138-159; Vance, *op. cit.*, pp. 363-364; Cilento, Rejoinder to Professor Huntington.

[33] Griffith Taylor: The Control of Settlement by Humidity and Temperature, *Commonwealth of Australia, Bur. of Meteorology, Bull. No. 14*, Melbourne, 1916, p. 9.

[34] C. P. Yaglou: The Influence of Atmospheric Conditions on Health and Growth, *Heating, Piping, and Air Conditioning*, Vol. 3, 1931, pp. 926-932.

[35] Dr. Huntington considers that the term "laboratory" should be extended to include "experiments" that may in future be conducted on a large scale on white groups in the tropics and not necessarily by laboratory work.

[36] In conversation with the writer, Harvard, 1932.

[37] A. Brienl and W. J. Young: Tropical Australia and Its Settlement, *Medical Journ. of Australia*, 6th Year, 1919, Vol. 1, pp. 253-259, 375-382, and 395-404.

NOTES

CHAPTER II

PRESCIENTIFIC INVASIONS OF THE TROPICS

[1] In this work no effort will be made to examine the white invasions of the tropics that took place in prehistoric or early historic times. It is tempting to adopt clear-cut explanations, such as Lionel Curtis's account of the Aryan settlement of India, or such theories as the view that the contact between northern and tropical races in India produced the caste system by the drawing of a color line by the conquerors to keep their lineage and culture pure. The latter thesis might afford plausible explanation of the stratification visible today in the West Indies and other tropical regions of racial

mixture. Unfortunately, the writings of A. L. Kroeber and other trained anthropologists reveal the uncertainty and unscientific character of the existing evidence on problems such as that of the early white invasions of India. It is this lack of proved scientific facts that makes the attractive generalizations of such writers as Professor A. J. Toynbee matters of speculative interest rather than of practical importance.

For details see A. J. Toynbee: A Study of History, 3 vols., London, 1934; Lionel Curtis: Civitas Dei, 3 vols., London, 1934, especially Vol. 1, pp. 12-14; also pp. 20-32, above.

[2] Meredith Townsend: Asia and Europe, New York, 1904, pp. 85-86. J. A. Prescott notes, however, that some cities in India contain a few white trading families that are permanent in character.

[3] Toynbee, op. cit., Vol. 1, p. 212.

[4] Report of Indian Statutory Commission (Cmd. 3568), Vol. 1, London, 1930, pp. 42 and 46.

[5] C. A. Vlieland: British Malaya, A Report on the 1931 Census, London, 1932, p. 36.

[6] Indisch Verslag (Netherlands Indian Report) 1937, II: Statistical Abstract for the Year 1936, Batavia, 1938, Table 8A, p. 16.

[7] A. G. Keller: Colonization, Boston, New York, etc., 1908, pp. 104-105.

[8] R. S. Whiteway: The Rise of Portuguese Power in India, 1497-1550, Westminster, 1899, pp. 74-75 (quoted by Keller, op. cit., p. 117).

[9] Keller, op. cit., p. 105.

[10] Ibid., p. 108.

[11] Ibid., p. 87.

[12] A. D. A. de Kat Angelino: Colonial Policy, 2 vols., The Hague, 1931.

[13] Sir Charles Lucas: Introduction, The Cambridge History of the British Empire, New York and Cambridge, England, Vol. 1, 1929, pp. 1-21; reference on p. 4.

[14] Toynbee, op. cit., Vol. 1, pp. 211-212.

[15] Sir Harry Johnston: The Negro in the New World, London, 1910, pp. 110-129.

[16] Mark Jefferson: Recent Colonization in Chile, Amer. Geogr. Soc. Research Ser. No. 6, 1921, p. 3.

[17] J. W. Gregory: The Menace of Colour, 2nd edit., London, 1925, pp. 112-120.

NOTES

CHAPTER III

BRITISH FAILURES IN THE WEST INDIES

[1] See, for example, Lord Olivier: Jamaica: The Blessed Island, London, 1936.

[2] A. P. Newton: The European Nations in the West Indies, 1493-1688, London, 1933, p. 149.

[3] C. S. S. Higham: The Development of the Leeward Islands under the Restoration, Cambridge, 1921.

[4] F. Cundall: Historic Jamaica, London, 1915, p. 6.

[5] Bryan Edwards: The History, Civil and Commercial, of the British Colonies in the West Indies, 2 vols., London, 1793; reference in Vol. 1, p. 244.

[6] L. J. Ragatz: The Fall of the Planter Class in the British Caribbean, 1763-1883, New York, 1928, p. 3.

[7] J. A. Williamson: The Beginnings of an Imperial Policy, in The Cambridge History of the British Empire, New York and Cambridge, England, Vol. 1, 1929, pp. 207-238; reference on p. 236.

[8] Henry Whistler's Journal, March, 1654-5, in C. H. Firth, edit.: Narrative of General Venables, London, 1900, pp. 145-147 (quoted from F. W. Pitman: The Development of the British West Indies 1700-1763, New Haven, London, etc., 1917, p. 6).

[9] Ragatz, op. cit., p. 33.

[10] Ibid., pp. 31-32.

[11] Richard Ligon: A True & Exact History of the Island of Barbados, London, 1657, pp. 43-45.

[12] Calendar of State Papers, Colonial Series, America and West Indies, London 1693-1696, No. 1738; reference on p. 446.

[13] R. P. du Tertre: Histoire général des Antilles, Paris, 1667-1671, Vol. 1, pp. 78-81.

[14] V. T. Harlow: History of Barbados, Oxford, 1926, Chapter 7.

[15] Calendar of State Papers, 1693-1696, p. 447

[16] J. C. Jeaffreson: A Young Squire of the Seventeenth Century, London, 1878, Vol. 1, Chapter 7.

[17] Calendar of State Papers, Colonial Series No. 7, 1669-1674.

[18] Harlow, op. cit., p. 306.

[19] Higham, op. cit., pp. 143-144.

20 Pitman, *op. cit.*, p. 55.

21 *Ibid.*, Chapter 2.

22 J. A. Williamson: The Colonies after the Restoration, *in* The Cambridge History, Vol. I, pp. 239-267; reference on p. 243.

23 Harlow, *op. cit.*, pp. 339-340.

24 Address to Assembly Dec. 5, 1724, Leeward Islands, 1691-1782, Original Correspondence with the Board of Trade, Colonial Office Papers, Class 152, Vol. 15, R. 130 (quoted from Pitman, *op. cit.*, p. 100). See also Ragatz, *op. cit.*, Chapter 2, for evils of "large estates, monoculture, absenteeism and antiquated methods."

25 Jamaica, 1689-1782. Original Correspondence with the Board of Trade, Colonial Office Papers, Class 137, Vol. 16, R. 8 (quoted from Pitman, *op. cit.*, p. 108).

26 Pitman, *op. cit.*, pp. 108-109.

27 Edward Long: The History of Jamaica, 3 vols., London, 1774, Vol. 2, p. 22.

28 Ragatz, *op. cit.*, pp. 7-8.

29 *Ibid.*, p. 13.

30 Ligon, *op. cit.*, pp. 43-44.

31 Higham, *op. cit.*, p. 144.

32 Harlow, *op. cit.*, p. 309.

33 *Ibid.*, p. 295.

34 Newton, *op. cit.*, p. 197.

35 Harlow, *op. cit.*, p. 309.

36 Edwards, *op. cit.*, Vol. 2, pp. 21-22.

37 See pp. 92-94, above.

38 H. R. Carter: Yellow Fever: An Epidemiological and Historical Study of Its Place of Origin, Baltimore, 1931, p. 53.

39 *Ibid.*, p. 72.

40 Du Tertre, *op. cit.*, Vol. I, pp. 78-81.

41 Ligon, *op. cit.*, p. 21.

42 Calendar of State Papers, 1685-1688, Nos. 374, 540, 871; 1693-1696, No. 1738; quotation from No. 540, 1686, p. 139.

43 Ragatz, *op. cit.*, p. 32.

44 Pitman, *op. cit.*, p. 61.

45 Ragatz, *op. cit.*, p. 3.

46 Jeaffreson, *op. cit.*, Chap. 7.

47 Calendar of State Papers, 1689-1692, No. 977; reference on p. 293.

48 Report of the Lords of the Committee of the Council Appointed for the Consideration of All Matters Relating to Trade and Foreign Plantations, 1788-9, Part 3, A 37, 39.

49 *Ibid.*, Appendix, Q. 37, 38, 39.

50 *Ibid.*, Paper No. 1, Appendix, p. 30, Questions 32, 33, Aug. 18, 1787-8.

51 Edwards, *op. cit.*, Vol. 2, pp. 10-14.

52 R. W. Cilento: The White Man in the Tropics, *Commonwealth of Australia Dept. of Health, Service Publ. (Tropical Division) No. 7*, [1925], pp. 73-74.

NOTES

CHAPTER IV

THE SCIENTIFIC INVASIONS OF THE TROPICS

1 See pp. 133-134, above.

2 C. L. Jones: Civilization in the Caribbean, *in* A. C. Wilgus, edit.: The Caribbean Area, Washington, 1934, pp. 488-503; *idem:* The Economic Significance of the Caribbean, *ibid.*, pp. 446-458; C. F. Jones: Economic Conditions in the Caribbean Area, *ibid.*, pp. 79-106; C. D. Kepner: The Banana Industry in the Caribbean, *in* A. C. Wilgus, edit.: Modern Hispanic America, Washington, 1933. For popular accounts see F. U. Adams: Conquest of the Tropics, New York, 1914; Samuel Crowther: The Romance and Rise of the American Tropics, New York, 1929.

3 See pp. 49 and 68, above.

4 A. G. Price: Pioneer Reactions to a Poor Tropical Environment, *Geogr. Rev.*, Vol. 23, 1933, pp. 353-371; reference on p. 357.

5 See pp. 158-160, above.

6 [See R. W. Boyce: Mosquito or Man? The Conquest of the Tropical World, 2nd edit., New York, 1910; S. H. Daukes: Interrelations between the Hygiene of the Tropics and Temperate Climates, *Journ. of Tropical Medicine and Hygiene*, Vol. 33, 1930, pp. 35-40 (a history of the fight against tropical diseases); R. P. Strong: The Modern Period of Tropical Medicine, *Amer. Journ. of Tropical Medicine*, Vol. 40, 1937, pp. 113-115; R. Y. Stones: Twenty-five years of Tropical Medicine, *East African Medical Journ.*, Vol. 13, 1937, pp. 271-281; A. Hauer: Die tropenmedizinischen Prob-

leme in der Gegenwart, *Deutsche Medizinische Wochenschrift*, Vol. 63, 1937, pp. 1717-1726; P. Manson-Bahr: Notes on Some Landmarks in Tropical Medicine, *Proc. Royal Soc. of Medicine*, Vol. 30, 1937, pp. 1181-1184; C. Schilling: Problemi da risolvere nel campo della medicina tropicale, *Terapia*, Vol. 27, 1937, pp. 225-232.—R. G. S.]

7 R. B. Vance: Human Geography of the South, Chapel Hill, N. C., 1932, p. 375. [See also B. de Rudder: Grundriss einer Meteorobiologie des Menschens, Berlin, 1938, for a thorough discussion of seasonal incidence of diseases.—R. G. S.]

8 R. DeC. Ward: The Acclimatization of the White Race in the Tropics, *Ann. Rept. Smithsonian Instn. for 1930*, Washington, 1931, pp. 557-576; reference on p. 561.

9 Sir Patrick Manson: Tropical Diseases, 5th edit., London, New York, etc., 1914, p. xxi. [See also R. P. Strong: The Importance of Ecology in Relation to Disease, *Science*, Vol. 82, 1935, pp. 307-317, and E. Martini: Wege der Seuchen, Lebensgemeinschaft, Kultur, Boden und Klima als Grundlagen von Epidemien unter Berücksichtigung der Tropenkrankheiten dargestellt, Stuttgart, 1936; W. A. Sawyer; Importance of Environment in the Study of Tropical Diseases, *Amer. Journ. Trop. Med.*, Vol. 18, 1938, pp. 9-18.—R. G. S.]

10 D. B. Blacklock: Health in West Africa, *Lancet*, Vol. 218, 1930, p. 844.

11 Epidemiological Report of the Health Section of the Secretariat, League of Nations, No. 7-9 (R. E. 179), Geneva, 1935.

12 See pp. 64-65, above. Dr. Huntington considers that the use of crude death rates is not justified and that it gives an entirely wrong impression. A rate of 8.3 in Queensland, if it were a real rate, would indicate an average life of nearly 125 years. Unfortunately, it is impossible in many cases to obtain standardized rates.

13 W. C. Gorgas: Sanitation in the Canal Zone, *Journ. Amer. Medical Assn.*, Vol. 49, 1907, pp. 6-8.

14 Sir R. W. Cilento: Australia's Orientation, *State of Victoria, Dept. of Public Health, Health Bull. 35-36*, Melbourne, 1933, pp. 1039-1066; reference on p. 1065.

15 H. G. James: Brazil After a Century of Independence, New York, 1925, p. 262.

16 Brazil, *Pan American Union Amer. Nation Ser. No. 3*, Washington, 1932, p. 15.

17 See pp. 157-160, above.

18 See pp. 73-74, above.

NOTES

CHAPTER V

THE TRADE-WIND MARGINS: I. FLORIDA

1 R. B. Vance: Human Geography of the South, Chapel Hill, N. C., 1932, pp. 25-26.

2 O. E. Baker: Agricultural Regions of the United States (map), *in* Yearbook of Agriculture, United States Dept. of Agriculture, Washington, 1928, p. 641. This map also appears in Vance, *op. cit.*, p. 13.

3 A. A. Miller: Climatology, London, 1931, p. 65; C. W. Thornthwaite: The Climates of North America According to a New Classification, *Geogr. Rev.*, Vol. 21, 1931, pp. 633-655.

4 E. A. Ackerman: Influences of Climate on the Cultivation of Citrus Fruits, *Geogr. Rev.*, Vol. 28, 1938, pp. 289-302; reference on pp. 292-293.

5 R. S. Atwood: Population Changes in Florida from 1920-1930. Manuscript, University of Florida, 1933.

6 J. K. Small: Cypress and Population in Florida, *Journ. New York Botanical Gardens*, Vol. 21, 1920, pp. 81-86; reference on p. 83.

7 J. B. Browne: Key West, the Old and the New, Miami, Fla., 1912, contains an account and some statistics.

8 Vance, *op. cit.*, p. 21, gives the percentages for 1920 as white, 69.6; negro, 30.4

9 Atwood, *op. cit.*

10 Interviews with Professor H. H. Hume, Agricultural Experiment Station, University of Florida, Gainesville, Fla., March 6 and 7, 1933.

11 Interviews with Professors H. H. Hume and J. E. Turlington, University of Florida, March 7, 1933.

12 Vance, *op. cit.*, pp. 410-441.

13 A. N. J. den Hollander: The Tradition of "Poor Whites," *in* W. T. Couch, edit.: Culture in the South, Chapel Hill, N. C., 1934, pp. 403-431; reference on pp. 430-431. See also the same: De landelijke arme blanken in het Zuiden der Vereenigde Staten, Groningen, etc., 1933 (reviewed in *Geogr. Rev.*, Vol. 26, 1936, pp. 320-321).

[It should be noted that American climatologists and geographers do not regard the South as typically subtropical in character, except perhaps the extreme southern margin. Summer heat is generally more intense in the central part of the United States than in the lower South (M. F. Meyer: "The" South and "The" North, *Science*, N. S., Vol. 80, 1934, pp. 438-439; see also note on "Air-conditioning of Hospitals," *Bull. Amer. Meteorol. Soc.*, Vol. 18, Nos. 6-7, 1937, pp. 243-244).—R. G. S.]

[14] A. E. Parkins: The South: Its Economic-Geographic Development, New York and London, 1938, pp. 212-213; Bertram Schrieke: Alien Americans, New York, 1936, pp. 104-157.

[15] U. B. Phillips: Life and Labor in the Old South, Boston, 1929-1930, p. 35.

[16] Den Hollander, *op. cit.*, p. 426.

[17] C. F. Ahmann, O. D. Abbott, and Georgia Westover: A Nutritional Study of the White School Children in Five Representative Counties of Florida, *University of Florida, Agric Exper. Sta. Bull. 216*, Gainesville, 1930.

[18] See also pp. 217-223, above, and p. 266, note 3, below.

NOTES

CHAPTER VI

THE TRADE-WIND MARGINS: II. QUEENSLAND

[1] For a recent brief discussion of white settlement in the Australian tropics from the medical point of view and with reference to vital statistics and economic problems see James Barrett: White Colonisation in the Tropics, *Comptes Rendus Congrès Internatl. de Géogr., Amsterdam, 1938*, Vol. 2, Section III c, pp. 3-13; and W. W. Williams: The White Man in the Australian Tropics: History of Colonisation, *ibid.*, pp. 337-344. See also Griffith Taylor: Possibilities of Settlement in Australia, *in* Limits of Land Settlement: A Report on Present-day Possibilities, New York, 1937, pp. 195-227; L. H. Pike: White Australia and Tropical Queensland, *Journ. Royal Soc. Arts*, Vol. 86, 1938, pp. 719-739; W. W. Williams: The Bogey of Empty Spaces, *Australian Quarterly*, March, 1937.

[2] *Official Year Book of the Commonwealth of Australia, No. 30*, 1937, p. 34. J. B. Brigden and W. Wynne Williams increase the area of the Queensland tropics and calculate the total area of the Australian tropics as 1,173,008 square miles. (J. B. Brigden and W. W. Williams: Tropical Settlement in Australia, manuscript of a paper prepared for the British Commonwealth Relations Conference, Promoted by the Royal Institute of International Affairs, Sydney, August, 1938, p. 3.)

[3] Letters to W. Wynne Williams from the Director of Agriculture, Ibadan, Nigeria, Feb. 14, 1936; from the Director of General Observations, Poona, India, Feb. 4, 1936; and from the Director of Agriculture and Fishery Service, Batavia, Java, Nov. 25, 1935.

[4] For other recent maps illustrating factors in the Australian climate, see J. A. Prescott: Single Value Climatic Factors, *Trans. Royal Soc. of South Australia*, Vol. 58, 1934, pp. 48-61.

[5] Brigden and Williams, *op. cit.*, p. 1.

[6] See also Dorothy Harwood: The Possibility of White Colonization in the Tropics, *Comptes Rendus*, pp. 131-142; Augustin Lodewyckx: Die weisse Rasse in den australischen Tropen, *ibid.*, pp. 209-222.

[7] James Davidson: Climate in Relation to Insect Ecology in Australia, II, Bioclimatic Zones in Australia, *Trans. and Proc. Royal Soc. of South Australia*, Vol. 60, 1936, pp. 88-92.

[8] W. H. Bryan: The Geological Basis of Queensland Industry, *The Australian Geographer*, Vol. 1, Part 4, 1932, pp. 48-57.

[9] John Andrews: Tropical and Sub-Tropical Agriculture in Coastal Queensland, *The Australian Geographer*, Vol. 1, Part 3, 1931, pp. 62-68.

[10] For descriptions of the region see the following works by Griffith Taylor: The Australian Environment, (*Commonwealth of Australia Advisory Council of Science and Industry, Memoir No. 1*), Melbourne, 1918; Australia in Its Physiographic and Economic Aspects (The Oxford Geographies), 5th edit., Oxford, 1928; A Geography of Australasia, *ibid.*, 1914; also Bryan, *op. cit.*, and Andrews, *op. cit.*

[11] E. O. G. Shann: Economic and Political Development [of Australia], 1860-1885, *in* The Cambridge History of the British Empire, New York and Cambridge, England, Vol. 7, Part 1, 1933, pp. 296-323, particularly p. 310; *idem:* An Economic History of Australia, Cambridge, 1930, pp. 246-248.

[12] R. W. Cilento: Australia's Orientation, *State of Victoria Dept. of Public Health, Health Bull. 35-36*, Melbourne, 1933, pp. 1039-1066; reference on p. 1058.

[13] For the development of this important point see Report of the Federal Health Council of Australia, Fifth Session, Canberra, 1931; Cilento, *op. cit.*; and the same: The White Man in the Tropics, *Commonwealth of Australia Dept. of Health, Service Publ.* (*Tropical Division*) *No. 7*, Melbourne, [1925].

[14] Cilento, The White Man in the Tropics, particularly pp. 86-87.

[15] C. V. Hives: The White Australia Policy, manuscript.

[16] A. Breinl: An Inquiry into the Effect of High Wet Bulb Temperatures upon Pulse Rate, Rectal Temperature, Skin-Shirt Temperature, and Blood Pressure of Wharf Labourers in North Queensland, *Medical Journ. of Australia,* 8th Year, 1921, Vol. 1, pp. 303-312.

[17] It should be noted, however, that in "West of the Pacific" (New York, 1925), pp. 363-365, and in "Season of Birth" (New York, 1938), pp. 187-189, Ellsworth Huntington puts forward death-rate figures for a "standard population" to show that although "taken as whole the people whose *residence* is in Queensland have a very low death-rate, those who were *born* there have a high death-rate."

[18] Professor J. A. Prescott, Waite Agricultural Institute, University of Adelaide, notes (November 23, 1936): "There is one community in tropical Australia that has managed to settle down to family life and make itself comfortable, and that is the pastoral community centered in Charters Towers. The Upper Burdekin, the cattle country south to Mirtna and across the plateaux as far as Hughenden and north to Chudleigh Park, has a number of homesteads and fine families who would probably resent any imputation that they were fit subjects for a special study. These people are in a semi-humid region and there are plateaux up to 2,000 feet in height connecting up along a range probably with Herberton. Winters can be quite cold with severe morning frost at times. The climate along the northern margin as at Croydon is probably very like that of Salisbury, Rhodesia. I have also visited the pastoral people between Meekatharra and Port Hedland (Western Australia)—these people are definitely on an arid fringe. The family units north of the tropic strike me as being less stable and a good deal of reliance is placed on aboriginal labour."

[19] C. V. W. Brown: Some Suggestions on the Prevention of Maternal Morbidity with Special Relation to Queensland, *Medical Journ. of Australia,* 23rd Year, 1936, pp. 529-537.

[19a] [However, it should be noted that Professor C. A. Mills of the University of Cincinnati has recently given much study to the statistics of puberty, menarche, and menstruation in various climates and that his conclusions contradict those stated here (see his papers in *Amer. Journ. of Hygiene,* Vol. 15, 1932, pp. 593-600; *Human Biology,* Vol. 9, 1937, pp. 43-56; and *Archives of Internal Medicine,* Vol. 46, 1930, pp. 921-929).—R. G. S.]

[20] Dr. L. J. Jarvis Nye notes that certain observers in Queensland consider that the tropical sun has a detrimental effect on the Betz cells of the cerebral cortex (conversation with Dr. Nye, Brisbane, April, 1936).

[21] Report of the Sugar Inquiry Committee, *Commonwealth of Australia, Parliamentary Paper No. 240,* Melbourne, 1931, p. 14.

[22] *Ibid.,* p. 13. See also Report of the Royal Commission Appointed to Inquire into and Report on the Social and Economic Effect of Increase in the Number of Aliens in Northern Queensland, Alien Immigration Commission.

[23] Cilento: The White Man in the Tropics, pp. 73-74.

[24] W. W. Williams: Settlement of the Australian Tropics, *Economic Record,* Vol. 11, 1935, pp. 20-34; reference on p. 27.

[25] *Ibid.,* p. 34.

[26] Dr. Ellsworth Huntington stresses the point that coal fields are not essential to manufacture.

[27] Sir George Buchanan: Northern Territory Development and Administration, *Commonwealth of Australia, Parliamentary Paper No. 48,* Melbourne, 1925, p. 10.

NOTES

CHAPTER VII

THE TRADE-WIND ISLANDS OF THE WEST INDIES

[1] Theodore Roosevelt: Land Problems in Puerto Rico and the Philippine Islands, *Geogr. Rev.,* Vol. 24, 1934, pp. 182-204.

[2] Rafael Picó: Geographical and Economic Factors Influencing Puerto Rican Agriculture, *Proc. Pan American Inst. of Geogr. and History, 2nd General Assembly (Department of State Conference Ser. No. 28),* Washington, 1937, pp. 280-288; reference on p. 281. This paper is also published as part of the same author's "Studies in the Economic Geography of Puerto Rico," *Bull. Univ. of Puerto Rico, Ser. 8, No. 1,* 1937, pp. 13-22; reference on p. 14.

[3] *Ibid.,* pp. 282 and 15, respectively.

[4] K. Mixer: Porto Rico, New York, 1926, p. 31.

[5] *Ibid.*, p. 35.

[6] *Ibid.*, p. 41.

[7] J. C. Rosario: The Porto Rican Peasant and His Historical Antecedents, *in* V. S. Clark and others: Porto Rico and Its Problems, The Brookings Institution, Washington, 1930, pp. 537-575; reference on p. 554.

[8] Mixer, *op. cit.*, p. 50.

[9] *Ibid.*, p. 51-52.

[10] Rosario, *op. cit.*, p. 540.

[11] S. J. Crumbine and others: Porto Rico: An Enquiry into the Health, Nutritional and Social Conditions in Porto Rico as They May Affect Children, American Child Health Association, New York (report now in the library of the Russell Sage Foundation, New York), p. 5.

[12] G. J. Miller and A. E. Parkins: Geography of North America, New York, 1934, p. 613.

[13] Crumbine and others, *op. cit.*

[14] Rosario, *op. cit.*, p. 558.

[15] Rosario, *op. cit.*, p. 565. See also Crumbine and others, *op. cit.*

[16] L. H. Jenks: American Rule in Puerto Rico, *in* A. C. Wilgus, edit.: The Caribbean Area, Washington, 1934, pp. 142-157; reference on p. 142.

[17] *Ibid.*, pp. 142-148.

[18] Rosario, *op. cit.*, p. 558.

[19] Jenks, *op. cit.*, p. 144.

[20] *Ibid.*, p. 156.

[21] Mixer, *op. cit.*, p. 222.

[22] Clark and others, *op. cit.*, p. 11. See also W. H. Haas: The Jibaro, an American Citizen, *Scientific Monthly*, Vol. 43, 1936, pp. 33-46.

[23] The writer's observations and interviews in St. Martin, May, 1933.

[24] The section on Saba has been reprinted with a few alterations from the author's article "White Settlement in Saba Island, Dutch West Indies," *Geogr. Rev.*, Vol. 24, 1934, pp. 42-60.

[25] W. M. Davis: The Lesser Antilles, *Amer. Geogr. Soc. Map of Hispanic America Publ. No. 2*, 1926, pp. 35-36.

[26] West Indies Pilot, Vol. 2, *U. S. Hydrogr. Office Publ. No. 129*, 4th edit., Washington, 1929, p. 123. Earlier editions give the altitude as 2820 feet.

[27] J. H. J. Hamelberg: De Nederlanders op de West-Indische Eilanden, Narrative and Documents, Amsterdam, 1903, Narr., p. 18.

[28] J. B. Labat: Nouveau voyage aux isles de l'Amérique . . . . , The Hague, 1724, Vol. 5, pp. 341-345.

[29] G. T. Raynal: A Philosophical and Political History of the Settlements and Trade of the Europeans in the East and West Indies (translated by J. O. Justamond), Dublin, 1784, Vol. 4, pp. 250-251.

[30] C. B. Davenport, Morris Steggerda, and others: Race Crossing in Jamaica, *Carnegie Instn. Publ. No. 395*, Washington, 1929.

[31] The account of the German settlements is largely based on: Wahrhold Drascher: Deutsche Siedlungen auf Jamaika, *Ibero-Amerikanisches Archiv*, Vol. 6, No. 1, 1932, pp. 84-90; republished with other references to German settlements in Jamaica and the West Indies in *The Daily Gleaner*, Kingston, Dec. 17, 1932; Davenport and Steggerda, *op. cit.*, pp. 12-14; the writer's observations and interviews with British officials and doctors and with medical scientists of the Rockefeller Foundation, Jamaica, 1933.

[31a] Drascher, *op. cit.*, p. 88.

[32] Davenport and Steggerda, *op. cit.*, p. 14.

[33] *Ibid.*

[34] Drascher, *op. cit.*, pp. 89-90.

[35] This section is based on official papers of the United States in regard to the Virgin Islands, particularly "General Information Regarding the Virgin Islands of the United States," Dept. of the Interior, Washington, 1932; Lubin Pickwood: Social Survey of the French Settlements at Carenage and the Northside, 1934, manuscript; E. B. Shaw: The Chachas of St. Thomas, *Scientific Monthly*, Vol. 38, 1934, pp. 136-145; the writer's observations during a visit to St. Thomas, May, 1933.

[36] Pickwood, *op. cit.*, p. 12.

[37] Shaw, *op. cit.*, p. 145.

[38] Letter from Administrator, Colonial Secretary's Office, Grenada, Jan. 21, 1935.

[39] Letter from Colonial Secretary, Barbados, Jan. 17, 1935.

[40] In justice to the British it should be noted, however, that their work on behalf of their West Indian peoples has many fine aspects. Figure 32 illustrates the replacement in St. Christopher of disgraceful negro housing by decent and sanitized dwellings.

[41] Davenport and Steggerda, *op. cit.,* pp. 14-17, and the writer's interviews with the Rev. H. Hughes, Jamaican Education Department, Dr. J. M. Hall, Jamaica, and Mr. Webster and his son, of the Cayman Islands.

[42] Davenport and Steggerda, *op. cit.,* p. 17.

[43] *Ibid.,* p. 15.

[44] *Ibid.,* pp. 14-17.

[45] Report of The Lords of the Committee of the Council Appointed for the Consideration of All Matters Relating to Trade and Foreign Plantations, 1788-9, Part 3, Appendix, Evidence No. 2. Paper from Edward Lang, Jamaica, notes the pernicious custom of "dirt eating" brought by imported Africans to Jamaica. The symptoms that follow clearly indicate hookworm.

[46] H. N. Coleridge: Six Months in the West Indies, London, 1832, p. 273.

[47] G. P. Paul: Report on Ankylostomiasis Inspection Survey of Barbados, September 4, 1916–November 16, 1918, International Health Board, Rockefeller Foundation.

[48] *Ibid.,* p. 5.

[49] *Ibid.,* p. 49-50.

[50] *Ibid.,* p. 52.

[51] See also Peter Keenagh: Mosquito Coast: An Account of a Journey Through the Jungles of Honduras, New York, 1938.

[52] Ellsworth Huntington: Civilization and Climate, New Haven, 1915, pp. 14-18.

[53] For causes of the decline other than climate see "The Bahama Islands," Geographical Society of Baltimore, New York, 1905; M. Moseley: The Bahama Handbook, Nassau, 1926. Dr. Huntington points out that the text frequently alludes to the possibility of ethnic differences in origin accounting for some of the contrasts shown by various white groups in similar tropical environments. He believes that his studies show that migration is often accompanied by selective action which manifests itself in the descendants for hundreds of years. For example, a recent study of the Puritans who came to southern New England between 1620 and 1635 and those who came from 1636 onward shows a "remarkable and extraordinary difference." Similar results have been obtained by Australian writers who have studied British emigration to the Commonwealth. Valuable as might be an examination of the differing ethnic, social, and cultural origins of northern white groups in the West Indies, such a study would be extremely difficult, owing to the lack of historical data.

NOTES

CHAPTER VIII

THE ARID AND WET-DRY TROPICS: TROPICAL AUSTRALIA

[1] See above, p. 246, note 1.

[2] [Actually the evaporation is less. These figures give what the evaporation would be if the surface were open water; i.e., the evaporating power or evaporability, as it may be called.—R. G. S.]

[3] Griffith Taylor: Agricultural Regions of Australia, *Econ. Geogr.,* Vol. 6, 1930, pp. 109-134 and 213-242; reference on p. 116.

[4] Bessie Threadgill: South Australian Land Exploration, 1856-1880, (*Historical Compilations Based Upon the Study of Original Documents,* No. 3), Adelaide, 1922, p. 169.

[5] For explorations in northern Australia see bibliographies in The Cambridge History of the British Empire, New York and Cambridge, England, Vol. 7, Part 1, 1933, and Threadgill, *op. cit.*

[6] Ernest Scott: The Exploration of Australia, 1813-1865, *in* The Cambridge History of the British Empire, Vol. 7, Part 1, pp. 95-119; reference on p. 142.

[7] For pastoral development see references in The Cambridge History of the British Empire, Vol. 7, Part 1; S. H. Roberts: History of Australian Land Settlement (1788-1920), Melbourne, 1924; E. O. G. Shann: An Economic History of Australia, Cambridge, 1930; A. G. Price: History and Problems of the Northern Territory, Australia, Adelaide, 1930; and Threadgill, *op. cit.*

[8] F. G. Clapp: In the Northwest of the Australian Desert, *Geogr. Rev.,* Vol 16, 1926, pp. 206-231; reference on p. 209.

[9] See map, Australia, Showing Areas and Months in Which Rainfall Exceeds Evaporation As Determined by Saturation Deficit, *in* James Davidson: The Monthly Precipitation-Evaporation Ratio in Australia, As Determined By Saturation Deficit, *Trans. and Proc. Royal Soc. of South Australia,* Vol. 58, 1934, pp. 33-36, map on p. 36.

[10] A. Despeissis: The Nor'west and Tropical North, Perth, 1921, pp. 8, 34, and Appendix C.

[11] *Ibid.*, p. 43.

[12] W. R. Easton: Report on the Kimberley District of Western Australia, Perth, 1922, p. 32 and 50. Some experienced Australians believe that the East Kimberley division and the Victoria River area are more suitable for sheep than the Barkly Tableland, as they have more undulating country and more shelter.

[13] Despeissis, *op. cit.*, p. 43.

[14] Census of the Commonwealth of Australia, Part 5, Canberra, 1933.

[15] Royal Commission on Meat Industry in Western Australia, *Western Australia, 13th Parliament, 3rd Session,* Vol. 1, Perth, 1928, pp. v-xxiv.

[16] References to soil and agriculture in Price, *op. cit.*

[17] Griffith Taylor: The Australian Environment, *Commonwealth of Australia, Advisory Council of Science and Industry, Memoir No. 1,* Melbourne, 1918, pp. 67-68. Professor J. A. Prescott of the Waite Agricultural Institute, Adelaide, notes (December 23, 1936) that this quotation from Taylor "represents a theory of soil formation which is still held by some, but which is being increasingly challenged. . . .The main thing is that tropical countries have their due measure of poor soils." He considers that Australians have never fully realized the implications of the soil and climatic conditions of the Northern Territory. They have always thought of plantation crops instead of dry-farming crops so common in the corresponding parts of India and Africa. Unfortunately, the crops so produced are not usually considered to be white man's food, and with modern transport Australians are less likely to emulate the Pilgrim Fathers in discovering a crop like maize from which to make corn cakes in the absence of wheat.

[18] Letter from Director of Agriculture, Bombay Presidency, Poona, India, to W. Wynne Williams, February 4, 1936.

[19] For details see Price, *op. cit.*, p. 47.

[20] W. W. Williams: The Settlement of the Australian Tropics, *The Economic Record,* Vol. 11, pp. 20-34; references on pp. 27-28.

[21] Letter from the Director of Agriculture, Ibadan, Nigeria, to W. Wynne Williams, Bureau of Industry, Brisbane, February 14, 1936. Professor J. A. Prescott, who is studying comparative climatic conditions in the Australian and Nigerian tropics, is already convinced that the Australian rainfall is less reliable than the Nigerian.

[22] Letter from Director of Agriculture, Bombay Presidency, Poona, India, to W. Wynne Williams, February 4, 1936.

[23] Report of the Board of Inquiry Appointed to Inquire into the Land and Land Industries of the Northern Territory of Australia, Canberra, 1937, p. 77.

[24] Williams, *op. cit.*, pp. 28-30.

[25] R. B. Kelley: Zebu (Brahman) Cross Cattle and their Possibilities in North Australia, *Commonwealth Council for Scientific and Industrial Research, Pamphlet No. 27,* Melbourne, 1932, p. 33.

[26] Report of the Board of Inquiry.

[27] Williams, *op. cit.*, pp. 29-31.

[28] Price, *op. cit.*, p. 51, and *idem:* Pioneer Reactions to a Poor Tropical Environment, *Geogr. Rev.,* Vol. 23, 1933, pp. 353-371; reference on p. 364.

[29] Sir W. Denison to Sir E. B. Lytton, April 6, 1859, quoted in Shann, *op. cit.*, p. 236.

[30] Brigden and Williams estimate the number of aboriginal full bloods in the Australian tropics as follows: Queensland tropics, 11,303; Northern Territory, 17,422; Western Australia, 15,458; total, 44,183 (J. B. Brigden and W. W. Williams: Tropical Settlement in Australia, manuscript of a paper prepared for the British Commonwealth Relations Conference, Sydney, August, 1938, p. 3).

[31] Price, Pioneer Reactions to a Poor Tropical Environment, pp. 361-363.

[32] See, however, above, p. 247, note 19a.

[33] Report of the Administration of North Australia, Parliamentary Papers, Vol. 4, 1930, pp. 417-448.

NOTES

CHAPTER IX

TROPICAL PLATEAUS: I. COSTA RICA AND SOUTH AMERICA

[1] Costa Rica, Union of American Republics, Washington, 1931; A. C. Wilgus, edit.: Studies in Hispanic American Affairs (Vol. 1: Modern Hispanic America; Vol. 2: The Caribbean Area; particularly R. R. Hill: Geographic and Historic Background of Central America), Washington, 1934; Ricardo Fernández Guardia: History of the

Discovery and Conquest of Costa Rica, New York, 1913, p. 2; Karl Sapper: Klima-kunde von Mittelamerika (W. Köppen and R. Geiger, edits.: Handbuch der Klima-tologie, Vol. 2, Part H), Berlin, 1932, p. 64.

[2] These data on the history and population of Costa Rica are based in part on the works of Fernández Guardia, Jones, and Wilgus; also on the author's interviews with Don Ricardo Fernández Guardia, Don Cleto Gonzáles Víquez, Dr. Solon Nuñez, Señor José Guerrero, Señor Gonzales de Zeledon, and British and American agents in Costa Rica. Statistics are from *Anuario Estadistico,* Direccion General de Estadistica, Costa Rica, Vol. 33, 1929, San José, 1930; Compendio Estadistico, 1932; and Poblacion de la Republica de Costa Rica, *Costa Rica Oficina Nacional del Censo, Publ. No. 2,* San José, 1927.

[3] Luciano Beeche: Tropical Diseases of Costa Rica, *Proc. Internatl. Conference on Health Problems in Tropical America,* Boston, 1934, p. 573 (quoted from C. L. Jones: Costa Rica and Civilization in the Caribbean, *Univ. of Wisconsin Studies in the Soc. Sciences and Hist., No. 23,* Madison, 1935).

[4] León Fernández: Collección de documentos para la historia de Costa Rica, Vol. 7, Barcelona, 1907, pp. 258-286.

[5] Cleto Gonzáles Víquez: President's Message, May 3, 1931, quoted by Jones, *op. cit.,* p. 63.

[6] The data on health are based on the interviews cited in note 2 and with doctors of the Rockefeller Foundation in Costa Rica; see also Jones, *op. cit.,* and H. R. Carter: Yellow Fever; An Epidemiological and Historical Study of Its Place of Origin, Baltimore, 1931. Statistics are from sources cited in note 2 and from Estadistica Vital (1906-1925). *Costa Rica Oficina Nacional del Censo, Publ. No. 1,* San José, 1927.

[7] Jones, *op. cit.,* p. 133.

[8] *Ibid.,* p. 46.

[9] J. Guerrero in *La Tribuna,* San José, August 13, 1930.

[10] *Ibid.,* April 10, 1934.

[11] For recent discussions see: Isaiah Bowman: Possibilities of Settlement in South America, *in* Limits of Land Settlement, Council on Foreign Relations, New York, 1937; also H. v. Freeden: Über Möglichkeiten der Kolonisation für die weisse Rasse in der tropischen Zone, *Comptes rendus, Congrès Internatl. de Géogr. Amsterdam, 1938,* Vol. 2, Section III c, pp. 111-121 (deals primarily with the American tropics); P. Cool: De hollandsche boerenkolonisatie in Nederlandsch Guyana, *ibid.,* pp. 30-32; W. R. Menkman: Les Pays-Bas et le problème de la colonisation de blancs sous les tropiques, *ibid.,* pp. 246-254; Th. Lens: Deux colonisations de blancs aux Indes Occidentales, *ibid.,* pp. 192-198 (mainly on Curaçao); E. F. Verkade-Cartier van Dissel: De mogelijk-heid van volksplantingen door blanken in de tropen, *ibid.,* pp. 74-86. The last three references deal mainly with Surinam (Netherlands, Guiana). See also note 13, below.

For details concerning the establishment of settlements in South America by colonists from the Confederate States at the time of the American Civil War, see: Mark Jefferson: An American Colony in Brazil, *Geogr. Rev.,* Vol. 18, 1928, pp. 226-231, and L. F. Hill: Confederate Exiles to Brazil, *Hisp. Amer. Hist. Rev.,* Vol. 7, 1927, pp. 192-210.

[12] J. W. Gregory: The Menace of Colour, London, 1925, p. 112.

[13] C. F. Jones: South American Economic Prospects and Possibilities, *in* A. C. Wilgus, edit.: Modern Hispanic America, Washington, 1932, pp. 139-155; reference on p. 151. [It should be noted, however, that Dutch farmers who settled in the low equatorial tropics near Paramaribo, Surinam, in 1849 have met with some degree of economic success and, although not altogether healthy, show few signs of degeneration even to the fourth and fifth generations. This community is discussed in an important, de-tailed, and critical study by E. F. Verkade-Cartier van Dissel: De mogelijkheid van landbouw-kolonisatie voor blanken in Suriname, Amsterdam, 1937.—EDIT.]

[14] Isaiah Bowman: South America (Lands and Peoples Ser.), Chicago, 1915, map facing p. 317.

[15] *Ibid.,* pp. 306-308.

[16] H. W. Bates: The Naturalist on the River Amazons, London, 1875, pp. 260-261.

[17] R. Nash: The Conquest of Brazil, New York, 1926, p. 38.

[18] W. S. Robertson: History of the Latin American Nations, New York, 1925, p. 86.

[19] Mark Jefferson: Recent Colonization in Chile, *Amer. Geogr. Soc. Research Ser. No. 6,* 1921, p. 3.

[20] Bartolomé Mitre: Historia de Belgrano y de la independencia Argentina, 6th edit. Buenos Aires, 1913; Vol. 1, p. 9.

[21] H. G. James: Brazil After a Century of Independence, New York, 1925, p. 260.

[22] R. H. Whitbeck: Economic Geography of South America, 2nd edit., New York, 1931, p. 26.

23 Gregory, *op. cit.*, p. 115.

24 C. F. Jones: South America, New York, 1930, pp. 423-437.

25 L. L. Bernard and J. S. Bernard: The Negro in Relation to Other Races in Latin America, *Annals Amer. Acad. of Polit. Sci.*, Vol. 140, 1928, pp. 306-318; reference on p. 317.

26 P. Sorokin: Contemporary Sociological Theories, New York, 1928, p. 297.

27 *Ibid.*, p. 298.

28 G. M. McBride: The Agrarian Indian Communities of Highland Bolivia, *Amer. Geogr. Soc. Research Ser. No. 5*, New York, 1921, pp. 11-12.

29 A. A. Adams: The Plateau Peoples of South America, London, 1915, pp. 86-87. [An excellent review of this question appears in D. B. Dill: Life, Heat and Altitude, Cambridge, Mass., 1938, pp. 144-174.—R. G. S.]

30 *West Coast Leader*, Mar. 3, 1925, p. 17. On white settlement in Brazil, see Pierre Deffontaines: La population blanche au Brésil, *Comptes rendus*, pp. 33-37; Otto Fischer: Kann der Mensch weisser Rasse in tropischen Ländern leben?, *ibid.*, pp. 87-100; G. Königk: Das Deutschtum in Brasilien, *Auslandsdeutsche Volksforschung*, Vol. 1, 1937, pp. 311-318.

31 O. M. Miller: The 1927-1928 Peruvian Expedition of the American Geographical Society, *Geogr. Rev.*, Vol. 19, 1929, pp. 1-37; reference on pp. 28-29. The experiences of German colonists in the tropics are considered by various authors, for example, by Dietzel, Fischer, Freeden, Jaeger, Karstedt, Lindequist, Lufft, Niedermayer, Sapper, and Ziemann, in the *Comptes rendus.*

32 *West Coast Leader*, April 7 and 28, 1925.

33 *Ibid.*, February 19, 1924.

34 Interview with R. R. Platt at the American Geographical Society, New York, December 10, 1932.

35 For Ford's experiment see: Fordlandia, Brazil, *Bull. of the Pan Amer. Union*, Vol. 67, 1933, pp. 4-15; reference on p. 11.

36 Interviews with G. Cutter, President of the United Fruit Company, and Dr. R. C. Connor, Medical Officer, Boston and New York, 1932. F. U. Adams: The Conquest of the Tropics, New York, 1914, and S. Crowther: The Romance and Rise of the American Tropics, New York, 1919, contain popular accounts of the company's work.

NOTES

CHAPTER X

TROPICAL PLATEAUS: II. AFRICA

1 For recent discussions see J. H. Wellington: Possibilities of Settlement in Africa, *in* Limits of Land Settlement, Council on Foreign Relations, New York, 1937, pp. 229-291; the same: Some Geographical Aspects of the Peopling of Africa, *South African Journ. of Sci.*, Vol. 34, 1937, pp. 29-60; also Daniel Hall: The Possibilities of Colonisation in Africa by the White Races, *Comptes rendus, Congrès Internatl. de Géogr.*, Amsterdam, 1938, Vol. 2, Section III c, pp. 122-124; M. M. Moreno: Le possibilita' di colonizzazione a mezzo della razza bianca nella zona tropicale (Sunto), *ibid.*, pp. 255-261 (deals mainly with Italian territory).

2 C. Southworth: The French Colonial Venture, London, 1931, pp. 26-27.

3 Sir Harry Johnston: Africa (Britain Across the Seas), London, 1910, p. 263.

4 W. C. Willoughby: Race Problems of the New Africa, Oxford, 1920, p. 149.

5 Sir Charles Lucas: Introduction, The Cambridge History of the British Empire, New York and Cambridge, England, Vol. 1, 1929, pp. 1-21; reference on p. 17.

6 H. C. Darby: Pioneer Problems in Rhodesia and Nyasaland, *in* Pioneer Settlement, *Amer. Geogr. Soc. Special Publ. No. 14*, New York, 1932, pp. 192-220; reference on pp. 192-193.

7 [See M. Mackinnon: European Children in the Tropical Highlands, *The Lancet*, Vol. 199, 1920, p. 944; E. Weigt: Die Kolonisation Kenias, Leipzig, 1932; Oskar Karstedt: Die Möglichkeiten der Kolonisation Ostafrikas durch Weisse, in *Comptes rendus*, pp. 171-180; Max Salvadori: White Settlement in the Colonial Territories of the Tropics, *ibid.*, pp. 305-316; Karl Sapper: Über die Möglichkeit der Besiedlung der Tropen durch die weisse Rasse, *ibid.*, pp. 317-326; and also the very frank and sane paper by A. Walter: Climate and White Settlement in East African Highlands, *East African Medical Journ.*, Vol. 11, 1934, pp. 210-225. Walter begs for more research, for better selection of types of peoples suited for the colony, and for more sensible clothing habits and buildings; he also implies that the possibilities for alleviating the disadvantages of the climate through science have hardly been touched and

that the resources of the colony would make the effort worth while. A rather extensive series of instrumental observations of the solar radiation and the cooling power made for a year in Kenya by Gertrud Riemerschmid are discussed by H. Machetanz: Zur Klimatologie des tropischen Hochlandes von Kenya (Ostafrika), *Bioklimatische Beiblätter*, Vol. 4, 1937, pp. 66-72. Miss Riemerschmid used the Pfleiderer-Büttner frigorigraph in Kenya for six months, December 1934 to May 1935; judged by Pfleiderer's "sensation scale" determined at Kiel, Germany, all these months were "comfortable" by midday and "cool" at night. Owing to acclimatization and other differences it is a question whether the Kiel scale is strictly applicable at Nairobi. At any rate these results show that Nairobi has a comfortable climate from December to May and that the daily range of cooling power is about five times as great as the seasonal range. The extreme high values were only "warm" according to the above-mentioned scale, and these occurred on only 21 per cent of the hours between 7 a. m. and 6 p. m. for the whole six months! The scale applies only to naked or lightly clothed persons at rest; for exercise the scale would be shifted one whole step toward the less comfortable—"comfortable" would become "warm," etc. The radiation intensities are very high, but the author thinks they should be of prophylactic and heliotherapeutic value. See p. 261, note 30, below.

See also T. W. Wallbank: American Reflections on Kenya, *Suppl. to Journ. Royal Afr. Soc.*, Vol. 37, 1938; H. B. Thomas and R. Scott: Uganda, London, 1935; K. Arning, edit.: Deutsche Ostafrica, Gestern und Heute, Berlin, 1936.—R. G. S.]

[8] Dr. A. M. Fleming in a note published by Dr. A. Balfour, 1923, quoted in Gregory, *op. cit.*, p. 143.

[9] W. M. Hewetson: Environmental Influences Affecting Blondes in Rhodesia and Their Bearing on the Future, Salisbury and London, 1922, p. 4.

[10] *Ibid.*, pp. 10-11.

[11] Joint Select Committee of the Lords and Commons on Closer Union in East Africa: Papers Relating to the Question of the Closer Union of Kenya, Uganda and the Tanganyika Territory, *Colonial Office No. 57*, London, 1931.

[12] Hewetson, *op. cit.*, p. 15.

[13] Joint Select Committee, Papers, p. 31, quoting from Sir Daniel Hall, in an address to the Royal Society of Arts. See, for example, E. G. Malherbe: Education and the Poor White, *South African Journ. of Sci.*, Vol. 26, 1929, pp. 888-903; reference on p. 893. Dr. Malherbe notes that the white is prepared to dig but not in the employment of another.

[14] Joint Select Committee, Papers, p. 31.

[15] Darby, *op. cit.*, p. 213. See also E. G. Malherbe: Education and the Poor White (The Poor White Problem in South Africa: Report of the Carnegie Commission, Vol. 3), Stellenbosch, 1932, p. 295.

[16] Hewetson, *op. cit.*, p. 21.

[17] *Ibid.*

[18] *Ibid.*, p. 24.

[19] Joint Select Committee, Papers, p. 704. This statement applies, of course, to the high plateaus and not to the low hot plains.

[20] R. L. Buell: The Native Problem in Africa, Bur. of Internatl. Research of Harvard Univ. and Radcliffe College, New York, 1928, Vol. 1, pp. 527-528.

[21] Dr. E. G. Malherbe, officer in charge of the National Bureau of Education, Pretoria, South Africa, who has been kind enough to read and comment upon the manuscript of this work, disputes the accuracy of this statement.

[22] Darby, *op. cit.*, p. 219.

[23] *Ibid.*, p. 220.

[24] Hewetson, *op. cit.*, p. 27. L. S. Norman, writing from Luchenza, Nyasaland, February 25, 1935, stresses the influence of the native as a reservoir of diseases such as malaria and emphasizes the low moral and ethical sense of the native, particularly as regards theft. He alleges that in some areas the whites cannot grow the same crops as the natives owing to the fact that the pilfering is so frequent.

[25] Indians in Kenya: Memorandum, Cmd. 1922, London, 1923, p. 10. (This document is generally referred to as the "White Paper of 1923.")

[26] Future Policy in Regard to Eastern Africa, Cmd. 2904, London, 1927, p. 7.

[27] Memorandum on Native Policy in East Africa, Cmd. 3573, London, 1930.

[28] On this complex problem see also L. P. Mair: Native Policies in Africa, London, 1936, pp. 77-100, and the detailed and comprehensive discussion by M. R. Dilley: British Policy in Kenya Colony, New York, 1937, particularly pp. 179-208 and 275-285. Dilley makes it clear that the official pronouncements from London cannot invariably be taken at their face value. "Official policy might provide that native interests constituted a trust which required that their interests should receive first attention and serve as a guide to general policy, but such procedure has never been followed" (*ibid.*, p. 279).

29 Wellington, Possibilities of Settlement in Africa, pp. 255-256.

30 Some authorities—for example, Dr. Malherbe—consider that some of these white communities, particularly those of Rhodesia, will survive (conversation, Adelaide, June 5, 1937).

31 Dr. Malherbe differentiates between the British and South African points of view. In his opinion, the *Grond-wet* was a safeguard against social equality in so far as it might lead to miscegenation, which was utterly abhorrent to the Boer mentality. It was also a protest against the point of view of the London Missionary Society, one of whose leading missioners married a black woman. In Dr. Malherbe's opinion the British were socially much more free in their association with the blacks than were the Boers.

32 Willoughby, *op. cit.*, pp. 220-221. Dr. Malherbe notes that this legislation came from the trade unions, which were predominantly English. The English feared economic competition, and, although socially liberal, had no compunction in downing the natives economically. The Dutch were in general tolerant and at least indifferent in the matter of economic competition, as they were not artisans by tradition.

33 *Ibid.*, pp. 233-235.

34 See L. Curtis and M. Perham: The Protectorates of South Africa, Oxford, 1935.

35 General Hertzog: Speech at mass meeting at Potchefstroom, June 4, 1924, reported in the *Glasgow Herald* and quoted by Gregory, *op. cit.*, p. 133.

36 C. T. Loram: Native Labor in Southern Africa, *in* Pioneer Settlement, pp. 169-177; reference on p. 169.

37 J. H. Wellington: Pioneer Settlement in the Union of South Africa, *in* Pioneer Settlement, pp. 146-168; reference on p. 161.

38 Willoughby, *op. cit.*, pp. 198-199.

39 See Report of Colored Commission in South Africa, 1936.

40 Director of the Census of 1921, quoted by R. L. Buell: Black and White in South Africa, *Annals, Amer. Acad. of Polit. and Soc. Sci.* Vol. 140, 1928, pp. 299-305; reference on p. 304. Dr. Malherbe notes, however, that this viewpoint has been criticized by Professor J. du Plessis. Subsequent census figures seem to indicate that the conclusions from the 1921 census were incorrect.

41 The Poor White Problem in South Africa: Report of the Carnegie Commission (5 vols. on economics, psychology, education, health, and sociology), Stellenbosch, 1932.

42 *Ibid.*, Vol. 4, pp. v-xi. Dr. E. G. Malherbe considers that the South African system of subdividing landholdings among the children of the owners and so continuously reducing the size of the holdings is a main cause of the "poor-white problem" and that for similar reasons a "poor native problem" is evolving.

43 *Ibid.*, p. 86.

44 *Ibid.*, p. xiv.

45 *Ibid.*, p. xiv.

46 *Ibid.*, p. xxiv.

47 *Ibid.*, pp. xviii-xix.

48 *Ibid.*, p. xx. Dr. Malherbe comments: "but only in those few specific spots where there is propinquity of dwelling."

49 Dr. Malherbe notes, however, that entirely different causes are creating the problems on the African tropical plateaus and in South Africa. He considers that in the latter region the poor whites originated largely on account of a wrong tradition and that climate and racial contacts were only contributing factors.

50 Wellington, Possibilities of Settlement in Africa, pp. 229-291.

51 *Ibid.*, pp. 279-285.

52 T. A. Barnes: Angolan Sketches, London, 1928, p. 168.

NOTES

CHAPTER XI

THE AMERICANS IN PANAMA

1 C. F. Mason: Sanitation in the Panama Canal Zone, *in* G. W. Goethals: The Panama Canal, New York, 1916, Vol. 1, pp. 85-116; reference on p. 85.

2 H. R. Carter: Yellow Fever: An Epidemiological and Historical Study of Its Place of Origin, Baltimore, 1931, p. 21.

3 W. P. Chamberlain: The Health Department of the Panama Canal, *New England Journ. of Medicine,* Vol. 203, 1930, pp. 669-680; reference on p. 670.

[4] W. P. Chamberlain: Twenty Five Years of American Medical Activity on the Isthmus of Panama, 1904-1929, Mt. Hope, C. Z., 1929. [See also J. S. Simmons: The U. S. Army's War Against Mosquito-Borne Disease, *Amer. Journ. of the Medical Sci.,* Vol. 196, 1938, pp. 153-166 (contains instructive graphs on malaria in the Canal Zone). Of interest in this general connection is E. B. Vedder: A Synopsis of the Work of the Army Medical Research Boards in the Philippines, 1900-1928, *Army Medical Bull.,* Carlisle Barracks, Pa., 1929.—R. G. S.]

[5] Chamberlain, Twenty Five Years of American Medical Activity, p. 16, and Report of the Health Department, Panama Canal, 1931, Mt. Hope, C. Z., 1932, p. 35.

[6] Dr. Huntington criticizes the use of crude death rates made on this and the following pages. He notes: "The white death rate in Panama, if real, would indicate an average life of 150-300 years."

[7] R. P. Ashton: Some Lessons in Sanitation from the Panama Canal Zone, *Trans. Mining and Geol. Inst. of India,* Vol. 7, 1912-1913, pp. 176-216; reference on p. 204.

[8] Chamberlain, Twenty Five Years of American Medical Activity, p. 9.

[9] Mason, *op. cit.,* p. 114.

[10] *Ibid.*

[11] R. E. Wood: The Working Force of the Panama Canal, *in* Goethals, *op. cit.,* pp. 189-204; Extracts from the Hearings of the Committees on Appropriations of the Senate and House of Representatives Relative to Pay, Allowances, Health and Other Conditions of Employment of Skilled Labor on the Panama Canal, 63rd Congress, 2nd Session, Washington, 1914, p. 404 (evidence of Goethals).

[12] W. R. Scott: The Americans in Panama, New York, 1913, p. 193. The term "gold" employees refers to the Americans whose salaries were paid in gold, "silver" employees to the common and unskilled laborers, who received their wages in silver (Wood, *op. cit.,* p. 189).

[13] For southern Europeans see Wood, *op. cit.;* Cornish, *op. cit.;* Extracts from the Hearings of the Committees on Appropriations; and *Canal Record,* Oct. 28, 1914. Information was also furnished the writer by P. S. Wilson, Inspector of European labor during the construction period, Ancon, March 29, 1933.

[14] W. E. Deeks and W. M. James: A Report on Hemoglobinuric Fever in the Canal Zone: A Study of Its Etiology and Treatment, Dept. of Sanitation, Isthmian Canal Commission, Ancon, 1911, p. 12.

[15] Interviews at Madden Dam, Panama, April 4, 1933.

[16] Interview with P. S. Wilson.

[17] Wood, *op. cit.,* p. 196.

[18] Interview with P. S. Wilson.

[19] Vaughan Cornish: The Panama Canal and Its Makers, London, 1909, p. 107.

[20] See references in previous notes; also "Repatriating Laborers" (*Canal Record,* Oct. 28, 1914).

[21] Annual Report Isthmian Canal Commission, 1906 (quoted in Cornish, *op. cit.,* p. 102).

[22] H. W. Durham: Preliminary Municipal Engineering at Panama, *in* Goethals, *op. cit.,* pp. 117-125; reference on p. 135.

[23] Wood, *op. cit.,* p. 199.

[24] Annual Report of the Governor of the Panama Canal, Washington, 1932, p. 68.

[25] The Canal Diggers in Panama, Panama Canal Retirement Assn., Canal Zone, 1928, pp. 39-40.

[26] Report of the Survey of the Schools of the Panama Canal Zone, Columbia University, Mount Hope, C. Z., p. 202.

[27] Interview, Ancon, April 4, 1933.

[28] Canal Diggers in Panama, p. 44.

[29] Interview with Dr. George Eugene, who, with the authority of the Chief Health Officer, supplied evidence in hearings before the Committee on Interstate and Foreign Commerce, House of Rep. 67th Congress, 1922-1923. See also pp. 30-31, 73-74, above, for Edward's and Cilento's descriptions of tropical whites.

[30] Interview with Dr. H. Clark, Director, Gorgas Memorial Institute, Panama.

[31] Dr. Ellsworth Huntington considers that these sections presenting white births and deaths, and also the section on white children, do not stress sufficiently the highly selected character of the Canal population. This population is obviously highly selected. It includes comparatively small percentages of old and young people, and the standard of the children is high, owing to the fact that their parents form a group possessing high mentality and physical vigor. Dr. Huntington's criticisms indicate the need of further and more detailed research on this subject.

[32] The Census of 1930 showed that there were 2812 white and 7347 colored children in the Canal Zone, in the following age groups:

Age	White	Colored
1-4	712	1973
5	162	....
6	169	501
7	193	537
8	199	550
9	199	582
10	171	601
11	150	529
12	176	564
13	145	536
14	122	493
15	146	481
16	143	....
17	125	....
Total	2812	7347

[33] Report, p. 10.
[34] Ibid., p. 79.
[35] Deeks and James, op. cit., p. 12.
[36] Report, p. 33.
[37] Report of the Health Department, Panama Canal, 1930, p. 13, and interview with Dr. Kamp, Ancon, 1933.
[38] Annual Report of the Governor of the Panama Canal, 1932, p. 80.
[39] G. J. P. Barger: Living in Congoland, manuscript.
[40] West Africa, Vital Statistics of Non-Native Officials, Returns for 1932, Crown Agent for the Colonies, London. Similar trends appear in: East Africa, Vital Statistics of European Officials, London, 1931.

NOTES

CHAPTER XII

RACIAL PROBLEMS

[1] J. S. Huxley and A. C. Haddon: We Europeans, New York, 1936, pp. vii-viii.
[2] Ibid., p. 220.
[3] Ibid., p. 84.
[4] Aleš Hrdlička: Human Races, in E. V. Cowdry, edit.: Human Biology and Racial Welfare, New York, 1930, pp. 156-183; reference on p. 159. Dr. I. F. Phipps, Waite Agricultural Research Institute, University of Adelaide, notes, however, that predisposition to and immunity from a number of diseases are definitely inherited.
[5] H. S. Jennings: The Biological Basis of Human Nature, Boston, 1926, p. 284.
[6] A. J. Toynbee: A Study of History, Oxford, 1934, Vol. 1, p. 233.
[7] Pitirim Sorokin: Contemporary Sociological Theories, New York, 1928, p. 293.
[8] Gordon Harrower, Professor of Anatomy at Singapore, considers that Chinese and Tamil medical students are little inferior to white (interview, December, 1929).
[9] See pp. 112-135, above.
[10] C. B. Davenport and Morris Steggerda: Race Crossing in Jamaica, Carnegie Institution of Washington Publ. No. 395, Washington, 1929.
[11] E. A. Hooton: Up from the Ape, London, 1931, p. 596.
[12] [On the whole field of geographical psychology see Willy Hellpach: Geopsyche, Leipzig, 4th edit., 1935. See also his article "Generelle Erkenntnisse zur Individual- u. Sozial-, Rassen- u. Völkerpsychologie der kolonisatorischen Akklimatisation," Comptes rendus, Congrès Internatl. de Geogr., Amsterdam, 1938, Vol. 2, Section III c, pp. 143-154.—R. G. S.]
[13] Sir Aldo Castellani: Climate and Acclimatization, 2nd edit., London, 1938, pp. 122-144. See also H. J. Fleure: The Characters of the Human Skin in Their Relations to Questions of Race and Health, Oxford, 1927. [There is also a good review in E. R. Stitt: Diagnostics and Treatment of Tropical Diseases, 5th edit., Philadelphia, 1929, Appendix on "Tropical Hygiene," pp. 831-902. For an authoritative detailed review of the technical aspects of pigmentation see H. Laurens: Sunlight and Health, Scientific Monthly, Vol. 42, 1936, pp. 312-324. See also the same: Physiological Effects of

Radiant Energy, New York, 1933; K. W. Hausser: Strahlung und Lichterythem, Leipzig, 1934. The physical relation of solar radiation to the skin, apart from purely therapeutic questions, is well treated by K. Büttner in his "Physikalische Bioklimatologie," Leipzig, 1938, pp. 6-68.—R. G. S.]

[14] Castellani, *op. cit.*, p. 135.

[15] W. P. Chamberlain: Some Features of the Physiologic Activity of Americans in the Philippines, *Amer. Journ. of Tropical Diseases*, Vol. 1, 1913, pp. 12-32; see conclusions on p. 29. [Recent studies suggest an increase in red-cell count in the tropics, however. Sundstroem reviews all the evidence down to 1927 in "Physiological Effects of Tropical Climates," *Physiological Rev.*, Vol. 7, 1927, pp. 343-344.—R. G. S.]

[16] Castellani, *op. cit.*, p. 133. [See also A. Loewy and C. Dorno: Über Haut- und Körpertemperaturen und ihre Beeinflussung durch physikalische Reize, *Strahlentherapie*, Vol. 20, 1925, pp. 411-431.—R. G. S.]

[17] Castellani, *op. cit.*, p. 134.

[18] [For a thorough discussion of the physiology of sweating and the racial differences therein see Yas Kuno: The Physiology of Human Perspiration, London, 1934. Some more recent studies, by Dill, are summarized in Chapter XV and in Appendix I, below.—R. G. S.]

[19] Castellani, *op. cit.*, p. 132.

[20] For references to the publications upon which this discussion is largely based see above, note 13.

[21] [For experiences of Portuguese in Africa see C. R. Machado de Faria e Maia: Les possibilités de la colonisation par la race blanche dans la zone tropicale, *Comptes rendus*, pp. 223-233.—R. G. S.]

[22] See above, pp. 46-47, 62-63, and 72.

[23] See above pp. 84-100.

[24] See above pp. 158-160.

[25] See above pp. 136-145. [For a trenchant comment on the colored labor question in Africa see Sir Daniel Hall: The Possibilities of Colonisation in Africa by the White Races, *Comptes rendus*, pp. 122-124.—R. G. S.]

[26] Castellani, *op. cit.*, p. 6.

[27] A. M. Carr-Saunders: World Population, Oxford, 1936, p. 171.

[28] Jennings, *op. cit.*, p. 269.

[29] *Ibid.*, Chapter XII.

[30] Hrdlička, *op. cit.*, pp. 176-177.

[31] Davenport and Steggerda, *op. cit.*, p. 471.

[32] Jennings, *op. cit.*, p. 285.

[33] C. B. Davenport: The Mingling of Races, *in* Cowdry, *op. cit.*, pp. 553-565; reference on pp. 560-563.

[34] *Ibid.*

[35] *Ibid.*, p. 561.

[36] Jennings, *op. cit.*, p. 287.

[37] Dr. Jarvis Nye of Queensland considers that this statement does not hold good for white-Chinese crosses.

[38] Huxley and Haddon, *op. cit.*, p. 231.

[39] *Ibid.*, p. 235.

[40] Davenport and Steggerda, *op. cit.*, p. 472.

[41] C. B. Davenport: Race Crossing in Jamaica, *Scientific Monthly*, Vol. 27, 1928, pp. 225-238; reference on p. 237.

[42] See above, pp. 69-70, 90-91.

[43] L. Symes: What About Hawaii?, *Harper's Magazine*, Vol. 165, 1932, pp. 529-539; reference on p. 535.

[44] S. D. Porteus and M. E. Babcock: Temperament and Race, New York, 1926; L. C. Dunn: An Anthropometric Study of Hawaiians of Mixed Blood, *Peabody Museum Papers*, Vol. 11, No. 3, 1928; K. O. Moe: Problems of Social Adjustment in Hawaii, *Interocean*, Vol. 9, 1928, pp. 319-323; H. L. Shapiro: Race Mixture in Hawaii, *Natural History*, Vol. 31, 1931, pp. 31-48; A. W. Lind: Occupational Trends Among Immigrant Groups in Hawaii, *Social Forces*, Vol. 7, 1928, pp. 290-299; and R. C. Adams: The Peoples of Hawaii, Institute of Pacific Relations, Honolulu, 1925.

[45] H. L. Shapiro: Robinson Crusoe's Children, *Natural History*, Vol. 28, 1928, pp. 290-301; *idem:* Descendants of the Mutineers of the Bounty (*Memoirs of the Bernice P. Bishop Museum*, Vol. 11, No. 1) Honolulu, 1929; and *idem:* The Heritage of the Bounty, New York, 1936.

[46] See note "The Peoples of Norfolk Island," *Geogr. Rev.*, Vol. 20, 1930, pp. 679-680; also E. E. Muntz: Race Contact, New York, 1937.

NOTES

CHAPTER XIII

SOME ENVIRONMENTAL FACTORS

[1] G. H. Pitt Rivers: The Clash of Culture and the Contact of Races, London, 1927, pp. 86-100; reference on p. 86.

[2] As, for example, the recent emigration of 187 Danes to Venezuela reported in the *New York Times* for June 5, 1938.

[3] On the important question of humus in tropical (hot, wet) soils, see A. S. Corbet: Biological Processes in Tropical Soils, Cambridge, England, 1935. [The poverty of the soil with respect to various minerals may have a serious influence upon the mineral content of the food crops and in turn upon the health of the people. Dumont has written strong polemics to the effect that the Belgian Congo (especially Kivu, Ruanda, Ituri, Katanga, Loami, Uele) will never become a populous colony unless the soil is fertilized to make up for its calcium deficiency, which leads to great weaknesses in the present population subsisting on the local food plants (Robert Dumont: Série de cinq articles ayant trait à des constatations d'ordre médical faites en 1931-1932 dans le Kwango (Congo Belge), Brussels, 1937; reprinted from *Bull. Médical du Katanga*, 1935, *L'Avenir Coloniale Belge*, 1935, and *Rév. d'Hygiène et de Médicine Tropicale*, 1937).—R. G. S.]

[4] L. A. Wolfanger: Major Soil Groups and Some of Their Geographic Implications, *Geogr. Rev.*, Vol. 19, 1929, pp. 94-113; reference on p. 103.

[5] *Ibid.*, p. 106.

[6] J. A. Prescott: The Soils of Australia in Relation to Vegetation and Climate, *Australian Council for Scientific and Industrial Research, Bulletin 52*, Melbourne, 1931, p. 51.

[7] A. G. Price: History and Problems of the Northern Territory, Australia (Macrossan Lectures, University of Queensland), Adelaide, 1930, pp. 20, 34, 61 (note 27), and 65 (note 78).

[8] H. L. Shantz and C. F. Marbut: The Vegetation and Soils of Africa, *Amer. Geogr. Soc. Research Ser. No. 13*, 1923, p. 214.

[9] E. Huntington, F. Williams, and S. Van Valkenburg: Economic and Social Geography, New York, 1933, pp. 196-197.

[10] Prescott, *op. cit.*, p. 67.

[11] Wolfanger, *op. cit.*, pp. 110-111.

[12] C. F. Marbut: The Soils of the Amazon Basin in Relation to Agricultural Possibilities, *Geogr. Rev.*, Vol. 16, 1926, pp. 414-442; reference on p. 442.

[13] James Thorp: Soil Survey (Reconnaissance) of St. Croix Island, Virgin Islands, *United States Dept. of Agriculture Technical Bull. No. 315*, Washington, 1932; H. H. Bennett and R. V. Allison: The Soils of Cuba, Washington, 1928; and H. H. Bennett: Some Geographic Aspects of Cuban Soils, *Geogr. Rev.*, Vol. 18, 1928, pp. 62-82.

[14] Bennett and Allison, *op. cit.*, Foreword.

[15] [The general outlines of the climatic factors and their biological effects have been considered at length in several special works that should not be overlooked by those interested in these questions: M. Piéry and others, edits.: Traité de climatologie biologique et médicale, 3 vols., Paris, 1935; B. de Rudder: Grundriss einer Meteorobiologie des Menschen, Berlin, 1937; D. B. Dill: Life, Heat, and Altitude, Cambridge (Mass.), 1938; W. Hellpach: Geopsyche, 4th edit., Leipzig, 1935; W. F. Petersen: The Patient and the Weather, Vol. 1 (2 parts), Ann Arbor, 1935; C. A. Mills: Health and Disease as Influenced by Climatic Environment, *International Clinics*, Vol. 2, Ser. 46, 1936, pp. 143-167; W. Borchardt: Medizinische Klimatologie, *in* Köppen-Geiger Handbuch der Klimatologie, Vol. I, Part E, 1935, pp. 1-63; A. Loewy: Über Klimatphysiologie, Leipzig, 1931; Dietrich and Kaminer, edits.: Handbuch der Balneologie, medizinischen Klimatologie und Balneographie, 5 vols., Leipzig, 1916-1926; K. Büttner: Physikalische Bioklimatologie, Leipzig, 1938; Verhandlung der Klimatologischen Tagung in Davos 1925, Basel, 1926; O. Kestner: Die physiologische Wirkung des Klimas, *in* Handbuch der normalen und pathologischen Physiologie, Vol. 17, 1926; A. Loewy: Physiologie des Höhenklimas, Berlin, 1932; A. Aimes: Météoropathologie, Paris, 1932; J. Van Bebber: Hygienische Meteorologie, Stuttgart, 1895; C. Dorno: Grundzüge des Klimas von Muottas-Muraigl (Oberengadin), Braunschweig, 1927; *idem:* Das Klima von Agra (Tessin), Braunschweig, 1934; F. Lahmeyer and C. Dorno: Assuan, Braunschweig, 1932; H. I. Köhler: Das Klima von Bad Nauheim, 1937; W. Mörikofer: Zur Bioklimatologie der Schweiz (reprinted from the *Schweizerisches Medizinisches Jahrbuch* for 1931, 1933, and 1934); C. Haeberlin and P. Perlewitz: Klima-Atlas für die Meeresheilkunde an der deutschen Seeküste, Hamburg, 1932; P. Köhler and E. Flach: Atmosphärische Strömungsvorgänge im Zusammenhang mit Krankheitserscheinungen, *Strahlentherapie*, Vol. 48, 1933, pp. 541-564; A. Missenard: L'homme et le climat, Paris, 1937.

The climatic data are being summarized for the world on a uniform plan in the Köppen-Geiger "Handbuch der Klimatologie," Berlin, 1931- (to be in 5 volumes). Many of the papers in the *Comptes rendus, Congrés Internatl. de Géogr.,* Amsterdam, 1938, Vol. 2, Section III c., also discuss this subject. See below, p. 260, note 27, p. 261, notes 29 and 1.—R. G. S.]

[16] Griffith Taylor: The Control of Settlement by Humidity and Temperature, *Commonwealth of Australia, Bur. of Meteorol. Bull. No. 14,* Melbourne, 1916, p. 9.

[17] C. P. Yaglou: The Influence of Atmospheric Conditions on Health and Growth, *Heating, Piping, and Air Conditioning,* Vol. 3, 1931, pp. 926-932; reference on p. 931.

[18] Andrew Balfour: Personal Hygiene in the Tropics, *in* W. Byam and R. G. Archibald, edits.: Practice of Medicine in the Tropics, Oxford, 1921, Vol. 1, pp. 1 ff.

[19] [Climatic classifications of the type mentioned here are designed especially to meet the needs of economic, agricultural, and plant geography and therefore do not serve particularly well for defining the climatic zones according to human comfort or acclimatability in physiological terms, except very indirectly. There are numerous proposals extant for evaluating weather or climate with respect to the comfort or other physiological responses of man. These are of two types. The first is based on the use of some instrument that is exposed to the air and is designed to heat, cool, and evaporate approximately as would a human body similarly exposed. The other makes use of some formula for combining various ordinarily observed weather elements into an index that may be correlated more or less closely with some physiological sensation or index. Certain of the formulae of this kind are derived from experiments with the instruments and are intended to obtain similar results in places where an instrument cannot be afforded or has not been in use. The human body is such a complicated organism, however, that the instruments and formulae still leave much to be desired and tend to be so costly or unhandy that their use is still very limited. Some of the cruder and more frankly empirical formulae still have a qualitative utility and, until such time as the complicated thermodynamics of the instruments and their biological significance are elucidated on a more practical plane for ordinary climatic work, can still be recommended in geographical studies. However, some details of the experiments with the instruments and formulae are described in Appendix III, and an excellent technical review of the subject will be found in the works of Dorno, Büttner, and Mörikofer cited in note 15, above.

Of the simpler indices some manipulation of the wet-bulb temperature seems most convenient and valid, e. g. climograms plotting wet-bulb against dry-bulb temperature. Taylor gives climograms using wet-bulb against relative humidity (which, as Huntington has pointed out, gives double weight to humidity) for many stations over the world and classifies the climates accordingly (see Taylor, *op. cit.* For a discussion of the wet-bulb and comfort see below, p. 266, note 41, and Appendix II. J. W. Gregory cites many early references in: The Wet-Bulb Thermometer and Tropical Colonisation, *Journ. Scottish Meteorol. Soc.,* Vol. 16, 1912, pp. 3-8.

Eventually, however, it will be possible to classify the climates on the basis of data furnished by cooling-power and other bioclimatic instruments. Dorno first made a suggestive beginning in this direction by using the records of his frigorimeters for several cities (C. Dorno: Über spezifisch-medizinische Klimatologie, *Meteorol. Zeitschr.,* Vol. 39, 1922, pp. 344-348). Later he published more detailed results obtained with his own cooling-power instrument (the frigorimeter), from which Table XVIII, p. 298, is taken to show the contrast between the tropics and mid-latitudes (Die Abkühlungsgrösse in verschiedenen Klimaten nach Dauerregistrierungen mittels des "Davoser Frigorimeters," *ibid.,* Vol. 45, 1928, pp. 401-421). Dorno (with Lahmeyer) finally attained the acme of his method in a series of detailed practical computations and measures—complete model physiological-climatic studies—in a number of contrasted climates (Über die Grenzen und die Notwendigkeit der Zusammenarbeit von physiologischer Klimatologie und Klimaphysiologie, dokumentiert an einem praktischen Beispiel, *Schweizerische Medizinische Wochenschrift,* Vol. 62, 1932, pp. 474-506; see also his "Assuan").—R. G. S.]

[20] C. W. Thornthwaite: The Climates of the Earth, *Geogr. Rev.,* Vol. 23, 1933, pp. 433-440. Thornthwaite's formula is criticized by Professor Prescott in his paper "Single Value Climatic Factors" (cited in the following note).

[21] J. A. Prescott: Single Value Climatic Factors, *Trans. and Proc. Royal Soc. of South Australia,* Vol. 58, 1934, pp. 48-61; *idem:* The Climatic Control of the Australian Deserts, *ibid.,* Vol. 60, 1936, pp. 93-95; James Davidson: The Monthly Precipitation-Evaporation Ratio in Australia as Determined by Saturation Deficit, *ibid.,* Vol. 58, 1934, pp. 33-36; *idem:* Climate in Relation to Insect Ecology in Australia, *ibid.,* Vol. 58, 1934, pp. 197-210, Vol. 59, 1935, pp. 107-124, Vol. 60, 1936, pp. 88-92. Professor J. A. Prescott notes (November 23, 1936): "The factors that Davidson and I have studied, those relating rainfall to evaporation, are essentially moisture relationships of

importance to plants and insects but not to the mammalian thermostat, except in so far as the rate of evaporation plays a part in keeping him cool. Man's comfort is presumably determined by two laws: (a) Newton's Law: the rate of cooling is proportional to the difference between body temperature and air temperature; and (b) Dalton's Law: the rate of evaporation is proportional to the saturation deficit in water vapor of the atmosphere."

[A third (c) law, emphasized by Sir Leonard Hill's studies, should be added, namely that the wind affects the cooling of the body according to some exponential function of its velocity. These three laws can be summarized in a formula of the general form found by L. V. King for the cooling of a hot wire in an air stream ($H=$(a $+b\sqrt{v})\theta$, where H is the heat loss, v the wind, θ the difference in temperature between object and the air (or wet-bulb temperature of the air if the object is wet), and a and b are convection constants to be determined experimentally).

For the agricultural purposes in which Professor Prescott is interested several new indices have lately been proposed. Anders Angström (A Coefficient of Humidity of General Applicability, *Geografiska Annaler*, Vol. 18, 1936, pp. 245-254) suggests a "coefficient of humidity" based on the duration of precipitation in relation to mean temperature, and he finds it better, for northern climates at least, than De Martonne's index or Meyer's ratio. Also W. Haude and O. Moese propose a new formula for agronomic use, which has different coefficients for different soil-productivity types within the same climatic type (Allgemeine Betrachtungen über eine Formel für landwirtschaftliche Klimabewertung, *Bioklimatische Beiblätter*, Vol. 4, 1937, pp. 54-62, discussed by Arnold Court: Agricultural Evaluation of Climate for Taxation Purposes, *Geogr. Rev.*, January, 1939). Mention should likewise be made of E. E. Fedorov's "weather complex" method of correlating climate with crop growth (see summarized translation by E. S. Nichols: Das Klima als Wettergesamtheit (Climate as Totality of the Weather), *Monthly Weather Rev.*, Vol. 55, 1927, pp. 401-403). The British Agricultural-Meteorological Scheme set up by agronomists and statisticians of the Rothamstead Experiment Station envisages experiments with crop plots and microclimatic observations to rationalize the statistical correlations that have been made using R. A. Fisher's "analysis-of-variance"procedures. Such a program is now being initiated in America. But it is doubtful whether the specialized development of climatic studies in that direction can elucidate the problem of acclimatization in the tropics. Rather, the human-physiological aspects must be approached by special methods appropriate to the problem, along lines mentioned in note 19 above and discussed further in Chapter XV and in the Appendixes.—R. G. S.]

[22] Henry Barkely: Zones of Relative Physical Comfort in Australia, *Commonwealth of Australia, Bur. of Meteorol. Bull. No. 20*, 1934.

[23] See also Appendix II, below.

[24] [C. A. Mills has also constructed a world map of climatic stimulation based on the variability of temperature and has discussed the great importance of this factor in relation to health and disease in physiological terms (Health and Disease as Influenced by Climatic Environment, *Internatl. Clinics*, Vol. 2, Ser. 46, 1936, pp. 143-167; map on p. 151.—R. G. S.]

[25] J. E. Switzer: Weather Types in the Climates of Mexico, the Canal Zone, and Cuba, *Monthly Weather Rev.*, Vol. 53, 1925, pp. 434-437; reference on p. 434. [See also papers by C. F. Brooks, E. C. Donnelly, G. F. Howe, and E. S. Nichols, published under the general heading "Papers on the Relation of the Atmosphere to Human Comfort," of which Switzer's paper is a part, *ibid.*, pp. 423-433, and the reply to them by C. Dorno, *ibid.*, Vol. 54, 1926, pp. 39-43. Still another method is suggested by A. Gregor: Der Witterungscharakter nach Punkten, *Zeitschr. für Angewandte Meteorologie (Das Wetter)*, Vol. 50, 1933, pp. 97-105. However, all these methods are too cumbersome and empirical to justify their wide use; they await a better experimental and physiological basis (see also note 19, above, Chapter XV, and Appendixes II and III, for efforts in this direction. P. E. James has evaluated the frequencies of weather types at Port of Spain, Trinidad, in a simple and clear-cut manner similar to Switzer's (Climate of Trinidad, *Monthly Weather Rev.*, Vol. 53, 1925, pp. 71-75).—R. G. S.]

[26] Arthur Hunter: Extra Premiums for Americans and Canadians Residing in Tropical and Semi-Tropical Countries, *Trans. of the Actuarial Soc. of America*, Vol. 29, Part 1, 1928, pp. 4-25; reference on p. 20; see also below, p. 263, note 29.

[27] J. C. Elkington: The Mestizos of Kisar, Dutch East India, *Medical Journ. of Australia*, Vol. 1, 1922, p. 32; E. Rodenwaldt: Die Mestizen von Kisser [Kisar] und die Frage der Akklimatisation der europäischen Rassen und des tropischen Klimas, *Archiv. für Schiffs-und Tropen-Hygiene*, Vol. 27, 1923, pp. 202 ff. [See also W. Radsma: Gegevens omtrent den invloed van het tropenklimaat en van het verblijf in tropische kuststreken op het lichaamsgestel van den blanke, *Comptes rendus*,

pp. 272-291; W. M. F. Mansvelt: Kolonisatie door blanken in de tropen, *ibid.*, pp. 234-238; C. Bonne: Over de mogelijkheid van volksplantingen door blanken in de tropen, *ibid.*, pp. 14-20.—R. G. S.]

[28] R. deC. Ward: The Acclimatization of the White Race in the Tropics, *Ann. Rept. of the Smithsonian Instn. for 1930*, Washington, 1931, pp. 557-576; reference on p. 559.

[29] *Ibid.*

[The oft-made comparison of the subtropical (especially American Cordilleran) highland climates to one of "perpetual spring" (or "autumn") is often misleading because they are not without certain discomforts and unhealthful features. The mean annual or mean monthly temperature may, for example, be close to the optimum (in Huntington's sense), but where the diurnal range is fairly great (in semiarid regions especially) the temperature alternates above and below the optimum, forcing the body to shift rapidly every day from defense against chill to adaptation to heat. According to Huntington an interdiurnal or interseasonal variation of this type is presumably very stimulating, but when the variation comes too rapidly (intradiurnally) it is a question what benefit it has, since many people require many hours or days adequately to adjust their heat regulation to a new level. Such changes in the higher latitudes are said to favor many diseases and "breakdowns." On the tropical plateaus the intense radiation, the extremes of relative humidity or rainfall in some places, and the low pressure also affect many people adversely. A. Walter, Director of the British East Africa Meteorological Service, writes in his "Annual Report for 1937" (Nairobi, 1937, p. 19): "Problems connected with Medical Meteorology arise in determining the best time for work and rest, . . . whether some method could not be devised for utilising the health-giving solar radiation available in such profusion in these latitudes and altitudes. It appears probable that these great stores of solar energy are either not used at all, owing to excessive precautions, or are abused from ignorance of their effects. . . . The greatest temperature range recorded during any one day in 1937 at Kabete was 29.2° F., from 79.9° F. to 50.7° F., and the greatest humidity variation was 64% from 86% to 22%.

The expenditure of energy in effecting adaptation to these ever-recurring short period variations has never been a subject of close investigation. It may well be found to contain an explanation of some of the physiological phenomena ascribed to the climate of the high altitude tropical regions."—R. G. S.]

[30] [Note the unfavorable remarks quoted from various travelers as to the climate of Quito, Ecuador (K. Knoch: Klimakunde von Südamerika (Köppen-Geiger, Handbuch der Klimatologie, Vol. 2, Part G), Berlin, 1930, p. 121; E. Solly: A Handbook of Medical Climatology, New York, 1897, pp. 370-371; and W. Knoche: Klimatische Beobachtungen auf einer Reise in Ecuador, *Verhandl. deut. Wiss. Ver. Santiago de Chile*, N. F., Vol. 2, 1932.

Concerning East African plateaus see p. 252, note 7. With regard to "hill stations" in India, Blanford compares most of them to southern European climates in some ways. He finds only Ootacamund and Darjeeling in any way like England, and then the resemblance is "not very close," consisting chiefly in the coolness, dampness, and cloudiness "One could hardly desire" or "find within India or perhaps elsewhere, a more charming climate or one more fitted to the European constitution than that of the Nilgiri hills" (Climates and Weather of India, London, 1889, p. 120). The annual range at Ootacamund is only 11° F. and the mean 55° F. "But," he writes of most of the Indian hill stations, "except in the cold season, they are scarcely such as an European, free to select his place of residence, would probably choose as an abode" (*ibid.*, p. 126).

Karl Sapper discusses the effects of contrasts in highland and lowland climates in his "Auswanderung und Tropenakklimatisation," Würzburg, 1921, pp. 59-77 and *passim;* and also in "Die geographische Bedingtheit der Altamerikanischer Hochkulturen und Kulturstaaten, *Petermanns Mitt.*, Vol. 77, 1931, pp. 178-182 and 295-248.—R. G. S.]

NOTES

CHAPTER XIV

ACCLIMATIZATION AND HEALTH: I. CLIMATOLOGICAL AND
STATISTICAL STUDIES

[1] Many of the papers in the *Comptes rendus, Congrès Internatl. de Géogr.*, Amsterdam, 1938, Vol. 2, Section III c, discuss the problem of white settlement in the tropics from the medical point of view, but see more especially those of Barrett, Van Everdingen, Bonne, Fischer, Hellpach, Lampe, Radsma, Sapper, Winckel, and Ziemann. See also above, p. 244, note 6.

[2] See, for example, A. E. Parkins: The South, New York, 1938; C. W. Ramsdell: The Southern Heritage, *in* W. T. Couch, edit.: Culture in the South, Chapel Hill, N. C., 1934; R. B. Vance: Human Geography of the South, Chapel Hill, 1932; and H. W. Odum: Southern Regions of the United States, Chapel Hill, 1936.

[3] See above, pp. 65-76.

[4] See above, pp. 120-121.

[5] See above, pp. 161-168.

[6] Kenneth Black: Health and Climate with Special Reference to Malaya, *Malayan Med. Journ.*, Vol. 1, 1932, pp. 99-107; reference on p. 101. Sir R. H. Charles: Neurasthenia, and Its Bearing on the Decay of Northern Peoples in India, *Trans. Soc. of Tropical Medicine and Hygiene,* Vol. 7, 1913-1914, pp. 2-15. See also pp. 210-213, above.

[7] Interview with Dr. G. J. P. Barger, Washington, February 10, 1933. [See Durén: La situation sanitaire des Européens au Congo Belge, *Bruxelles Méd.,* Vol. 16, 1936, pp. 445-447.—R. G. S.]

[8] Cleveland Abbe: Introduction, *in* E. G. Dexter: Weather Influences, New York, 1904, p. xx.

[9] Sir Aldo Castellani: Climate and Acclimatization, London, 2nd edit., 1938, p. 15.

[10] Black, *op. cit.,* p. 100.

[11] Griffith Taylor: The Control of Settlement by Humidity and Temperature, *Commonwealth of Australia Bur. of Meteorology Bull. No. 14,* Melbourne, 1916, pp. 16-22. [Taylor's "tentative" scale of comfort in terms of the wet-bulb temperature is as follows: below 40° F., raw or keen; 40-45°, very rarely uncomfortable; 45-55°, ideal; 55-60°, very rarely uncomfortable; 60-65°, sometimes uncomfortable; 65-70°, often uncomfortable; 70-75°, usually uncomfortable. As Huntington points out, the plotting of wet-bulb against relative humidity gives double weight to humidity. Huntington uses dry-bulb against relative humidity in his climographs, but it would be better yet to use wet-bulb against dry-bulb (as in Figs. 82-85, pp. 285-291, below), since the wet-bulb is a thermodynamic quantity that can be linked directly to physiological experiments and also to the wet cooling power and the effective temperature (see Appendixes). A set of slanting iso-lines for relative humidity can be added to a wet-bulb—dry-bulb climogram making it an ordinary psychometric chart in addition. For further remarks on wet-bulb, see p. 266, note 41.—R. G. S.]

[12] For Huntington's views see his works cited above, p. 241, note 15, particularly his important summaries: The Effect of Climate and Weather, *in* E. V. Cowdry, edit.: Human Biology and Racial Welfare, New York, 1930, pp. 295-330; and Climate and the Evolution of Civilization, *in* G. A. Baitsell, edit.: The Evolution of Earth and Man, New Haven, 1929, pp. 330-383.

[13] Huntington, The Effect of Climate and Weather, p. 323.

[14] [For more direct evidence of the significance of variability and monotony of weather on health see C. A. Mills: Health and Disease as Influenced by Climatic Environment, *Internatl. Clinics,* Ser. 46, Vol. 2, 1936, pp. 143-167; C. A. Mills: Weather and Health, *Bur. Amer. Meteorol. Soc.,* Vol. 19, 1938, pp. 141-151; W. F. Petersen: The Patient and the Weather, Ann Arbor, Vol. 1, Parts 1-2, 1935; also note especially Ogle's and Mills' studies on rabbits and rats, which are very suggestive (C. Ogle and C. A. Mills: Animal Adaptation to Environmental Temperature Conditions, *Amer. Journ. of Physiology,* Vol. 103, 1933, pp. 606-612; and papers by Ogle, *ibid.,* Vol. 107, 1934, pp. 628-640, Vol. 117, 1936, pp. 285-291). Sundstroem and others have also experimented similarly with rats (see summary in *Physiological Rev.,* Vol 7, 1927, pp. 320-321, and *passim*).—R. G. S.]

[15] For criticisms of Ellsworth Huntington's views see P. Sorokin: Contemporary Sociological Theories, New York, 1928, pp. 137-159 (with important bibliographical references); R. B. Vance: *op. cit.,* pp. 351-441; S. S. Stevens: A Critique of the Climatic Theories of Ellsworth Huntington with Special Reference to the South (manuscript thesis), University of North Carolina, Chapel Hill, 1931; R. W. Cilento's works cited above, p. 242, note 23; C. H. Wickens: Dr. Huntington and Low Latitudes, *Econ. Record,* Vol. 6, 1930, pp. 123-127; and W. A. Murray: Health Factors in the Poor White Problem, Report of the Carnegie Commission on the Poor White Problem in South Africa, Vol. 4, 1932, pp. 23-46.

[16] Dexter, *op. cit.,* pp. 233-246. [See also W. Hellpach: Geopsyche, Leipzig, 1935, for a review of mental influences of climate and weather.—R. G. S.]

[17] L. N. Hines: Effects of School Room Temperatures on the Work of Pupils, *Psychological Clinic,* Vol. 8, 1909, quoted by Sorokin, *op. cit.,* p. 158, together with the findings of other authorities. [See also the philosophical discussion of optima for human mental work in Hellpach, *op. cit.,* pp. 38-46. Hellpach refers to an early study by Lehmann and Pedersen in Denmark, who found that for the performance of arithmetical addition the optimum was 8° C. lower than for muscular work (15° — 17°

vs. 7° — 10°). Hellpach believes that there is a certain optimum difference in air temperature between head, body, and feet, especially for sedentary workers and for sleeping, which accords with the findings of hygienists as to "comfortable" distributions of temperature in rooms.—R. G. S.]

[18] C. P. Yaglou: The Influence of Atmospheric Conditions on Health and Growth, *Heating, Piping, and Air Conditioning*, Vol. 3, 1931, pp. 926-932; reference on p. 931. [See also K. D. Blackfan, C. P. Yaglou, and K. McKenzie: The Premature Infant: A Study of the Effects of Atmospheric Conditions on Growth and on Development, *Amer. Journ. of the Diseases of Children*, Vol. 46, 1933, pp. 1175-1236.

Professor W. B. Cannon of Harvard University has recently pointed out (The Aging Process, New York, 1938) the extent to which the range of environmental variability (e. g., of temperature) that a person can tolerate well narrows with increasing age. This would imply that with age the optimum becomes of more significance and that there is certainly a lessening of adaptability to tropical climate. Dr. Cannon holds that the conditions that explain the decreased tolerance of heat with age are mainly atrophy of the skin, thickening of the surface blood vessels, etc., which reduce the ability of the body to regulate temperature in warm surroundings.

In a paper by G. W. Pickering (Peripheral Resistance in Persistent Arterial Hypertension, *Clinical Sci.*, Vol. 2, 1936, pp. 209-235) there are observations indicating a gradual reduction of the ability to lose heat to the surroundings as one grows older. G. C. Shattuck and M. M. Hilferty (Sunstroke and Allied Conditions in the United States, *Amer. Journ. of Tropical Medicine*, Vol. 12, 1932, pp. 223-245) present data on heat-stroke and sun-stroke deaths in the United States, indicating how the death rate increases rapidly with old age above the seventieth year or so. (See likewise C. J. Root: Deaths During the Heat Wave of July, 1936 at Detroit, *Bull. Amer. Meteorol. Soc.*, Vol. 18, 1937, pp. 232-236; especially Table 2, p. 233).—R. G. S.]

[19] Huntington, The Effect of Climate and Weather, p. 319.

[20] *Ibid.*, p. 328.

[21] *Ibid.*, p. 329.

[22] Stevens, *op. cit.*, p. 84. See also reference to Professor Cannon's work, note 18, above.

[23] See above, pp. 62-63.

[24] R. W. Cilento: The White Man in the Tropics, *Commonwealth of Australia Dept. of Health, Service Publ. No. 7*, Melbourne, 1925, p. 54.

[25] See review of P. D. Phillips and G. L. Wood, edits.: The Peopling of Australia (Pacific Relations Series, No. 1, Melbourne 1928), *Geogr. Rev.*, Vol. 20, 1930, pp. 168-169. [It is not clear that comfortable climates are necessarily healthful, for the principle of variability as a necessary stimulant to activity and civilization (Huntington) calls for a continual degree of discomfort to keep man on the move. In fact, the most generally comfortable climates are distinctly intolerable for certain types of persons. Cyclonic variability in the climatic zones supposedly most comfortable and productive of energy leads to a high incidence of "breakdown diseases" from overstimulation (Petersen, Mills). Furthermore, the comfort of climates is only relative and incomplete and not to be readily translated in terms of comfortable combinations of the weather elements at one time, such as air-conditioning engineers produce them for a room. The diurnal range of the atmospheric elements alone is often enough to cause a continual degree of discomfort. Dr. Cilento was attempting to measure tolerability by statistics, but comfort is a difficult and poor index of tolerability. The importance of comfort to health is widely assumed *a priori*, yet its fundamental biological rôle is still relegated to psychological theory (see for example conclusions of W. Strauss and K. Walther in "Klima und Arbeit," Part II (*Archiv für Gewerbepathologie und Gewerbehygiene*, Vol. 1), 1931, pp. 634-655). For more concrete evidence on this point see the discussion of "comfort zones" in Appendix II; also compare note 39, p. 265.—R. G. S.]

[26] Griffith Taylor: The Settlement of Tropical Australia, *Geogr. Rev.*, Vol. 8, 1919, pp. 84-115; reference on p. 112.

[27] See above, pp. 158-161.

[28] Ellsworth Huntington: Civilization and Climate, New Haven, 1915, pp. 27-34.

[29] Arthur Hunter: Extra Premiums for Americans and Canadians Residing in Tropical and Semi-tropical Countries, *Trans., Actuarial Soc. of America*, Vol. 29, Part 1, 1928, pp. 4-25. See also map accompanying J. Fairgrieve: The Geographer and the Actuary, *Geography*, Vol. 15, 1929-1930, pp. 282-284; also G. H. Macalester: Life Assurance, *Malayan Medical Journ.*, Vol. 3, 1928, pp. 105-106; J. F. C. Haslam and others: Discussion of Life Assurance in the Tropics, *Proc. Royal Soc. of Medicine*, Vol. 21, 1938, pp. 31-43.

[30] Hunter, *op. cit.*, p. 20.

[31] *Ibid.*, pp. 20-21.

[32] *Ibid.*, p. 22.

[33] *Ibid.*, p. 23.

[34] Medical Appointments, *Colonial Service, Recruitment No. 3*, London, 1931, p. 73.

[35] *Ibid.*, p. 61. [For a survey of the peculiar (for Oceania) situation as to health and racial problems in British Fiji, see P. A. Buxton: Researches in Polynesia and Melanesia, Parts V-VII, Human Disease and Welfare (Memoir Ser. London School of Hygiene and Tropical Medicine), Nov. 1928, pp. 95-117 on "Brown and White Man."—R. G. S.]

[36] *Ibid.*, p. 36.

[37] *Ibid.*, p. 40.

[38] D. B. Blacklock: Health in West Africa, *The Lancet*, Vol. 218, 1930, pp. 843-848.

[39] Medical Appointments, p. 52.

[40] *Ibid.*, pp. 22, 23, 56, 66.

NOTES

CHAPTER XV

ACCLIMATIZATION AND HEALTH: II. PATHOLOGICAL, PSYCHOLOGICAL
AND PHYSIOLOGICAL STUDIES

[1] [For a general handbook of tropical diseases consult E. R. Stitt: The Diagnostics and Treatment of Tropical Diseases, 5th edit. rev., Philadelphia, 1929; C. Mense, edit.: Handbuch der Tropenkrankheiten, 6 vols., Leipzig, 1924-1931; P. Manson-Bahr: Manson's Tropical Diseases, London, 1935; H. Ruge, Mühlens, and Zur Verth: Krankheiten und Hygiene der wärmen Ländern, 3rd ed., 1931; A. Castellani and I. Jacono: Manuale di clinica tropicale, Torino, 1937; L. Rogers and J. W. D. Megaw: Tropical Medicine, London, 1934; and Ch. Joyeau and A. Sicé: Précis de Médicine Coloniale, Paris, 1937.—R. G. S.]

[2] [The geography of disease is discussed in a number of special works such as F. G. Clemow: Geography of Disease (Cambridge Geogr. Ser.), Cambridge, England, 1903; J. Wütschke: Die geographische Verbreitung von Krankheiten, *Petermanns Mitt.*, Vol. 67, 1921, pp. 53-57; J. Guiart: Climatogéographie des Maladies, *in* M. Piéry, edit.: Traité de climatologique biologique et médicale, Paris, 1935, Vol. 2, pp. 1046-1071; W. F. Petersen: The Patient and the Weather, Ann Arbor, Vol. 1, Part 1, 1935; E. B. McKinley, edit.: A Geography of Disease, Washington, 1935.—R. G. S.]

[3] [See J. W. Bews: Human Ecology, London, 1935; also p. 245, note 9, above.— R. G. S.]

[4] Fourth Annual Report of the Rockefeller Foundation, International Health Board, 1917, New York, 1918, p. 126.

[5] A. S. Chandler: Hookworm Disease, New York, 1929, p. 2.

[6] Fourth Annual Report of the Rockefeller Foundation, p. 2-3.

[7] Chandler, *op. cit.*, pp. 16, 24, 165-167.

[8] *Ibid.*, p. 52.

[9] Thirteenth Annual Report of the Rockefeller Foundation, International Health Board, 1926, New York, 1927, p. 6.

[10] See H. R. Carter: Yellow Fever: An Epidemiological and Historical Study of Its Place of Origin, Baltimore, 1931, footnote p. 5, for recent experimental studies in yellow fever.

[11] See Elizabeth, Countess of Carnarvon: Malaria: Curse, Cause, Cure, London, 1927; Fourth General Report of the Malaria Commission, *Bull. Health Organisation of the League of Nations*, Vol. 6, 1938, pp. 895 ff., and B. Nocht and W. Mayer: Die Malaria, 2nd ed., Berlin, 1936.

[12] R. B. Vance: Human Geography of the South, Chapel Hill, N. C., 1932, p. 391.

[13] Twelfth Annual Report of the Rockefeller Foundation, International Health Board, pp. 71-72 (quoted in Vance, *op. cit.*, p. 390).

[14] Quoted by Vance, *op. cit.*, p. 391.

[15] [For details of the experiences of the United Fruit Company in combating malaria, etc., on its banana plantations see the annual reports of the Medical Department of the United Fruit Company, New York.—R. G. S.]

[16] Carter, *op. cit.*, pp. 34-35.

[17] A Decade of Public Health, 1923-1932, *Thirty-third Rept. of the Florida State Board of Health*, 1933, p. 77. [During the last few years large funds of the Works Progress Administration have been expended on malaria control in such states as Mississippi, where large areas have been treated and the people educated in anti-malaria hygiene. The cost of such work was probably prohibitive for the local or state governments alone, and hence the control is now much further advanced than could have been hoped for without federal aid.—R. G. S.]

[18] M. F. Boyd and Gerald Ponton: The Recent Distribution of Malaria in the Southeastern United States, *American Journ. of Tropical Medicine*, Vol. 13, 1933, pp. 143-166, with maps; references on pp. 143 and 147.

¹⁹ R. W. Cilento and A. H. Baldwin: Malaria in Australia, *Medical Journ. of Australia*, 17th Year, 1930, Vol. 1, pp. 247-282; reference on p. 281.

²⁰ Vance, *op. cit.*, p. 410.

²¹ [On sleeping sickness see: A. Sicé: La Trypanosomiase Humaine en Afrique Intertropicale, Paris, 1937 (excellent treatise; includes data on geographical distribution); C. F. M. Swynnerton: The Tsetse Flies of East Africa, a First Study of their Ecology with a View to their Control, *Trans. Royal Entomological Society*, London, Vol. 84, 1936 (a monumental and epochal work); F. Zumpt: Die Tsetsefliegen, Jena, 1936; E. Steudel: Der gegenwärtige Stand der Schlafkrankheitsbekämpfung in Afrika, *Archiv für Schiffs- und Tropen-Hygiene*, Vol. 35, 1931, pp. 114 ff.; E. Weigt: Schlafkrankheitsbekämpfung in Tanganyika, *Petermanns Mitt.*, Vol. 84, 1938, pp. 183-185.—R. G. S.]

²² R. DeC. Ward: The Acclimatization of the White Race in the Tropics, *Ann. Rept. Smithsonian Instn. for 1930*, Washington, 1931, pp. 557-576; reference on p. 565 (see also above, p. 241, note 9).

²³ Sir R. H. Charles: Neurasthenia, and Its Bearing on the Decay of Northern Peoples in India, *Trans. Soc. of Tropical Medicine and Hygiene*, Vol. 7, 1913-1914, pp. 2-15 See above p. 195.

²⁴ Kenneth Black: Health and Climate, with Special Reference to Malaya, *Malayan Medical Journ.*, Vol. 7, 1932, pp. 99-107; reference on p. 101.

²⁵ [See W. R. Jones: Notes on the Climate of Southern Burma and the Malay Peninsula, *Quart. Journ. Royal Meteorol. Soc.*, Vol. 61, 1935, pp. 381-386.—R. G. S.]

²⁶ Interview with Professor Gordon Harrower, Singapore, December 10, 1929.

²⁷ Morden Carthew: The Aetiology and Prophylaxis of Mental Irritability in the Tropics, *Journ. of Tropical Medicine and Hygiene*, Vol. 30, 1927, pp. 113-117; reference on p. 114.

²⁸ Dr. Huntington disputes this statement. He considers that the missionaries have been selected with extreme care and, as in Hawaii, have often left a biological heritage of great importance.

²⁹ Carthew, *loc. cit.*

³⁰ R. L. Buell: The Native Problem in Africa, 2 vols. New York, 1928, Vol. 2, p. 17.

³¹ Millais Culpin: An Examination of Tropical Neurasthenia, *Proc. Royal Soc. of Medicine*, Vol. 26, 1933, pp. 911-922. [The bibliography on p. 917 is good; note the table of statistics on West and East Africa. Further discussions on tropical neurasthenia appeared in the *British Medical Journ.*, Vol. 1, 1936, pp. 503-545, 595, 634, 676, 760, 846, 884, 920, and 1071, Vol. 2, 1936, pp. 236 and 328 (these are all part of a running symposium and correspondence). See also S. M. Vassallo: Tropical Neurasthenia: Its Possible Relation to Hyperthyroidism, *Trans. Royal Soc. Trop. Med. and Hyg.*, Vol. 27, 1934, pp. 625-627; and C. P. Emerson: Neurasthenia As Observed in the Orient, *Trans. Amer. Assoc. Physicians*, Vol. 48, 1933, pp. 239-247.—R. G. S.]

³² H. S. Stannus: Tropical Neurasthenia, *Trans. Royal Soc. of Tropical Medicine and Hygiene*, Vol. 20, 1926-1927, pp. 327-343; reference on p. 330.

³³ Culpin, *op. cit.*

³⁴ Letter from Dr. Shattuck to J. A. Fleming, November 25, 1929. See also G. C. Shattuck: The Possibility of White Settlement in the Tropics, *Comptes rendus, Congrés Internatl. de Géogr.*, Amsterdam, 1938, Vol. 2, Section III c, p. 327.

³⁵ Sir Aldo Castellani: Climate and Acclimatization, London, 2nd edit., 1938.

³⁶ C. K. Drinker: The Physiological Problems of Life in the Tropics Together with a Program of Investigation. Memorandum, Harvard, 1932. See also Appendix I.

³⁷ Castellani, *op. cit.*

³⁸ See Appendix III, below, for further details on the katathermometer and the cooling power.

³⁹ [The effect of increasing the air movement at high temperatures and humidities is an increased cooling which in some ways is "refreshing" or stimulating up to the point where the "warming power" sets in (i. e., wet-bulb >100° F. approximately), as Sir Leonard Hill has strikingly shown with the katathermometer (see Appendix III). However, there is recognition among those who have experimented in this line that this is partly if not entirely a psychological response, for high temperature, whether with high or low humidity and wind, will have a debilitating effect per se *if prolonged*. Under ordinary working conditions in temperate lands these extreme conditions have to be borne only for brief spells, and their effects are more transitory therefore; but in the tropics there is often no escape from a continual exposure to them except by air conditioning. Strauss and Walther particularly emphasize the difference between the physiological and psychological effect of air movement (quoted by R. R. Sayers in *U. S. Bur. of Mines, Information Circular No. 6645*, 1932, p. 61). There has been a good deal of misunderstanding on this point because of the tendency to confuse mere subjective "comfort" with true biological health.—R. G. S.]

[40] Castellani, *op. cit.*, p. 43.

[41] [See J. S. Haldane: The Influence of High Air Temperatures (No. 1), *Journ. of Hygiene*, Vol. 5, 1905, pp. 494-513. Haldane's use of the wet-bulb temperature has been criticized by J. L. Bruce (Humidity and Temperature of Air in Relation to Comfort and Health, quoted by L. Hill: Science of Ventilation and Open Air Treatment, Part I, *Medical Research Council Special Rept. No. 52*, London, 1919, p. 111), but a confirmation of the validity of the wet-bulb as a measure of the limits of heat toleration is given by the experiments of H. M. Vernon with the katather-mometer (The Index of Comfort at High Atmospheric Temperatures, *in* The Kata-Thermometer in Studies of Body Heat and Efficiency, *Medical Research Council Special Rept. 73*, London, 1923, pp. 116-114). Note Breinl's physiological correlations with the wet-bulb in Queensland, note 16, p. 247. The thermodynamics of the wet-bulb temperature has been studied especially by C. W. B. Normand (The Effect of High Temperature, Humidity, and Wind on the Human Body, *Quart. Journ. Royal Meteorol. Soc.*, Vol. 46, 1920, pp. 1-14; Wet-Bulb Temperatures and the Thermodynamics of the Air, *Memoirs India Meteorol. Dept.* Vol. 23, Part I, 1920, pp. 1-21); he finds that with wind and at high temperatures the wet-kata of Hill does not, for some strange reason, cool as fast and the wet-bulb thermometer, and he prefers the wet-bulb. Since others have found the wet-kata more sensitive to changes in wind and humidity than the moist human body, the wet-bulb likewise can be no more than a relative in-dication of the body sensation. The wet-kata is nowadays often calibrated in terms of the wet-bulb temperature, so that, knowing the wind velocity also, one may estimate the wet cooling power from the wet-bulb (see Appendix III, p. 295). The wet-bulb temperature of about 69° or 70° F. coincides roughly with the experimentally deter-mined limits of human comfort observed by Lancaster and by Tyler and also, if wind be considered, with the ASHVE (American Society of Heating and Ventilating Engineers) comfort limit at high humidities (see Fig. 82). Ordinarily, however, as Vernon and also the American experimenters have pointed out, it is desirable to consider the wind and the dry-bulb along with the wet-bulb; radiation may also be a factor, in the sun for example. The wet-bulb is nevertheless a fundamental and indispensable quantity.—R. G. S.]

[42] Castellani, *op. cit.*, p. 44.

[43] D. B. Dill, H. T. Edwards, and others: Physical Performance in Relation to External Temperature, *Arbeitsphysiologie*, Vol. 4, 1931, pp. 508 ff. A summary of Dill's work on this subject down to 1936 as well as his review of the whole subject appears in "The Economy of Muscular Exercise," *Physiological Rev.*, Vol. 16, 1936, pp. 263-291; see also his Life, Heat, and Altitude, Cambridge (Mass.), 1938, pp. 3-23; J. H. Talbott, H. T. Edwards, D. B. Dill and L. Drastich: Physiological Responses to High Environmental Temperature, *Amer. Journ. of Tropical Medicine*, Vol. 31, 1933, pp. 381-398; A. V. Bock and D. B. Dill, edits.: Bainbridge's Physiology of Muscular Exercise, 3rd edit., London, 1931.

[44] W. J. Crozier and T. J. B. Steir: Temperature and Frequency of Cardiac Contrac-tions in Embryos of Limulus, *Journ. of General Physiology*, Vol. 10, 1926-1927, pp. 501-524.

NOTES

CHAPTER XVI

DIET, CLOTHING, EXERCISE

[1] In 1935 a committee on the Problem of Nutrition was set up by the League of Nations. Their report is mainly concerned with countries of Western civilization, but the acuteness of the problem in "Asia, Africa, and tropical countries generally" is recognized, and the League's Health Organization is "actively engaged upon the prob-lem of nutrition in Eastern and tropical areas." Final Report . . . Relation of Nutri-tion to Health, Agriculture, and Economic Policy, Geneva, 1937.

[2] E. V. McCollum: The Newer Knowledge of Nutrition, New York, 1922, pp. 415-416.

[3] ["Character of metabolism on exposure to warmth: The tendency of individuals living in a warm climate to avoid high protein diets with their marked specific-dynamic action and to choose a diet richer in carbohydrates is well known. Fats are also less palatable in warm climates; they supply a large heat value in small bulk and are therefore less adapted for giving a normal stomach distension under conditions where a small number of calories are required; they also do not allow quite such a high standard of muscular efficiency (Krogh and Lindhard, *Biochemical Journal*, Vol. 14, 1920, p. 290) as do carbohydrates. Nothing is known of the mechanisms by which the appetite adjusts itself so that the more suitable diet is chosen." H. C. Bazett: Physiological Responses to Heat, *Physiological Rev.* Vol. 7, 1927, p. 557.—R. G. S.]

4 E. V. McCollum: The Reaction to Food, *in* E. V. Cowdry, edit.: Human Biology and Racial Welfare, pp. 331-347; reference on pp. 340-341.

5 *Ibid.,* p. 341. See also E. Rodenwaldt: Über Yaghurtgenuss in den Tropen, *Archiv für Schiffs-und Tropen-Hygiene,* Vol. 16, Beiheft 4, 1912, p. 488.

6 E. Huntington, F. Williams, and S. Van Valkenburg: Economic and Social Geography, New York, 1933, p. 126.

7 McCollum, quoted by E. S. MacLachlan: The Diet Pattern of the South, Thesis, University of North Carolina, 1932.

8 Again we must emphasize the lack of knowledge for generalization. In a report on the health of Uganda by the acting governor it is stated: "Here again it is impossible to generalize, and observations made in one district are not necessarily of much value in another. . . Difference of climate may account for some of the surprising variations, but I think the only conclusion which can be reached is that each tribe has its own 'national characteristics' which have developed from various causes through many generations." (Papers Relating to the Health and Progress of Native Populations in Certain Parts of the Empire, *Colonial No. 65,* London, 1931, p. 31.)

9 Henry Adams: History of the United States, 1801-1805, 9 vols. Vol. 1, New York, 1890, p. 43.

10 R. B. Vance: Human Geography of the South, Chapel Hill, N. C., 1932, pp. 438-441.

11 Dr. G. C. Shattuck, however, points out that one form of canned goods, evaporated milk, is a useful food for infants in the tropics, even though it is not available to the very poor (letter, December 30, 1937). [See also R. J. Blackham: Infant Feeding in Warm Climates, *Journ. State Med.,* Vol. 45, 1937, pp. 462-473.—R. G. S.]

12 Earl Hanson: Are the Tropics Unhealthy?, *Harper's Mag.,* Vol. 167, 1933, pp. 556-568; reference on p. 564.

13 Hanson, *op. cit.,* p. 563.

14 Earl Hanson: Social Regressions in the Orinoco and Amazon Basins, *Geogr. Rev.,* Vol. 23, 1933, pp. 578-598; reference on p. 593.

15 Earl Hanson, Are the Tropics Unhealthy?, p. 564.

16 R. W. Cilento: Australia's Orientation, *Department of Public Health, Bull. No. 35-36,* Victoria, 1933, p. 26.

17 Sir Aldo Castellani: Climate and Acclimatization, London, 1938, pp. 160-161.

18 W. T. Councilman and R. A. Lambert: The Medical Report of the Rice Expedition to Brazil, Cambridge, 1918, p. 106.

19 Roy Nash: The Conquest of Brazil, New York, 1926, p. 345.

20 See above, p. 258, note 3.

21 *Archiv für Schiffs- u. Tropen-Hygiene,* Vol. 41, 1937, pp. 385-386, 520-522.

22 Interview with Dr. G. J. P. Barger, Washington, February 10, 1933. See also A. Castellani: Brief Note on Tropical Helmets, *Journ. of Tropical Medicine and Hygiene,* Nov. 15, 1935.

23 [The differences in toleration with respect to exposure to sunlight in different tropical stations are well known and are often attributed to differences in the spectral composition or total intensity (for the same solar altitude) of the solar radiation, an entirely reasonable view but one that cannot be proved because there are insufficient data from the tropics on solar radiation. See the interesting symposium on this question in the *Archiv für Schiffs- und Tropen-Hygiene* (Vol. 40, 1936, pp. 81, 303, and 305; Vol. 41, 1937, pp. 385, and 520) by various authors. It is known that the depth of the moist and turbid lower atmosphere varies greatly in the tropics and could account for varying total intensity and varying proportions of both the "heat" and ultra-violet radiation, though measures made so far generally show about the same spectral proportions as in higher latitudes, the total intensities being higher only because the solar elevation is greater. Data on solar radiation in the tropics are summarized by H. H. Kimball in the *Monthly Weather Rev.,* Vol. 55, 1927, pp. 155-169; and Vol. 56, 1928, pp. 393-398; and by V. Conrad in the Köppen-Geiger Handbuch der Klimatologie, Vol. 1, Part B., pp. 2-44, Berlin, 1936.—R. G. S.]

24 G. C. Shattuck and M. M. Hilferty: Sunstroke and Allied Conditions in the United States, *Amer. Journ. of Tropical Medicine,* Vol. 12, 1932, pp. 223-245; *idem:* Distribution of Acute Heat Effects in Various Parts of the World, *New England Journ. of Medicine,* Vol. 214, 1936, pp. 458-468. [See also R. G. Stone: On the Causes of Deaths from Heat at Detroit, July, 1936, *Bull. Amer. Meteorol. Soc.,* Vol. 18, 1937, pp. 233-236; A. Castellani: Climate and Acclimatization, 2nd ed., 1938, pp. 72-93 (good review of literature); C. A. Mills and C. Ogle: The Climatic Bases of Susceptibility to Heat Stroke or Exhaustion, *Amer. Journ. of Hygiene,* Vol. 17, 1933, pp. 686-696; D. B. Dill: Life, Heat and Altitude, Cambridge (Mass.), 1938, pp. 24-119; L. Hill: Science of Ventilation and Open Air Treatment, Part 2, *Medical Research*

Council Special Rept. 52, London, 1920, pp. 1-110; especially pp. 98-110; M. Gover: Mortality During Periods of Excessive Temperature, *U. S. Public Health Reports,* Vol. 53, 1938, pp. 1122-1143.—R. G. S.]

[25] C. E. Woodruff: The Effects of Tropical Light on White Men, New York, 1905.

[26] [A review and a fresh discussion of the physics of clothing from the bioclimatic point of view is given by Büttner in his "Physikalische Bioklimatologie," Leipzig, 1938, pp. 128-138. The discussion of clothing, physics, and hygiene in Max Rubner's "Lehrbuch der Hygiene" (Leipzig, 1907) is still worth study; a modernized view appears in E. Brezina and W. Schmidt: Das künstliche Klima in der Umgebung des Menschen Stuttgart, 1937, pp. 42-53. Note also W. Mörikofer: Die Durchlässigkeit von Bekleidungstoffen für Sonnenstrahlung verschiedener Spektralbereiche, *Strahlentherapie,* Vol. 39, 1931, pp. 57 ff. The effects of different kinds of clothing materials on cooling power have been studied by W. Bachmann (Über das Wärmehaltungsvermögen von Bekleidungstoffen, *Archiv für Hygiene,* Vol. 103, 1930, pp. 336-348, Vol. 104, 1930, pp. 43-51, Vol. 105, 1931, pp. 181-201) and by Von Diringshofen (Das Kälteschutzvermögen verschiedener Bekleidungszusammenstellungen, *Zeitschr. für Hygiene,* Vol. 114, 1932-1933, pp. 179-194. Yaglou's experiments are also of interest in this connection (A Heated Globe Thermometer for Evaluating Comfort . . . , *Journ. of Industrial Hygiene,* Vol. 17, 1935, pp. 185-198); I. Tiggemann: Über die Durchlässigkeit von Sommerstoffen für UV-Strahlung, *Arch. Hyg.,* Vol. 113, 1935, pp. 354-364; A. P. Gagge and others: The Influence of Clothing on the Physiological Reactions of the Human Body to Varying Environmental Temperature, *Amer. Journ. Physiol.* Vol. 124, 1938, pp. 30-50.

A thought-provoking discussion of tropical climate and clothing, sometimes speculative, but based on available data, will be found in Hill, Science of Ventilation, Part 2, pp. 76-80, 102-104, 214-247, and *passim.* See also standard works on tropical hygiene (e. g. Balfour, Nocht, Hauer); the articles by G. C. Shattuck, W. J. Mixter, and G. P. Howe in the section on hygiene, medicine, and surgery, *in* Handbook of Travel, Harvard Travellers Club, Cambridge, 2nd ed., 1935, part 4, pp. 385-494; J. B. Christopherson: The Motive in Women's Dress in the Tropics, *Journ. of Tropical Medicine and Hygiene,* Vol. 33, 1930, pp. 201-207; Sir Aldo Castellani: Climate and Acclimatization, London, 2nd edit., 1938, pp. 151-164; R. Mouchet: Note sur la valeur hygiénique des differents étoffes employées pour les vêtements coloniaux, *Archiv für Schiffs- und Tropen-Hygiene,* Vol. 15, 1911, pp. 60 ff.; A. Junger: Kleidung und Umwelt in Afrika, Leipzig, 1926; A. L. de Barros Barreto: O vestuario, *Gazeta Clinica,* Vol. 32, 1934, pp. 13-15; G. P. Crowden: Insulation Against Heat and Cold for Human Comfort; Uses of Bright Metallic Surfaces, *The Lancet,* Vol. 1, 1934, pp. 37-40; J. B. Kirk: Hints on Equipment and Health for Intending Residents in the Tropics, London, 1926; G. A. P. Ross: Climate and Clothing in South Africa, *So. Afr. Med. Journ.,* Vol. 9, 1936, pp. 779-782.—R. G. S.]

[27] C. P. Yaglou: Ventilation in Hot Industries, *Fuels and Furnaces,* Vol. 3, 1925, pp. 569-575; C. P. Yaglou and Philip Drinker: The Summer Comfort Zone: Climate and Clothing, *Journ. of Industrial Hygiene,* Vol. 10, 1928, pp. 350-363; and C. P. Yaglou: The Comfort Zone for Men at Rest and Stripped to the Waist, *ibid.,* Vol. 9, 1927, pp. 251-263. Mom and Wiesenborn have determined the comfort zone of Europeans in Batavia and Bandoeng (see below, pp. 285-286).

[28] R. W. Cilento: The White Man in the Tropics, *Commonwealth of Australia, Dept. of Health Service Publ.* (*Tropical Division*) No. 7, 1925, Melbourne, Part II, pp. 106-124; D. B. Blacklock: An Empire Problem: The House and the Village in the Tropics, London, 1932 (deals mainly with native problems); *idem:* Presidential Address on Housing in the Tropics, *Journ. Royal Sanitary Inst.,* Vol. 58, 1937, pp. 296-304; Reports of the United Fruit Company, Boston and New York.

[29] C. S. Jarvis, late Governor of Sinai, during a temporary sojourn in the Kharga oasis in Egypt, constructed an underground house as a refuge from the heat. By an ingenious water-cooling device he succeeded in reducing the temperature inside the dugout to about 70° as compared with 115° outside. "I tried to sleep here in the afternoons and at night, but found the sudden change of temperature and moisture more than the ordinary constitution would stand, so that after a series of violent colds and inflamed throats I had to scrap the idea." C. S. Jarvis: Three Deserts, London, 1936, p. 66.

[Air conditioning is now being widely introduced in some tropical centers, and it should not be long before experience as to its possibilities and limitations in the tropics will become available (see, for example, notes in *The Engineer,* Vol. 164, 1937, p. 259; *The Heating and Ventilating Engineer,* Vol. 12, 1938, p. 33). The expense of air-conditioning installations will probably be its greatest limitation in the tropics.

"We must recognize that among civilized people the physiological devices for maintenance of constant temperature [of the body] may have little opportunity to function. . . . in summer, mechanically operated fans, cold drinks, ice cream and *refrigerated rooms* [editor's italics] lessen the use of the natural arrangements for keeping cool. It is not impossible that we lose important protective advantages by failing to exercise these physiological mechanisms, which were developed through myriads of generations of our less favored ancestors. The man who daily takes a cold bath and works until he sweats may be keeping 'fit,' because he is not permitting a very valuable part of his bodily organization to become weakened and inefficient by disuse" (W. B. Cannon: The Wisdom of the Body, New York, 1932, pp. 198-199).

Dr. W. F. Petersen warns of the dangers in the large temperature contrast between summer outdoors and refrigerated indoor rooms, which involves a definite metabolic strain and can be harmful for a considerable proportion of a group of subjects (What Weather Does to Man, *Heating, Piping, and Air-Conditioning*, Vol. 10, 1938, pp. 595-596). The reactions of office workers to air-conditioned offices in a hot summer in Milwaukee are of interest in this connection; see study by F. C. Houghten and others (General Reactions of 274 Office Workers to Summer Cooling and Air Conditioning, *ibid.*, pp. 552-556) and further references below. F. Vick (Uber die künstliche Klimatisierung in den Tropen, *Archiv fur Schiffs- und Tropen-Hygiene*, Vol. 38, 1934, p. 133) recommends that in the tropics indoor air should be cooled to only about 2° C. below the outside temperature. Yaglou recommends "dehumidification of the air with but little cooling . . . in tropical climates, as was first suggested by Tyler 35 years ago" (Physical and Physiological Principles of Air Conditioning, Part II, *Journ. Amer. Medical Assn.*, Vol. 109, 1937, pp. 945-960; reference on p. 959).

In America in summer it is considered good practice in air-conditioned offices to make the indoor temperature follow a sliding temperature scale from 2° to 15° F. below that outdoors, being at the higher value just after the workers enter in the morning and just before they leave in the evening; this avoids much of the "shock" on entering or leaving, of which there has been considerable complaint (see W. J. McConnell and I. B. Kagey: The Air Conditioning System of the New Metropolitan Building, First Summer's Experience, *Trans. Amer. Soc. of Heating and Ventilating Engineers*, Vol. 40, 1934, pp. 217 ff.; and the study of disturbances of metabolism due to chilling in summer, reported by Yaglou, Physical and Physiological Principles, pp. 957-958). Castellani (Climate and Acclimatization, p. 158) mentions the often-observed fact that "a few hours cooling daily counteracts to a great extent the depressive effects of a hot climate. In a factory in Manila some years ago, daytime cooling of the premises was introduced with the result that the output of workers increased by 28 per cent. . . . A mistake to be avoided is cooling the air inside premises and ships too much, as the sudden change from the severe heat outside to the cold inside may cause chills and muscular rheumatism. A drop of about 15° F. below the outside temperature is usually sufficient for comfort." However, this last recommendation is apparently unwise for the tropics, where it would lead to the very chills which Castellani admits are dangerous. Yaglou's recommendation of chiefly or only dehumidification is much safer and will usually afford adequate "comfort." Changes to a somewhat cooler environment are nevertheless desirable, if not too sudden; nightly or week-end trips to a higher elevation, such as residents of Batavia, Manila, Hongkong, Rio de Janeiro, and Petropolis may make, noticeably offset the enervating monotony, as many writers on the tropics testify (K. Sapper: Auswanderung und Tropenakklimatisation, Würzburg, 1921, pp. 59-77).

Mom gives the best technical discussion of air conditioning for the hot moist tropics (C. P. Mom: Luchtbehandeling in de Tropen, *De Ingenieure in Nederlandsch Indië*, 1937, No. 4). Note also: Temperature and Humidity Requirements for Air-Conditioning in the Philippines, *Heating, Piping and Air-Conditioning*, Vol. 7, 1935, p. 102; T. Chester: Air Conditioning Factors, *Journ. Instn. of Heating and Ventilating Engineers*, Vol. 5, 1938, pp. 538-592; H. Ruge: Das Verhalten der Lufttemperatur und Feuchtigkeit auf einem modernen Kreuzer in den Tropen, Berlin, 1932; D. V. S. Reddy: Comfort Standards in the Tropics, *Journ. Indian Medical Assn.*, Vol. 4, 1935, pp. 593-600; S. F. Dudley: Kata-Thermometer at Sea in the Tropics, *Journ. Royal Navy Medical Service*, Vol. 14, 1928, pp. 77-103; F. E. Giesecke and W. H. Badgett: Seasonal Variations in Effective Temperature Requirements, *Heating, Piping, and Air-Conditioning*, Vol. 10, 1938, pp. 677-680.—R. G. S.]

[30] Griffith Taylor: The Settlement of Tropical Australia, *Geogr. Rev.*, Vol. 8, 1919, pp. 84-115.

[31] See above, pp. 77-102.

[32] Hanson, Are the Tropics Unhealthy?, p. 561.

[33] Castellani, *op. cit.*, p. 157.

[34] E. R. Stitt: Diagnostics and Treatment of Tropical Diseases, Philadelphia, 5th edit., 1929, quoted by Castellani, *op. cit.*, p. 159.

35 Hanson, Are the Tropics Unhealthy?, p. 561.
36 *Ibid.*, p. 562.
37 See above, pp. 158-161.
38 See above, p. 247, note 16.
39 See above, pp. 62-73.
40 C. P. Yaglou: Ventilation in Hot Industries, *Fuels and Furnaces*, 1925, p. 572.
41 [There is a large body of experience now accumulated from military campaigns, mines, steamships, construction projects, and farming settlements in various tropical localities which overwhelmingly demonstrates the ability of white men to perform hard labor over a considerable period of time (years or months) with not only an absence of untoward effects but if anything a distinctly tonic result essential for acclimatization. Prevention of disease (i. e., sanitation) must be assured to realize this benefit, of course. See, for example, H. Werner: Soll der weisse Tropenbewohner körperliche Arbeit verrichten?, *Deutsche medizinische Wochenschrift*, Vol. 62, 1936, pp. 27-29; C. B. Huppenbauer: Beiträge zur Frage der Tropendienstfähigkeit, *in* Arbeit und Tropenkrankheiten, Festschrift B. Nocht, 1927, pp. 210-219; G. Giemsa and E. G. Nauck: Rasse und Gesundheitserhaltung sowie Siedlungsfragen in den warmen Ländern, *Archiv für Schiffs- und Tropen-Hygiene*, Vol. 41, 1937, pp. 9-22. Prominent hygienists have expressed the opinion that in the tropics the white man can work just as well as the native can, if he will simply dress like the native and overcome social aversion to manual labor. Neither blacks nor whites can expect to work as hard in a hot environment as in a colder one—moderation is necessary in tropical labor and it goes without saying that strict hygiene is essential. Gradual acclimatization by exposure to increasingly severe conditions and selection of most adaptable individuals are also generally necessary for success. See also A. Castellani: Hygienic Measures and Hospital Organisation of the Italian Expeditionary Forces during the Ethiopian War, 1935-36, *Journ. Royal Soc. Arts.*, Vol. 86, 1938, pp. 675-689, and his Climate and Acclimatization, 1938, pp. 163-174; A. Hauer: Die deutsch-ostafrikanische Feldzug in tropenhygienischer Beleuchtung, *Arch. Schiffs. Trop. Hyg.*, Vol. 26, 1922, pp. 313 ff.—R. G. S.]
"The white man must accustom himself as rationally as possible to the tropical sun in order to become pigmented and to obtain the necessary action of the skin capillaries and secretion of sweat. He should not avoid the tropical sun too timidly. Only in this way will his physical heat regulation conform to the needs of a correct acclimatization. In this respect, clothing plays a very important rôle. Further, the white man should work in moderation in order to avoid all undue demands upon his heat regulation. In the diet of the inhabitant of the tropics, the loss of salt should be replaced as far as possible by the plant salts or plant ash. Moreover, the diet must be richer in spices than in the temperate zones in order to prevent derangements of the appetite and of the stomach and intestines. From the standpoint of physiology a lasting acclimatization of a white person to the tropics appears only conditionally possible. Today as in times less advanced hygienically and medically, the climatic conditions are, strictly speaking, not altogether favorable for the growth of a healthy white race in the tropical coast and lowland regions. But today, because of easier and more efficient means of communication with the colonies, the question of permanent colonization by the Europeans is placed in a light entirely different from that of earlier times." W. Borchardt: Medizinische Klimatologie, *in* Köppen-Geiger, Handbuch der Klimatologie, Vol. 1, Part E, Berlin, 1930, p. 41.

NOTES

CHAPTER XVII

SOME ADMINISTRATIVE AND ECONOMIC PROBLEMS

1 S. L. Parrish: Self-Government in the Tropics, *64th Congr., 1st Sess., Senate Doc. No. 364,* Washington, 1916.
2 A. D. A. de Kat Angelino: Colonial Policy, 2 vols., The Hague, Vol. 1, p. 495.
3 *Ibid.*, p. 505.
4 A. G. Keller: Colonization, Boston, New York, etc., 1908; A. J. Toynbee: A Study of History, 3 vols., London, 1934.
5 Professor J. A. Prescott makes the following comment (November 23, 1936): "These remarks about American capitalism and mono-culture remind me of some Soviet criticisms of imperialism. Most people find it hard to make sense of the Russian colonial theory, but these researches throw a great deal of light on the problem . . . that is, whether we should develop tropical countries as reasonably self-contained units

or wholly as sources of cheap raw materials. Possibly the two halves of the Dual Mandate may be incompatible or not quite so reciprocal as we fondly hoped they might be."

[6] C. L. Jones: Costa Rica and Civilization in the Caribbean (Univ. of Wisconsin Studies in the Soc. Sci. and Hist., No. 23) Madison, 1935, p. 167; and *idem:* Civilization in the Caribbean, *in* A. C. Wilgus, edit.: The Caribbean Area, Washington, 1934, pp. 488-503.

NOTES
CHAPTER XVIII
SUMMARY AND CONCLUSION

[1] Lucien Febvre: A Geographical Introduction to History, London, New York, 1925, p. 368.

[2] See J. Legendre: Observation et expérimentation, leur valeur comparative en biologie coloniale, *Presse Médicale,* Vol. 37, 1929, pp. 1905-1906.

[3] Isaiah Bowman: Possibilities of Settlement in South America, *in* Limits of Land Settlement, New York, 1937, pp. 293-337; reference on p. 300.

[4] See A. J. Toynbee: A Study of History, 3 vols., London, 1934, Vol. 2, p. 213, for the progress of Polish immigrants in the Connecticut Valley.

APPENDIXES
By Robert G. Stone

APPENDIX I

SOME RESULTS OF MODERN PHYSIOLOGICAL RESEARCH IN RELATION TO ACCLIMATIZATION IN THE TROPICS *

THE BASAL METABOLISM

The heat needed to sustain the body in health and wonted action is produced in the liver, muscles, and other special tissues by chemical oxidation (*metabolism*) of originally ingested foodstuffs (proteins, fats, carbohydrates). The rate of metabolism, as computed from the measured heat loss or from the gaseous exchange of the body, is found to have a wide range according to varying circumstances, but a minimal value can always be obtained under certain conditions (fast, rest, etc.), and only prolonged fast, disease, or collapse will reduce the rate below this value. This is called the *basal metabolism*. It represents, according to prevailing biological interpretations, the lowest value of heat production needed to maintain the vital processes in a normal state. *Ipso facto* it probably also represents the heat needed to maintain the constant body temperature with a considerable margin of safety, since even at basal conditions there is a surplus of produced heat to be lost to the environment unless the latter is rather cold. Metabolism of stored energy in the tissues permits existence during fast or when the rate of heat loss is exceptional.

The basal metabolism of whites and some other races is definitely affected by climate: for instance, in high latitudes it is above the average for the northern United States, but it is below this average in the South, the Orient, and the tropics and subtropics in general. The tropical depression varies greatly in degree, being from 1 to 30 per cent lower than that of the northern United States throughout the year. A seasonal range is also noticeable in most climates. The tropical lowering in metabolism has been regarded by some as of fundamental significance with respect to acclimatization, but in the absence of an understanding of the mechanism of the lowering and its relation to other factors, such as diet and body temperature, solar radiation, etc., its significance cannot yet be taken for granted, however reasonable it may seem. Since there is apt to be a slight rise in body temperature in persons who fail to lower their basal metabolism after reaching the tropics, such persons would appear to be at some disadvantage in withstanding the tropical heat. Radsma has disproved the

---

* There is a vast body of physiological literature on such matters as the basal metabolism, body heat production and loss, body temperature regulation, sweating, etc., in relation to age, sex, diet, disease, etc., on the one hand, and to climatic and other environmental circumstances on the other, all of which has a direct bearing on the problem of physical acclimatization. Some excellent reviews of different phases of this subject have appeared recently, upon which the present discussion is largely based, notably: C. K. Drinker: The Effect of Heat and Humidity on the Human Body, *Journ. of Industrial Hygiene*, Vol. 18, 1936, pp. 471-485 (reprinted in "The Environment and Its Effect Upon Man," Baltimore, 1937, pp. 68-81); C. J. Martin: Thermal Adjustment of Man to Environment, *The Lancet*, 1930, Vol. 1, pp. 617, 673; E. Lahmeyer and C. Dorno: Assuan, Braunschweig, 1932; T. Deighton: Physical Factors in Body Temperature Maintenance and Heat Elimination, *Physiol. Rev.*, Vol. 13, 1933, pp. 427-465; H. Pfleiderer: Meteorophysiologie des Wärmehaushaltes, *Verhandl. Deutsche Gesellsch. für Innere Medizin*, Vol. 47, 1935, pp. 492-501; H. Laurens: Sunlight and Health, *Scientific Monthly*, Vol. 42, 1936, pp. 312-324; E. F. DuBois: Basal Metabolism in Health and Disease, Philadelphia, 1936; *idem*: The Mechanism of Heat Loss and Temperature Regulation, Stanford University, 1937; C. P. Yaglou: Physical and Physiological Principles of Air Conditioning, *Journ. Amer. Medical Assn.*, Vol. 108, 1937, pp. 1708-1713; K. Büttner: Physikalische Bioklimatologie, Leipzig, 1938; D. B. Dill: Life, Heat, and Altitude, Cambridge, Mass., 1938. W. Borchardt: Medizinische Klimatologie, in Köppen-Geiger Handbuch der Klimatologie, Vol. 1, Part E, Berlin, 1930, pp. 41 ff.; R. N. Chopra: The Physiology of the Individual in the Tropics, *Indian Med. Gaz.*, Vol. 73, 1938, pp. 40 and 102 (also in *Nature*, Vol. 141, 1938, p. 379; and *Current Science*, Vol. 9, 1938, pp. 479-480); W. B. Cannon: The Wisdom of the Body, New York, 1932 (especially Ch. 12, The Constancy of Body Temperature); H. C. Bazett: Physiological Responses to Heat, *Physiol. Rev.*, Vol. 7, 1927, pp. 531 ff. (critical summary of the subject up to 1927); R. Thauer: Die nervöse und hormonale Regulation der Körpertemperatur, *Bioklimat. Beibl.*, Vol. 4, 1937, pp. 1-7 (good review); J. D. Hardy and E. F. DuBois: Regulation of Heat Loss from the Human Body, *Science*, Vol. 86, 1937, p. 445 (abstract); C. A. Mills: Functional Insufficiency of the Suprarenal Glands, *Arch. Int. Med.*, Vol. 42, 1928, pp. 390-408; *idem*, High External Temperatures: The Suprarenals and Body Relaxation, *Journ. Amer. Med. Assn.*, Vol. 104, 1935, p. 251; E. S. Sundstroem: Physiological Effects of Tropical Climates, *Physiol. Rev.*, Vol. 7, 1927, pp. 320 ff. (bibliography); W. F. Petersen: The Patient and the Weather, Vol. 1, Part 2, Ann Arbor, 1935. See also pp. 300-301, below.

contention that the well-known avoidance of a rich protein diet in the tropics causes the lowered basal metabolism. White Queenslanders show the greatest reported reduction—proof that these settlers are of a well selected and adapted type.

This type of adjustment to warmer climatic levels takes place slowly and is not to be confused with the rapid responses to environmental stimuli that are supposed to be eliminated in the making of standard basal-metabolism tests.

These standard tests are taken in the "zone of thermic neutrality" (81°-95° F.; see Fig. 78 and Appendix II). But tests made after even brief exposures to temperatures well above the zone show a depressed metabolism—a fact that may also be of considerable significance for climatic adaptation. Ordinarily, however, it takes from a few days to several weeks after entering the tropics for the lowering of the basal metabolism to occur, but it comes back to the "normal" more quickly upon return to the cooler environment again.

Apparently an adjustment to a warm climate involves a shift of the upper limit of the zone of neutrality or comfort zone to a higher temperature (or lower cooling power), the extent of which may be seen in Figure 82. Full acclimatization (as characterized, for example, by those who have become so accustomed to the tropics that temperate conditions seem positively foreign to them) requires still longer exposure— anywhere from six months to even twenty years or more. Obviously this deeper acclimatization is not due merely to the basal metabolic factor. We have to seek further mechanisms to explain it, including nervous and psychic factors.

BODY-HEAT PRODUCTION

While the basal metabolism is a fundamental and readily evaluated quantity, for the actual conditions of everyday life we have to consider the actual or active metabolism, which is the energy level on which the atmosphere really plays.

According to the recent Mayo Foundation standards for basal metabolism in the United States the average 30-year-old American male produces nearly 40 calories per square meter per hour, and the same-aged female 35 or 36 calories. The same persons, however, will produce from 50 to 1000 calories at different times during the day according to the stimuli of cold, degree of activity, emotion, food, etc. (see Fig. 79, for example); it is typical even for sedentary workers to average between 75 and 150 calories. By working at an easier or more efficient pace, by eating less and less-heating food, by nervous relaxation, etc., a man may reduce his heat production when the warmer environment makes less heat needed and heat loss very difficult, these methods being quite independent from devices for increasing the rate of heat loss. Since, however, the basal value sets a relatively inflexible lower limit to any decrease in active heat production and cannot be approached too closely if normal activity has to be continued, it is obvious that means of increasing the rate of heat loss offer a greater potential field of relief from a hot environment than do means of reducing heat production. The possible lowering of heat production by diet, reduced activity, and acclimatization (lower basal metabolism, etc.) is insignificant when compared with the increase of heat loss that is possible through better ventilation, increased volume of sweat, lighter and fewer clothes, artificial air cooling and dehumidification, cooling baths, shade from irradiation, etc. It is for this reason that the physical factors of heat loss have been emphasized so much in the tropics. Only under extremely difficult conditions for heat loss do differences of heat production become obviously serious. They deserve much closer study, however, because they probably have a considerable bearing on acclimatization and the question of the degenerative effects of prolonged exposure to heat.

The metabolic rate is higher than "normal" in children and lower than "normal" in old age, which must be of some importance in the tolerance and acclimatization of different age groups to heat.

BODY-TEMPERATURE REGULATION

Man is provided with a remarkably complex mechanism for maintaining the body temperature at a nearly constant level, or homeostasis of body temperature, but in spite of such narrow requirements man can adjust himself to a wide range of temperatures, from — 70° to + 130° F. This is accomplished by a combination of autonomic physiological responses and conscious artificial (including cultural) devices; or, in other words, by a system of balancing variations in heat elimination by variations in heat production and vice versa, according to whichever is the more dynamic at the time.

The body temperature, however, is not kept perfectly constant but ranges within a degree or so even in health, there being diurnal and seasonal cycles related to muscular, thermal, and possibly cosmic stimuli. It is increased temporarily by exercise and by the specific-dynamic action of food (especially proteins), by irradiation from the environment, by disease, and by storage of heat due to a slow rate of heat removal by the atmosphere. Unless the rise is to over 102° F. or so the heat-regulating mechanisms are not fundamentally disturbed and the body responds by its usual defenses: sweating, flushing of the capillaries, more rapid breathing (*polypnoea*), seeking a cooler place, less clothing, less food, less activity, etc. Acclimated persons show less rise of body temperature under hot conditions and work, etc. Thus we may look upon upon

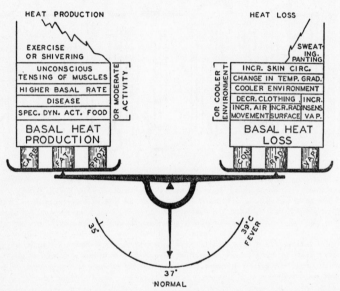

FACTORS INCREASING

FIG. 77—The balance between the factors increasing body heat production and loss (from E. F. Du Bois: The Mechanism of Heat Loss and Temperature Regulation, *Ann. of Internal Medicine*, Vol. 12, 1938, p. 389; reproduced by courtesy of the author and editor). There is a tendency for heat production and loss to balance closely so as to maintain the normal body temperature of 37° C. or 98° F. If the heat loss remains constant but the heat production is raised by exercise, the body temperature rises a little. This sets the sweat glands into activity by autonomic nervous reflexes, and the great consequent rise in cooling by vaporization restores the balance (see Fig. 79). If the temperature of the environment increases to 95° F., which is about the skin temperature, then radiation and convection cease to function as channels of heat loss (see Figs. 78 and 79), and vaporization of sweat must bear the burden of heat loss. If the humidity is high and the wind light or calm the rate of vaporization and hence of the cooling is low, and the body temperature rises. Above an air temperature of 98° F., the air adds heat to the body, since the gradient between them is reversed, and heat stroke is likely.

the body temperature as a sort of equilibrium, narrowly fluctuating in response to opposing tendencies. Figure 77 illustrates this effectively.

Much of the time a man's heat loss and production are considerably out of balance, a typical example of which, under exercising conditions in warm weather, is shown in Figure 79. A person of sedentary occupation commonly suffers similar if smaller dislocations, especially during and after meals and when walking or riding in the sun, strong wind, or cool air. Hence the rate of heat loss is always either lagging behind or exceeding the rate of heat production. Provided the disparity does not reach the fever or frostbite stage the constant shake-up of metabolic and heat-losing organs is healthful, because it keeps the heat-regulating machinery alert and responsive for the purposes that nature intended it to serve, and thus seems to have a generally stimulating effect on all human activity (cf. Huntington's "variability" effect on civilization). For infants and for weak, atonic, diseased, and aged people, the range of tolerable metabolic stress is less. Disuse of the responses to a high rate of heat loss, such as befalls those who have been in a uniformly warm, moist environment for a few weeks or more, leads to their partial atrophy, so that a sudden chill, which would not harm one used to it, may have a serious effect. Indeed, the dangers of "chills" are familiar to every tropical resident. Likewise those used to cold, when suddenly exposed to oppressive warmth, can neither suppress heat production nor speed up heat loss as rapidly as they can after acclimatization to heat.

It is clearly worth while, therefore, to look into the potentialities of training the adjustive mechanisms to take care of extreme stimuli without ultimate harm. Here we run into a truly difficult field, which in spite of much study remains relatively un-

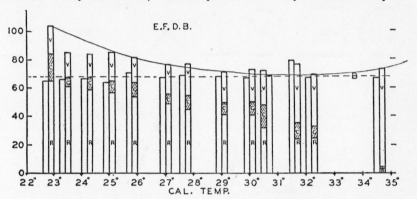

FIG. 78—Heat production (blank columns) and heat loss (columns divided to show radiation, convection, and vaporization) of a normal man, naked, under basal metabolic conditions in a calorimeter chamber, exposed to air from 22° to 35° C. (71.6° F. to 95° F.). The broken line shows average basal metabolism. (From Du Bois, *op. cit.* in title to Fig. 77, p. 392.) The solid curving line shows the rise in basal heat loss at the extremes of air temperature. The zone from 27°-35° C. (80.6°-95° F.) is called the "zone of thermic neutrality," in which basal heat production and loss balance. The importance of radiation at the lower temperatures and of vaporization at higher ones is very striking. Convection is nearly constant, owing to the absence of any forced draft or wind in the experiment illustrated. A breeze outdoors, or from a fan indoors, would, however, greatly increase the convection percentages at the expense of those of radiation and vaporization.

fathomed as far as the effects of prolonged exposures are concerned. Nevertheless, the now rapidly increasing knowledge of the short-time responses is illuminating the question of the long-time ones.

There are nerve endings in the skin that are specially sensitive to temperature. These stimulate a "heat center" in the brain, which in turn, via other nerves, stimulates the heat-producing organs and tissues, the sweat glands, the lungs, and the blood-circulation system. Also, there are direct nervous connections by which the nerve ends in the skin sympathetically stimulate these various organs. The secretions of the thyroid and adrenal glands control the rate of heat production, and these glands are coupled in with the nervous relays mentioned. Other hormones may be likewise involved. According to some, the heat-regulating reflexes are also set off by the stimulus on the brain of slight variations in the temperature of the blood coming from the skin.

The integration of all these factors in body-temperature regulation is still obscure, but its great importance for an understanding of acclimatization is unquestionable— indeed, some physiologists believe, for example, that changes in endocrine and hormonal activity are most important in adaptation to climate. Excess thyroid and adrenal activity is dangerous in the tropics because it stimulates metabolism and inhibits sweating; there is some evidence that the usual lowered metabolism may be related to changes in endocrine secretion; the suprarenal glands are also said to affect metabolism. This is called a "chemical regulation" of the body temperature.

Thus we may visualize the heat center of the brain, along with the sympathetic nervous system, as a thermostat responsive to small changes in skin and blood temperature, a thermostat which shuts off or turns on the heat-production or heat-loss mechanisms and likewise prevents over-compensation, so that the body temperature is kept steady.

Since the reactions to heat rest basically upon the nervous sensitivity of the skin to temperature, the variations in this sensitivity must partly explain the effects of acclimatization as suggested by the shift in the "comfort zone" (see below, p. 286). The sensitiveness of the skin to temperature normally increases with increasing skin temperature and with increasing contrast between air and skin temperature. The sensation of comfort or discomfort, however, is more closely related to the average gradient of temperature through the outer tissues than to skin-surface temperature.

The more striking effects of the stimulus of a rise in air or skin temperature begin usually with the dilatation of the blood vessels of the skin, so that more blood flows into them from the deeper heat-producing tissues. The skin temperature thereby increases (unless possibly it is already higher than the blood temperature, or the cooling power is high), whence more heat can be lost through the skin to the air by convection and radiation. With the body at rest when the temperature exceeds 87°-91° F. (or, in case of exercise or irradiation at an even lower temperature), the sweat glands break out, and the evaporation of sweat immediately affords a much higher rate of cooling (see Fig. 79). The volume of sweat increases irregularly with a continued rise of temperature and the insensible perspiration (invisible diffusion of water through the skin) also increases its evaporation, affording a small fraction of the cooling under warm conditions. Increased warmth of the blood stimulates more rapid breathing (*polypnoea*), which accelerates heat loss from the lungs, though this rarely becomes much more than 10 per cent or so of the total heat loss. In time the heat depresses the thyroid and adrenal activity, reducing metabolism somewhat (see Fig. 78). By all these means (see Fig. 77) the body temperature is kept within normal limits, unless the environment becomes too hot (as, for example, when the wet-bulb temperature surpasses 85° F.) or when the mechanisms fail from atrophy, disease, exhaustion, or weak heart, etc. As the heart works harder under heat in furnishing blood faster to the skin and lungs, a weak heart is a liability under very hot conditions.

Inability to keep the body temperature from rising after some length of tropical residence, with moderate activity and diet, proper clothing, etc., is generally taken as evidence of inherently poor acclimatability. Individuals vary greatly in this respect, owing to differences, inherited or acquired, in the efficiency and flexibility of their heat-regulating mechanism.

The Avenues of Heat Loss—Physical Factors

We have mentioned some "chemical" (endocrine-metabolic) as well as "physical" means of body-temperature regulation (perspiration, sweating, capillary suffusion, breathing). For warm environments it is patent that the physical heat regulation is the more important and that the physical properties of the skin and of the atmosphere and clothing must largely determine its efficiency. Really great progress has of late been made in the study of this subject.

The physics of the skin is especially illuminating. The penetration of radiation in relation to pigmentation has already been described (see above, pp. 175-176). Since the heat from the blood must be passed through the skin in order to reach the atmosphere, any factors affecting the thermal conductivity of the skin are important. The conductivity of the outer tissues varies with their temperature; with warmth they swell with water, which is a better conductor. Fat layers delay cooling in proportion to their thickness and temperature. Women with their greater accumulations of fat stand cold better and wear lighter clothing than men but suffer more from heat. Obese persons generally are poorly adapted to hot climates, owing both to adipose tissue and to higher metabolism—heat deaths in the United States are more common among those of short stocky build. The reduction of fat tissue is presumably part of the generally-observed loss of weight consequent upon prolonged tropical residence and may be looked upon as a means of acclimatization to heat. However, not all heavy people have special difficulty in tolerating hot climates. The tall thin build that whites often develop in the tropics is supposed to be an adaptation because it affords a greater surface for heat loss per unit of body weight and heat production.

The more liquid state of the outer tissues that results from the suffusion of the capillaries with blood and of the skin with sweat and water under warm conditions, facilitates heat loss by "internal convection"; also, blood is thinner and hence flows more freely in a warm environment. The thickness of the outer skin, or horny *corneum*, sometimes decreases in the tropics, with correspondingly greater ease of heat transmission. There is a fairly widespread belief among medical men that flexibility of the vessels, their capacity to accommodate a larger volume of blood in the skin and to do so more rapidly, can be developed by use (or may decline with disuse) and may be a powerful means of acclimatization. The general atrophy of the skin and hardening of the capillaries with age makes older people less adaptable to extremes and changes of temperature.

The disadvantage of the body in absorbing both short-wave and long-wave radiation while radiating only in the long-wave region, is to be especially noted (see above, p. 175). The skin is thus partly a trap for solar-radiational energy, which is a help in cold climates but a serious handicap in sunny tropical ones. Martin has published some striking figures on the effect of different fabrics and skins on solar radiation (*Lancet*, 1930, Vol. I, p. 617). A white cotton shirt (2 thicknesses) diffusely reflects 71 per cent of the radiation and absorbs 29 per cent; a khaki shirt reflects 43 per cent; a dress

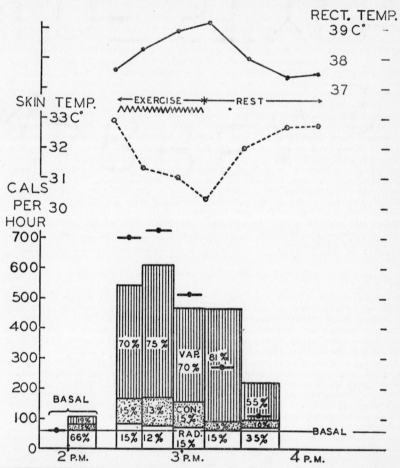

Fig. 79—Effect of violent exercise at squash for 36 minutes on a hot day (from Du Bois, *op. cit.* in title to Fig. 77, p. 391). Heat production is indicated by the dots with short horizontal lines, heat loss by the columns divided into the radiation, convection, and vaporization components. Note the changing balance between heat production and heat loss (70% of the energy produced by exercise must be lost in the form of surplus heat); also the rise in body (rectal) temperature and fall in skin temperature, with rapid restoration to normal after exercise ceased. The skin temperature falls as a result of cooling by evaporation, in spite of the greater blood supply to the capillaries when the heat production increases with exercise.

suit, 5.5; a fine white skin, 45; an average blond skin, 43; a dark brunette (semitic) skin, 35; a Hindu's skin, 22; and a negro's, 16 per cent.

In regard to the physical behavior of convectional and evaporational cooling of an inanimate object (e. g. an instrument) at body temperature (98° F.), see the note 41, p. 266, above, and Appendix III, pp. 293-299, below. In the case of the human body, however, there are complications, due to its varying physical surface properties and internal physiological responses that no instrument can be expected to imitate very accurately.

Within the "zone of thermic neutrality" (81°-95° F.) under basal metabolic conditions, but above 90° F., the skin temperature changes but slightly with temperature (assuming no air movement), so that the regulation of body temperature is now taken care of largely by increased capillary dilatation and by sweating. The mechanism is so sensitive in this zone that a 4° F. rise in air temperature increases sweat by about 50 per cent and the peripheral blood flow by about 20 per cent (Hardy and Du Bois). This is a remarkable demonstration of the physical heat-regu-

Fig. 80—Heat production and heat loss of healthy young men in relation to temperature and "effective temperature" (see below, p. 284). Curve A shows the basal metabolism of normal men, curves B and C are for men seated at rest indoors.

Fig. 81—Normal heat loss of men seated at rest indoors; proportions of loss by evaporation, radiation, and convection, in relation to temperature and humidity.

These figures, based on experiments made by Houghten, Teague, Miller, and Yant, are reproduced by courtesy of the American Medical Association from C. P. Yaglou: Physical and Physiological Principles of Air Conditioning, *Journ. Amer. Med. Assn.*, Vol. 108, 1937, pp. 1708-1713.

Note increase of heat production and decrease of heat loss above 98° F. (88° E. T.), the result of high temperature in increasing metabolism of unacclimatized subjects. Although discomfort begins at 87° F., when sweating starts, at least with most people, the body temperature and balance of metabolism and heat loss are maintained without difficulty up to 98° F., under the combination of temperature, humidity, and wind indicated here. Above 98° F. the pulse and body temperature tend to rise. The effect of high versus low relative humidity on the evaporational heat loss,

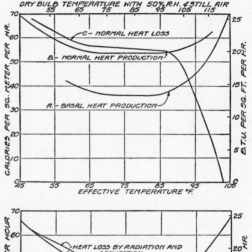

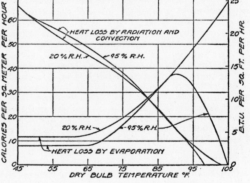

once sweating starts, is very strikingly shown in Figure 81; but at lower temperatures it is quite unimportant, the small observed difference being due to greater conductivity of moister clothing or skin at the higher relative humidity.

lation powers under warm conditions, and the effects upon acclimatization of training this mechanism to even greater response or to respond at a lower temperature, or of its unwonted atrophy, are obvious. It may seem artificial to minimize wind, as in the basal-metabolism experiments, but it must be recognized that wind cannot remove any more heat than is supplied to the surface of the skin by the blood and by the sweat glands (latent heat of vaporization).

The physics of the three avenues of heat loss (radiation, convection, and evaporation) may be summarized in a simple heat-balance equation for the body: W (the energy formed in the body by metabolism) $+ I$ (radiation to the body from the environment) $\times F$ (area of heat-losing surface) $= [S$ (radiation from the skin) $+ L$ (heat loss by conduction and convection) $+ V_h$ (heat loss by evaporation from skin)] $\times F$ $+ A$ (heat loss via the mouth) $+ V_L$ (heat loss by vaporization of the breath) $\pm S$ (the "storage" of heat due to rising or lowering of the body temperature).

The proportionate losses by the three avenues at different air temperatures under basal conditions are shown in Figure 78, under exercise in Figure 79, and under comfortable conditions, with clothing and at sedentary work, indoors, in Figures 80 and

81. The last two figures are especially interesting in that they show how rapidly the disparity between heat production and heat loss widens above 85° F. or so, the heat loss decreasing rapidly while the heat production increases, in spite of augmented cooling by evaporation of sweat.

We have seen how temporary and permanent adjustments to such conditions can be made, but the question of the effects of exposure for years and generations is not answerable. A tolerable adjustment to a brief strain is merely a defense, often harmless; but the same adjustment prolonged indefinitely may be very degenerating, though it has not been measured except by inference or by historical observations (such as those summarized by Dr. Price). Apparently the rise in metabolism during periods of exercise is tonic and stimulating in a tropical environment, even though uncomfortable. It may serve the same purpose as variability of the environment in cooler climates (Huntington). In other words, a variability of heat production may be substituted for variability of heat loss as a stimulus. Experiments with rats and other animals bear out these conclusions, but in general great caution must be observed in drawing inferences for man from such studies. Their value is largely suggestive.

SWEATING

"In man the chief areas of the skin where heat is to be dissipated are abundantly provided with sweat glands. . . . The sweat varies in composition depending on its rate of production, the degree of acclimatization and personal idiosyncrasy. Its composition appears also to be influenced by external temperature, physical activity, and degree of exposure to sun. In hot weather, salt depletion is high not only because of the large volume of sweat produced but because this sweat is unusually high in salt content. While the sweat glands excrete lactic acid it is believed [contrary to the opinions of some] that this is of little or no value to the economy of muscular exercise. . . . The rate of sweat secretion is not always precisely adjusted to the needs of the organism. A comparison made of the performance of three subjects showed that one of them always lagged behind the others in rate of sweat production and consequently underwent a greater and sometimes an unpleasant increase of body temperature. Adaptation to high temperature involves an increased capacity to produce sweat, a greater sensitivity of the temperature regulatory apparatus, and an economy of salt. The effectiveness of adaptation varies from one person to another. . . . In acute failure such as that due to excessive salt loss or to a steadily rising [body] temperature the sweat glands may be primarily at fault; but the chronic effects of heat may be observed even when sweat secretion and temperature regulation are adequate. Failure that comes after days or weeks of exposure may be due to a slight downward trend in the 24-hour cycles which describe the course of fatigue and recovery. Anyone exposed to high temperature should take warning . . . if his degree of recovery decreases with each night of rest." (D. B. Dill: Life, Heat and Altitude, pp. 47-49.)

Dill notes, as many others before him, that the heat-regulating apparatus improves with training. Work which brought on complete exhaustion in an hour at Boston in summer could be carried on easily after a month's training at Boulder City, Colorado. Dill is sure that the high rates of chloride loss found by so many previous workers in hot environments are incorrect or else represent lack of acclimatization, for such high losses over many days would be disastrous. Indeed, he demonstrated that the body learns after a few days or more to sweat more volume but less chloride, a most important fact which C. K. Drinker emphasizes as "one of the few definite adaptations to high temperatures known to exist in man." But just how the body learns so to adapt its sweat volume and content is still a mystery; possibly it does so through increased nervous sensitivity to temperature, histological changes in the sweat glands, the effects of the dilatation, blood, and endocrine changes. The sweat glands can become so exhausted as to stop secreting, in which case heat stroke soon follows.

The cooling effect of sweating is only in proportion to the amount of sweat actually evaporated; the sweat that runs off the body serves no advantage. There is a hint in the opinions of some writers that the dark-skinned tropical races may have a mechanism for regulating the volume of sweat so that it is somewhat proportional to the amount that can be evaporated, maintaining a thin, even film which delivers more cooling to the skin than to the water itself and avoids waste of sweat and evaporating power. Such remains to be proven, and it is more likely that varying individual rather than racial powers of regulating sweat are in question here. The darker races are said to have more sweat glands, but the advantage of this has not been proved.

Production of sweat and insensible perspiration are under closest nervous control in the comfort zone (Fig. 82), where the heat losses balance heat production without sensibly straining the physical heat-regulating mechanisms. In this zone there is a close integration of the automatic reflexes from skin temperature and skin-temperature gradients that control perspiration, sweat glands, breathing, blood flow, and metabolism. Above the zone the regulation is not so perfect.

SOME TROPICAL EFFECTS ON BLOOD, VISCERA, AND BODY TONE

Blood pressure generally becomes somewhat lower in the tropics, probably owing to capillary flushing (although Mills maintains that the lowering is an indication of the relaxation of metabolism and general tone under endocrine control). Presumably in hot climates the blood volume increases to compensate for the supply withdrawn from the viscera to fill the dilated capillaries with plasma and fluid for perspiration and sweat. Failure adequately to maintain blood volume would lead to a steady impairment of the internal organs as the capillaries and sweat take their toll. The rise in blood volume is accompanied by a decrease in haemoglobin (from dilution) and the entrance of more new red corpuscles from the spleen into the active circulation. Such a diluted blood is an adaptation making greater sweat volume possible. The decreased blood viscosity also facilitates heat transfer to the extremities. There is increased alkalinity (pH) of the blood, which may increase the mental irritability ("choler") and sexual libido (Petersen), but disappears with exercise. Breathing is slightly deeper, economizing energy and facilitating cooling by evaporation from lungs. Oxygen is less per cubic foot in hot air than in cold air; less available O_2 restricts all functions and affects the blood, which may be a factor in tropical fatigue (Balfour); also, according to the remarkable studies of Duerst, even a moderately lower O_2 climate develops profound anatomical, blood, and endocrine adaptations.

Sweating removes much sodium, chlorine, potassium, and calcium from the blood and serum; loss of the last two may impair the nervous system and thus help to explain the effects of fatigue in the hot climate. Loss of calcium is serious in view of the calcium-deficient diets in many parts of the tropics. The loss of sodium chloride may be serious under active sweating and cause heat cramps, if salt is not adequately supplied in the diet or drinking water. The losses of minerals and the relative withdrawal of blood from the viscera lead to a reduction in gastric secretion, which impairs digestion and appetite, and to an atonic condition of the intestine (stasis, constipation). The high external temperature and rich carbohydrate diet alter the bacterial flora and favor infection in the intestines.

It is of interest to note that the most effective mechanisms of physical heat regulation, sweating and peripheral dilatation, also seem to have the most markedly deleterious effects on the blood homeostasis and on the tone of the internal organism, with a consequent generally lowered resistance to infection in the tropics. One is inclined to conclude that man was not made for hot climates, however adequate the temporary defenses against heat may be.

APPENDIX II
COMFORT ZONES AND ACCLIMATIZATION *

Engineers and hygienists have in recent years carried out a series of ingenious empirical studies in order to determine proper standards of comfort and health indoors. The katathermometer and other cooling-power instruments have been extensively used for such purposes abroad (see footnote references on p. 293), but in this country the famous "effective temperature index" and "comfort zones" of the American Society of Heating and Ventilating Engineers (ASHVE) seem to be somewhat more successful for indoor problems. They give us, incidentally, an unexpectedly welcome measure of the degree of acclimatization in quantitative terms. In this case we are dealing not with the scientific study of special physiological mechanisms of acclimatization but rather with the subjective response to the combined effects of all the factors, bodily and atmospheric—i. e., the approach is empirical.

Houghten, McConnell, and Yaglou (Yagloglou) in the ASHVE-U. S. Bureau of Mines laboratories first determined an arbitrary index, the "effective temperature" (E.T.),† for equating various combinations of humidity, temperature, and air movement that give the same sensation of warmth. A large number of persons of representative types, normally clothed or stripped to the waist, passed from one room to another in which air conditions were controlled and systematically varied; each person voted his sensation in each room and combination of conditions. A correlation of the results gave the desired "scale", which is always presented in the form of a graph instead of a formula.

Any given E. T. is assumed to indicate an equivalence of physiological heat or cold effect, for the majority of a population. This is roughly the case when the subjects are acclimatized (by the short-period type of adjustment), normally clothed, indoors, and in radiation equilibrium with the environment, and are not under conditions extrapolated far beyond those for which the E. T. was originally determined. Outdoors, with very high wind speeds, with solar radiation, or with very low temperatures, these limitations are not even approximately met. Nevertheless, the "comfort zones" that have been determined in terms of the E. T. are of great interest to the student of tropical settlement in spite of the restricted conditions to which they specifically apply.

Figure 82, which shows among other things the summer and winter comfort zones for the northeastern United States and the comfort zone for Batavia, Java, affords as significant a comparison as we could ask for.

The dry-bulb and wet-bulb temperatures, being fundamental and instrumentally-observed absolute quantities, are the coördinates in Figure 82, and the corresponding

* Selected references to important publications dealing with comfort zones follow (see also the references to the works of Bradtke and Liese, Büttner (1938), Conrad, Grimm, Hill, Müller, Vernon, and von Vintschgr, in the footnote on p. 293 below): C. Badham, C. F. Assheton, and H. E. Rayner: On the Index of Comfort In Ventilation of Theaters in Sydney, N. S. W., *Studies in Hyg.*, No. 10, *Rept. Dir. Publ. Health, N. S. W. for 1926, Sect. I-C, Ind. Hyg.*, 1928, p. 49 (deals with the comfort zone in terms of katathermometer readings, but is based on only one subject); F. C. Houghten, W. W. Teague, W. E. Miller, and W. P. Yant: Heat and Moisture Losses from Men at Work, and Application to Air Conditioning Problems, *Heating, Piping, and Air Conditioning*, Vol. 3, 1931, pp. 493 ff. (gives comfort zone for men at work); A. Lancaster: De la manière d'utiliser les observations hygrométriques, (Rapport lu au Vᵉ Congrès International d'Hydrologie, de Climatologie, et de Géologie Médicales de Liége . . . . 1898), Liége, 1899; F. Linke: W. F. Tylers Zonen der thermischen Unbehaglichkeit nach Beobachtungen in Shanghai, *Biokl. Beibl.*, Vol. 1, 1934, pp. 114-115; R. C. Partridge and D. L. MacLean: Determination of the Comfort Zone for School Children, *Journ. Indust. Hyg.*, Vol. 17, 1935, pp. 66 ff.; H. Ruge: Das Verhalten der Lufttemperatur und Luftfeuchtigkeit auf einem modernen Kreuzer in den Tropen, *Veröffentlichungen aus dem Gebiete des Marine-Sanitätswesens*, Heft 22, Berlin, 1932; W. F. Tyler: Bracing and Relaxing Climates, *Quart. Journ. Royal Met. Soc.*, Vol. 61, 1935, pp. 309-315, discussion, pp. 331-343; *idem*, A Means for the Comparison of Hot Climates, London, 1936 (abstract in *Rept. Brit. Assoc. for the Advancement of Sci.*, 1936, pp. 406-407); J. Vincent: La détermination de la température climatologique, *Ann. l'Obs. Royal de Belgique pour 1890; idem*, Nouvelles récherches sur la température climatologique, *Ann. l'Obs. Royal de Belgique pour 1907*, (reprinted by the Service Meteorologique de Belgique, 1907); C. P. Yaglou, W. H. Carrier, E. V. Hill, F. C. Houghten, and J. H. Walker; How to Use the Effective Temperature Index and Comfort Charts, *Heating, Piping, and Air Conditioning*, Vol. 4, 1932, pp. 433-434, with charts (a very useful summary which brings out the proper interpretation of the earlier studies by these authors).

† Note that this is an empirically determined value expressed in terms of arbitrary "degrees," which are not to be confused with the ordinary degrees of the Fahrenheit or Centigrade scales.

relative humidities are drawn upon the grid for convenience, thus forming an ordinary psychrometric nomogram. This nomogram may also be used as a base for plotting climograms (as in Figs. 83, 84, and 85), and when employed in this way is specially applicable for warm climates, where the humidity is important in comfort and health. (For climograms for the colder climates a dry cooling-power nomogram, such as

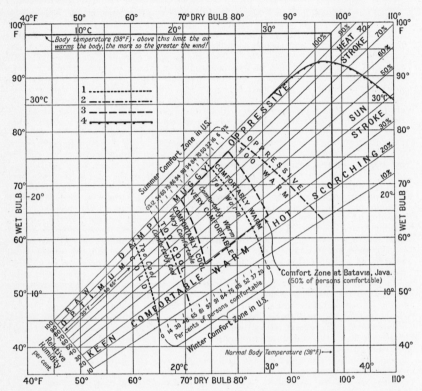

FIG. 82—Comfort and subjective sensations at various temperatures and humidities, for normally clothed and resting persons according to indoor chamber experiments and ordinary experience outdoors (see text for further details). Explanation: 1: "Winter Comfort Zone" indoors in the United States (Pittsburgh); 2: "Summer Comfort Zone" indoors in the United States (Boston); 3: "Comfort Zone" indoors at Batavia, Java. 4: Limit beyond which body temperature and pulse rate will rise rapidly with continued exposure and heat stroke is very likely to result. The terms parallel to the comfort-zone boundaries and in capital letters locate the distribution of subjective sensations within and just outside of the United States summer comfort zone; the similar terms in italic letters locate the same sensations with respect to the United States winter comfort zone. The terms parallel to the relative-humidity isolines locate very roughly the outdoor sensations in warm seasons and climates, as well as the range of optimum conditions for mental and physical effort, all based on the suggestions of Griffith Taylor and Ellsworth Huntington and the experience of the writer and other climatologists. Compare with Figures 83, 84, 85. (Comfort-zone data taken from C. P. Yaglou and P. Drinker, The Summer Comfort Zone: Climate and Clothing, *Jn. Ind. Hyg.*, Vol. 10, 1928, pp. 350-363; and C. P. Mom, Luchtbehandeling in de Tropen, *De Ingenieur in Nederlandsch-Indië*, No. 4, 1937.)

Figure 87, should be used as a base. The wet cooling-power nomogram shown in Figure 88 is in principle the most significant for climograms of warm climates, but the data for computing and interpreting it accurately are as yet inadequate).

The comfort zones shown on Figure 82 were determined from subjective votes of resting, normally clothed persons in controlled chamber experiments. The "too-warm" and "too-cold" limits of the American zones coincide with certain isolines of the arbitrary "effective-temperature index," and the corresponding comfort limits for Java are also almost parallel to E. T. lines. When plotted on a chart like Figure 82, the many comfort limits determined in other ways by other workers would not agree well because they are based on poorly controlled experiments with non-homogeneous conditions and subjects, or else on pure assumption; many, moreover, were determined in the temperate zone without allowance for acclimatization, so that their extrapolation to extremes of heat and humidity gives results that are more or less fictitious and contrary to experience.

The zone limited by Lines No. 1 is the winter comfort zone of the ASHVE, determined at Pittsburgh in 1923 by Houghten and Yagloglou. It was made for "still air" (≦ 25 ft. per min. velocity) and for normal healthy men and women of sedentary pursuits, at rest and with customary indoor clothing; they were given two hours indoor exposure before voting. Lines No. 2 limit the summer comfort zone based on sensations of a large group of men and women at Boston, Mass., wearing customary warm-weather clothing and engaged in sedentary pursuits. Their ages ranged from 22 to 72 years, but were for the most part between 22 and 37 years. The tests were made on summer afternoons during 1926-27. The percentages of the groups who were comfortable at different effective temperatures within the zones are marked on the chart; the limits of both zones are those beyond which not a single person was comfortable. These tests were made only between 30 and 75 per cent relative humidity; but the zones are extended to the extreme humidities by extrapolation along E. T. isolines; however, probably few people would be comfortable at relative humidities of more than 75 per cent or of less than 30 per cent, and the "average comfort zone" including a majority (50 per cent or a few more) of the people, as in the case of the Java zone, does not include such extremes. However, the Java zone reaches a relative humidity of 90 per cent, indicating that more people feel comfortable there at high humidities than in the United States—no doubt a mark of adaptation to the higher average humidity of the Java climate. The centers of the zones may be taken as the optimum conditions for comfort. The spread between the winter and the summer zones is a good measure of the degree of acclimatization due both to change of clothing and to physiological adaptations to the season in the United States. Similar spreads have been found in Europe by Vernon, Lange, and others, using similar as well as different methods.

Lines No. 3 give the comfort zone for Batavia, Java, found by Mom in the same manner as the American zones; the area is smaller than that of the summer zone in the United States because Mom includes only the area in which 50 per cent or more of the people are comfortable, but the optimum is about the same. This is a most striking fact, for it suggests that Americans become acclimatized to their summer much as people do to the tropic heat, in respect to comfort at least. Effects of more prolonged exposure are not revealed by this method, of course. Mom's subjects were clad in light tropical dress and included Javanese, Chinese, and Europeans, whose comfort zones he found were very nearly the same.

Line No. 4 is the limit above which continued exposure (at rest in a room) for an hour or more leads to a steady rise in body temperature and pulse rate, and hence to early heat stroke if collapse does not occur sooner (based on data by McConnell and Houghten). Above this limit the level of the wet-bulb temperature alone determines how soon collapse will take place in a healthy person, i. e., in "still air" and without marked irradiation from sun or walls (which would lower the limit in terms of temperature, wind, and humidity).

The effect of wind and sunshine on these zones is of course important for outdoor conditions and can be indicated approximately by the use of some instrument for measuring the wet cooling-power. In general, wind skews all the zones toward the right of the chart, more so at lower humidities; sunshine shifts them considerably to the left.

The present writer has attempted to indicate roughly on Figure 82 the types of sensation a person experiences outdoors in summer or warm climates, assuming normal clothing, moderate wind, and the sunshine likely to occur for various temperatures at high and low humidities; this, however, is only a personal impression reënforced by the results of observations and experiments of others. The general range of conditions including the "optimum" of Taylor and Huntington is also shown, except that for mental work this reaches down to below 38° F., which is off the chart. The sensations inscribed parallel to the relative-humidity lines apply chiefly to the extremes of humidity; the intermediate humidities give either less clear-cut sensations or else the same sensation that the same wet-bulb temperature gives at the lower humidities.

It is noteworthy that Mom finds similar comfort conditions for Javanese, Chinese, and Europeans. This may be taken to indicate either that the optimum climate is the same for these races or else, if we accept Huntington's data (see p. 197 above), that the comfort zone and the optimum for civilization or health cannot be entirely the same thing. The air-conditioning authorities do not hold that comfort and health are necessarily the same, and when one considers the various deleterious effects claimed for tropical climates (in spite of acclimatization through mechanisms of metabolism and heat loss), one must conclude that comfort and health should not be assumed to be synonymous.

The indoor comfort zone, according to actual tests, coincides with a range of conditions over which the total bodily heat production and heat loss just about balance at the same caloric value (range approximately 63°-85° F. in Figs. 80 and 81; compare Figs. 78 and 82). This fact leads the engineer to define comfortable indoor air conditions as those under which the body is able to maintain such a normal balance at normal body temperature without sensations of undue effort on the part of the heat-regulating mechanism. The use of the engineer's E. T. chart (see ASHVE Annual Guide) may mislead one into thinking that it makes no difference to comfort or health what the proportions of heat lost by radiation, convection, and evaporation are, so long as the index shows a comfortable combination of temperature, humidity, and air movement (loss and gain by radiation are assumed to balance and hence are not accounted for by the E. T.), and so long as heat production is balanced by heat loss. This is not true, however, for if one is losing nearly all of one's heat production by evaporation, for example, one is not likely to feel comfortable and such a condition would not be healthful if prolonged.

Here again we run directly into the dilemma that comfort and health are not always the same, for a very high temperature is deleterious, as we know, even if the humidity is low enough and the wind high enough to make it feel comfortable (after acclimatization). Strauss and Walther (see note 39, p. 265, above), in studying the significance of the cooling power for work in hot environments, stated the same opinion and warned that there is no assurance that the katathermometer is a safe guide to the healthfulness of working conditions even when it shows them to be comfortable. However, since work in comfortable but hot rooms or mines is usually alternated daily with a change to the cooler outdoors, this criticism does not have the force for air conditioning in the temperate zone that it does for acclimatization in the tropics, where the heat is apt to be ceaseless. Another criticism of the use of the comfort zone as an index of the healthfulness or the optimum of climates is already implied by Huntington's work, viz., that a certain amount of variability about the optimum is desirable; practically all physiologists recognize that some limited shakeup of the metabolism at intervals is healthful, even if it necessitates exercising in a hot climate.

Through correlation of the E. T. with certain physiologic conditions and with efficiency in work suggestive results have been obtained, as, for example, the discovery that ability for mental work does not diminish at an E. T. of as high as 68°, but with a rise from 68° to 75° there is a decrease of 15 per cent in physical efficiency. However, since the E. T. has been evaluated only over the limited range needed for indoor problems and all correlations made with it are likewise limited, it is difficult and unwise to infer their definite significance for the problem of outdoor climatic effects, especially in view of the solar radiation and wind found outdoors but not indoors, and the possible deteriorating effects of long exposures.

The research of the air-conditioning laboratories, while directed to the practical solution of problems much smaller in scope than those of climate in general, nevertheless has the virtue of being undogmatically empirical, on the whole free from useless speculations, and fairly well subsidized financially owing to the large commercial interest in the background. The field of outdoor bioclimatology is vastly more complex and needs more scientific methods and a better coördination with physiology. On the physical-climatic side, the magnitude and behavior of each factor has to be accurately measured over a period of time before we can say that the climatological stress on the body is adequately known; this stage of research has just begun—the rough estimates attempted by Dorno (see Lahmeyer and Dorno, "Assuan," Braunschweig, 1932) were pioneering ones and show us the kind of data that must be gathered before the effects of a climate can be scientifically studied. In the meantime, resort must be had to indirect and empirical statistical studies which are rarely conclusive because the specific effects of the various factors are neither isolated properly nor revealed in physically or physiologically proven mechanisms.

EXPLANATION OF FIGS. 83-85—Climograms for selected stations in the tropics, with (in Fig. 83) Professor Griffith Taylor's "type-white climogram." Professor Taylor defines a climograph, or climogram, as "a graph in which the twelve Mean Monthly Values of Wet-bulb Temperatures and Relative Humidity at a given place, are plotted as a twelve-sided polygon, with Wet-bulb Ordinates and [Relative] Humidity Abscissae" (Griffith Taylor: The Control of Settlement by Humidity and Temperature, Commonwealth Bureau of Meteorology, *Bull. No. 14,* 1916, p. 16, note). On the present climograms, however, dry-bulb temperatures are the abscissae and the relative humidities may be determined by reference to the sloping percentage scale. The "type-white climogram" is plotted from data of 12 places, five in the southern hemisphere, seven in the northern, which are "typical of the regions where white energy is at its best." (*Ibid.,* p. 18.)

An index letter for each station and the abbreviation "Jan." for the type-white climogram (here marked as for the southern hemisphere) indicate the position of January. The positions of the succeeding months, in order in the directions indicated by the arrowheads, are shown by the angles made by the lines (angles of approximately 180° are shown by ticks, or, on the type-white climogram, by dots). See also Fig. 82.

Long, narrow climograms are representative of stations having a considerable range of temperature, whereas wide climograms indicate a comparatively large range in humidity. The climograms for stations at high altitudes owing to lower temperatures tend to occur near the lower left-hand corners of the charts and those for stations near sea level are nearer the upper right-hand corners.

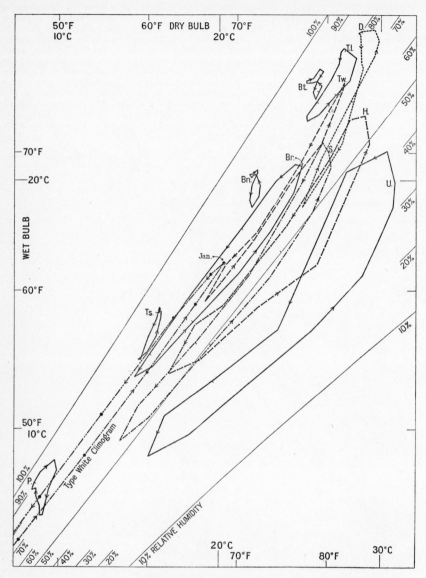

FIG. 83—Climograms for selected stations in Australia and Java. See also explanation, opposite. Based on data from the Köppen-Geiger "Handbuch der Klimatologie," Vol. IV, Part R and Vol. 4, Part S, and the Australian Council for Scientific and Industrial Research, *Pamphlet No. 42.* Key to stations: Bn., Bandoeng, Java (6° 55′ S, 107° 40′ E, elev. 2420′); Br., Brisbane, Queensland (27° 28′ S, 153° 02′ E, 137′); Bt., Batavia, Java (6° 12′ S, 106° 50′ E, 22′); D., Darwin, Northern Territory (12° 28′ S, 130° 51′ E, 97′); H., Hughenden, Queensland (20° 51′ S, 144° 13′ E, 1074′); P., Pangerango, Java (10,000′); S., Springsure, Queensland (24° 07′ S, 148° 20′ E, 1057′); Ts., Tosari, Java (7° 50′ S, 112° 50′ E, 5693′); Tw., Townsville, Queensland (19° 14′ S, 146° 49′ E, 72′); U., Urandangie, Queensland (21° 35′ S, 138° 24′ E, 550′).

20

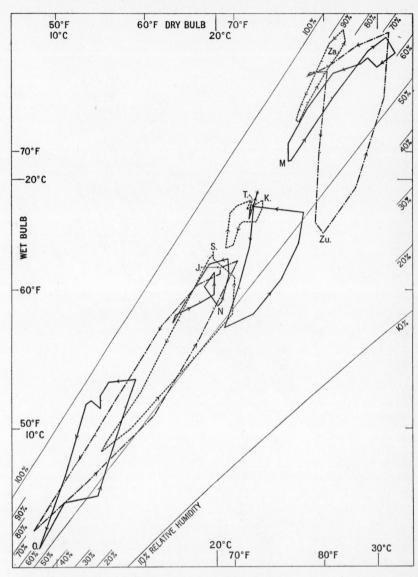

FIG. 84—Climograms for selected stations in Africa and India. See also explanation, p. 288. Based on figures from the Köppen-Geiger "Handbuch der Klimatologie," Vol. V, Part X; the South and East African Yearbook and Guide for 1938; A. Walter: The Climate of British East Africa, *Quart. Journ. of the Royal Meteorological Soc.*, January, 1938; C. E. P. Brooks: The Distribution of Temperature over Nigeria, *ibid.*, April, 1920; and A. Knox: The Climate of the Continent of Africa, 1911. Key to stations: J., Johannesburg, South Africa (26° 13′ S, 28° 56′ E, elev. 5735′); K., Kampala, Uganda (0° 19′ N, 32° 35′ E); M., Madras, India (13° 4′ N, 80° 7′ E, 22′); N., Nairobi, Kenya (1° 18′ S, 36° 52′ E, 5495′); O., Ootacamund, India (11° 24′ N, 76° 44′ E, 7252); S., Salisbury, Southern Rhodesia (17° 54′ S, 31° 30′ E, 4894′); T., Tabora, Tanganyika (5° 3′ S, 32° 53′ E, 4035′); Za., Zanzibar, East Africa (6° 0′ S, 39° 20′ E, sea level); Zu., Zungeru, Nigeria (9° 45′ N, 6° 5′ E, 608′).

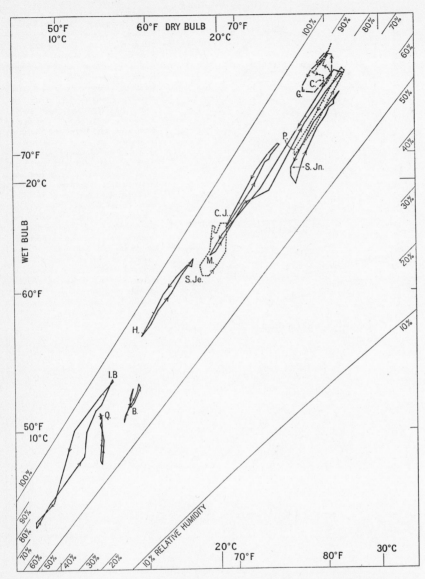

Fig. 85—Climograms for selected stations in tropical America. See explanation, p. 288. Based on data from the Köppen-Geiger "Handbuch der Klimatologie," Vol. II, Part G, and Vol. II, Part I, and U. S. Weather Bureau: Summaries of Climatological Data by Sections, *Bulletin W*. Key to stations: B., Bogotá, Colombia (4° 34′ N, 74° 5′ W, elev. 8727′); C. J., Camp Jacob, Guadeloupe (16° N, 61° 50′ W, 1756′); C., Colon, Panama (9° 21′ N, 79° 56′ W, sea level); G., Greytown, Nicaragua (10° 58′ N, 83° 47′ W, sea level); H., Hill Gardens, Jamaica (18° 0′ N, 77° 0′ W, 492′); I. B., Itatiaya, Brazil (22° 30′ S, 43° 0′ W, 7480′); M., Miami (25° 46′ N, 80° 12′ W, 83′); P., Philipsburg, St. Martin (18° 0′ N, 63° 3′ W, sea level); Q., Quito, Ecuador (0° 10′ S, 78° 35′ W, 9350′); S. Je., San José, Costa Rica (9° 58′ N, 84° 2′ W, 3725′); S. Jn., St. John, Antigua (17° 9′ N, 61° 51′ W, 79′).

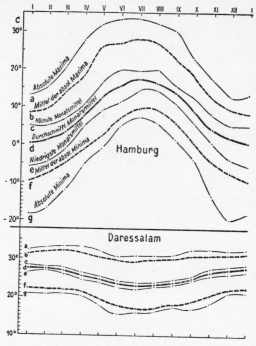

FIG. 86—The annual march of temperature (centigrade) at Hamburg, Germany, and at Dar-es-Salaam, Tanganyika Territory (from Fig. 2 in Gerhard Castens: Vom monatlichen Wetter- und Witterungs-Spielraum in den heimischen Breiten und in den Tropen: Hamburg und Daressalam (Ostafrika), *Zweites Köppenheft der Ann. der Hydrogr. und marit. Meteorol.*, 1936, p. 8). The figure illustrates the even temperatures throughout the year at a station typical of the equatorial coastal lowlands as contrasted with the wide range characteristic of a cool-temperate climate. Compare with climogram for Zanzibar, about 50 miles from Dar-es-Salaam (Fig. 84).

Explanation: For each month the diagram shows: a, absolute maxima (highest temperatures on record); b, means of absolute maxima (means of highest temperatures recorded each year of record); c, highest monthly means; d, average monthly means; e, lowest monthly means; f, means of absolute minima; g, absolute minima.

APPENDIX III

A NOTE ON THE COOLING POWER *

The "cooling power" may be defined as the net rate at which heat can be taken up from any body by its environment. In climatology and human physiology it is conventionally measured with respect to some standard object, such as a glass thermometer or copper sphere, which is heated at a constant rate to maintain a temperature of 98° F., on the analogy of the human body. When the object or body is dry and does not evaporate any moisture, it is said to be subjected to a "dry cooling power," and when fully wet to a "wet cooling power." The small glass "katathermometer" invented by Sir Leonard Hill is the simplest and most widely used of the standard cooling-power instruments both in climatological studies and in public health and ventilation work.

This instrument does not imitate the human body very closely because it is too small and has a somewhat different behavior with respect to radiations and to its surface temperature. Consequently, it gives heat losses from one third to ten times higher than those that actually take place from the human body for the same unit of area and time. However, all bioclimatologists believe that the katathermometer gives

* There follows a selection of references to certain of the more important publications dealing with the cooling power and its evaluation and interpretation. T. Bedford and C. G. Warner: The Influence of Radiant Heat and Air Movement on the Cooling of the Kata-thermometer, *Journ. Hyg.*, Vol. 33, 1933, pp. 330 ff.; F. Bradtke and W. Liese: Hilfsbuch für raum- und aussenklimatische Messungen, mit besonderer Berücksichtigung des Katathermometers, Berlin, 1937 (very useful summary of German studies); K. Brose: Der jährliche Gang der Windgeschwindigkeit auf der Erde, *Wiss. Abhandl. Reichsamt für Wetterdienst*, Vol. 1, No. 4, Berlin, 1936 (guide to the wind-velocity data for the whole world); K. Büttner: Kritisches über Abkühlungsgrösse, *Met. Zeitschr.*, Vol. 50, 1933, pp. 129-130; *idem*, Physikalische Bioklimatologie, Leipzig, 1938 (best technical discussion from physiological and physical point of view); V. Conrad: Physikalische und Klimatische Abkühlungsgrösse, *Zeitschr. Angew. Met. (Das Wetter)*, Vol. 54, 1937, pp. 206-216 (see also the same author's summary of the subject in the Köppen-Geiger Handbuch der Klimatologie, Vol. I, Pt. B, pp. 547-554); C. Dorno: über geeignete Klimadarstellungen, *Zeitschr. Physik. und Diätet. Therapie*, Vol. 26, 1922, pp. 293 ff.: *idem*, Über spezifisch-medizinische Klimatologie, *Met. Zeitschr.*, Vol. 39, 1922, pp. 344-346; *idem*, Papers on the Relation of the Atmosphere to Human Comfort, *Mo. Weather Rev.*, Vol. 54, 1926, pp. 39-43; *idem*, Über kombinierte meteorologisch-physikalisch-physiologische Klimastudien, *Zeitschr. Gesch. Physik. Therapie*, Vol. 31, 1927; *idem*, Grundzüge des Klimas von Muottas-Muraigl (Oberengadin): Eine meteorologisch-physikalisch-physiologische Studie, *Schweizerisches Inst. Hochgebirges Physiolog. und Tuberkulose-Forschung in Davos*, Heft 3, Braunschweig, 1927; *idem*, Das Klima von Agra (Tessin): Eine dritte und letzte meteorologisch-physikalisch-physiologische Studie, Braunschweig, 1934; C. Dorno and R. Thilenius: Das Davos Frigorimeter, *Zeitschr. Gesch. physikalische Therapie*, Vol. 29, 1925, Heft 2; S. F. Dudley: The Katathermometer at Sea in the Tropics, *Journ. Royal Navy Med. Serv.*, Vol. 14, 1928, pp. 77-103 (see also *Bull. Hyg.*, Vol. 3, 1928, p. 671); H. Grimm: Abkühlungsgrösse und Kleidung im Unterricht, *Zeitschr. Angew. Met. (Das Wetter)*, Vol. 52, 1935, pp. 362-364; Leonard Hill: The Science of Ventilation and Open Air Treatment, Parts I and II, *Med. Res. Council Repts. 32*, and *52*, London, 1919, 1920 (classic and indispensable work on the cooling power in human bioclimatology in the tropics and temperate zones); L. Hill, T. C. Angus, and E. M. Newbold: Further Experimental Observations to Determine the Ratio Between Kata-cooling Power and Atmospheric Conditions, *Journ. Ind. Hyg.*, Vol. 10, 1928, pp. 391 ff.; The Katathermometer in Studies of Body Heat and Efficiency, *Med. Res. Council Spec. Rept. Ser. No. 73*, London, 1923 (papers by L. Hill, H. M. Vernon, and others); F. Lahmeyer and C. Dorno: Assuan: Eine meteorologisch-physikalisch-physiologische Studie, Braunschweig, 1932; H. Lehmann: Mikroklimatische Untersuchungen der Abkühlungsgrösse in einem Waldgebiete, *Veröffentl. Geophysik. Inst. Univ. Leipzig*, 2nd Ser., Spezialarb. aus d. Geophysik. Inst. u. Obs., Vol. 7, No. 4, 1936 (best recent study of the katathermometer); F. Linke: Physikalische Abkühlungsgrösse und Wärmeabgabe des menschlichen Körpers, *Zeitschr. Gesch. Physik. Therapie*, Vol. 39, 1930, pp. 287-293; W. J. McConnell and C. P. Yagloglou: The Katathermometer: Its Value and Defects, *U. S. Bur. of Mines Repts. of Investigations, Ser. No. 2565*, January, 1924; W. Mörikofer: Zur Klimatologie der Abkühlungsgrösse, *Acta Davosiana*, Vol. 1, No. 3, Oct. 1933; A. Müller: Die Anwendung des "Davoser Frigorimeters" zur Bestimmung des Wärmehaltungsvermögens von Kleiderstoffen, *Arb. Reichsgesundheitsamt*, Vol. 57, 1926, pp. 314-317; J. Siegenthaler: Ein Beitrag zur Frage der Abkühlungs-Wirkung des Windes bei Bekleidung, *Bioklimat. Beibl.*, 1934, pp. 25-28; *idem*, Zur Frage der abkühlenden Wirkung des Windes auf mehrfach bekleidete Körper, *ibid.*, 1936, p. 53; H. M. Vernon: Is Effective Temperature or Cooling Power the Better Index of Comfort?, *Journ. Indust. Hyg.*, Vol. 8, 1926, pp. 392 ff.; *idem*, The Estimation of Solar Radiation in Relation to its Warming Effect on the Human Body, *Quart. Journ. Royal Met. Soc.*, Vol. 59, 1933, pp. 239 ff.; H. M. Vernon, T. Bedford, and C. G. Warner: The Influence of Cooling Power and of Variability of Air Currents on Sensations of Air Movements, *Med. Res. Council, Spec. Rept. Ser. No. 100*, Part III, London, 1926; J. von Vintschgr: Das Wärme-Isolierungsvermögen der Kleidungsstoffe gemessen mit Hilfe des "Davoser Frigorimeters," *Arch. für Hyg. u. Bakter.*, Vol. 101, 1929, pp. 261-289; C. P. Yagloglou [now Yaglou]: The Thermal Index of Atmospheric Conditions and Its Application to Sedentary and Industrial Life, *Journ. Indust. Hyg.*, Vol. 8, 1926, pp. 5 ff.; *idem*, Effective Temperature Versus Katathermometer: A Reply to H. M. Vernon, *ibid.*, Vol. 8, 1926, p. 402; C. P. Yaglou, A. P. Kratz, and C. E. A. Winslow: Instruments and Methods for Recording Thermal Factors Affecting Human Comfort, *Year Book Amer. Publ. Health Assn.*, 1936-37, pp. 84 ff.

a good idea of the strain that the atmosphere puts upon the body's metabolism and heat-regulating mechanisms. Other instruments (the Davos frigorimeter, Pfleiderer-Büttner frigorigraph, heated-globe thermometer, etc.) have been invented to reproduce the bodily reactions somewhat more closely than does the "kata," but they are more complicated and expensive. In the last analysis there is no "normal body," and it is probably impossible to make any instrument that would imitate such a body, even if it did exist. Although the "kata" is a simple instrument, its use is now on the wane for both indoor ventilating studies and climatological observations. Indeed, for

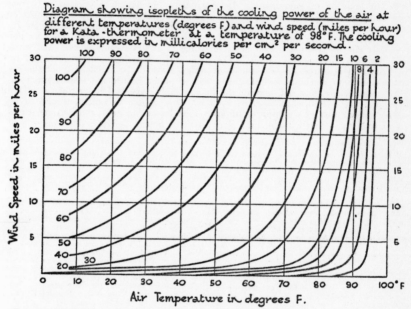

Diagram showing isopleths of the cooling power of the air at different temperatures (degrees F) and wind speed (miles per hour) for a Kata-thermometer at a temperature of 98° F. The cooling power is expressed in millicalories per cm² per second.

FIG. 87—A nomogram for computing the dry cooling power in the shade (reproduced from Gold: The Effect of Wind, etc., p. 317). See text for explanation.

general climatic purposes the computation of the cooling power with the aid of nomograms such as Figures 87 or 88 is recommended in preference to measuring it with instruments. Maps and statistics of the cooling powers in different climates would be of the utmost value with respect to many problems of settlement.

Under cold or cool conditions when the body does not sweat and the clothes are dry, it is the dry cooling power that directly applies to man (Fig. 87). For warm or moist conditions that lead to sweating the wet cooling power must be used (see Fig. 88); customarily both dry and wet cooling powers are computed. Above 98° F. (body temperature) the dry cooling power ceases and a dry warming power sets in. Since the body always sweats before such a condition is reached, the dry warming power is not ordinarily considered, though actually it operates to warm the body even while evaporation is cooling it. The wet cooling power above 98° F. is thus in reality the net difference between the dry warming power and the evaporating power.

The interpretation of the cooling-power values may be simplified and generalized by expressing them in terms of the human subjective sensations with which they are correlated, though such correlations can never be anything more than approximate owing to many other variable factors that also affect sensations. "Sensation scales" based on outdoor correlations of the readings of a katathermometer or other cooling-power instrument with the simultaneous feelings of representative persons have been published for a number of places, but they do not agree very closely. In general, in western Europe a dry "kata" cooling power of less than 5 may be either very warm or unbearably hot, 10-20 is pleasant, bracing, or slightly cool, and higher than 30 is cold. Between these intervals there is much overlapping of the scales for different climates.

For Vizagapatam, in India, Reddy gives the following sensation scale for the dry "kata" (shade readings): "intolerable," 0.9 in summer; "sultry," 1.4 in summer and 2.7 in winter; "just tolerable," 2.9 in summer and 3.8 in winter; "fine, pleasant," 4.4 in summer and 6.5 in winter; "cool, bracing," 6.6 in summer and 7.8 in winter. These fig-

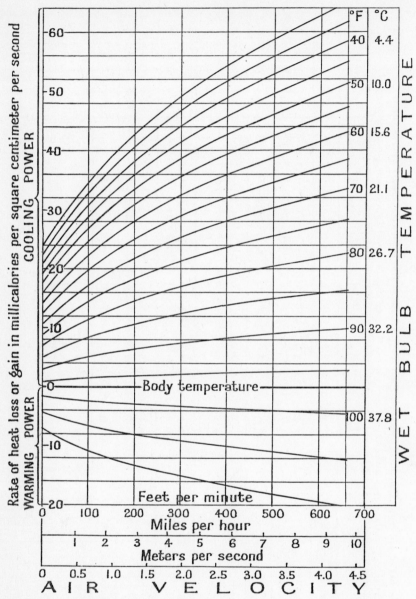

FIG. 88—A nomogram for computing the wet-cooling power in the shade (adapted from C. P. Yaglou and K. Dokoff: Calibration of the Kata-thermometer Over a Wide Range of Air Conditions, *Journ. Ind. Hygiene*, Vol. 10, 1928, p. 289). See text for explanation.

ures show a definite acclimatization to the small seasonal range of the cooling power in this climate. The wet "kata" averaged (for the entire year) 5.0 for "sultry," 7.0 for "just tolerable," and 9.6 for "fine, pleasant." On the Bengal Bay coasts the wet kata reading of 8 marks about the lower limit of comfort. The wet cooling-power, however, cannot be correlated so well with the feelings, because the degree of wetness of the human body varies so much.

In Table XVII are presented mean monthly cooling powers as determined with the katathermometer for various stations in the tropics and also for comparison for stations in England and Canada. Table XVIII gives cooling-power averages for Rio de Janeiro

TABLE XVII—MEAN MONTHLY COOLING POWERS AT VARIOUS STATIONS AS DETERMINED BY THE KATATHERMOMETER

All data "in the shade" and average for the day except as noted. D=dry kata, W=wet kata cooling power, respectively

Place	Element	Jan.	Feb.	Mar.	Apr.	May	June	July	Aug.	Sept.	Oct.	Nov.	Dec.
Madras[a], India (daily average)	D	11.4	10.2	8.6	7.3	5.0	4.7	6.2	6.7	6.6	7.7	10.4	11.2
Madras 2 P.M.[b] (in sun)	D	5.4	5.9	3.9	4.8	0.0	0.1	1.2	1.1	2.2	4.7	5.3	5.2
	W	21.2	21.8	21.2	18.1	18.3	18.1	16.3	16.5	18.3	16.9	21.0	20.2
Darjeeling[a], India	D	24.9	28.8	28.0	25.5	22.1	20.3	16.0	16.2	16.9	18.4	19.8	22.5
Vizagapatam[b], India (17°42′N, 83°20′E)	D min.	...	...	...	...	0.4	1.2	1.7	0.7	1.1	2.1	3.4	3.7
	D max.	...	...	...	...	5.0	5.8	8.8	14.2	7.0	9.4	10.0	9.6
	D av.	...	...	...	...	1.6	2.6	3.0	3.2	2.8	3.6	5.4	6.1
Sierra Leone[a], West Africa	D	7.7	8.0	8.1	8.4	8.7	9.4	10.6	12.2	10.4	9.0	7.9	7.4
	W	20.8	21.3	20.8	20.8	21.8	21.8	24.3	26.2	23.5	21.4	19.6	19.0
Kimberley[a], South Africa	D	13.7	12.9	15.4	17.8	22.1	25.2	25.1	24.2	22.4	19.9	17.2	13.5
	W	40.6	37.7	39.5	41.4	49.2	53.9	53.8	53.1	51.0	48.3	45.2	41.0
Witwatersrand, South Africa	D	23.9	23.9	24.7	27.3	31.5	34.5	36.0	35.4	31.1	28.4	26.4	26.4
Dar-es-Salaam[c], Tanganyika	D 7 A.M.	12.0	...	12.0	...	14.0	...	16.0	...	15.0	...	11.0	...
	D 2 P.M.	10.0	...	9.0	...	11.0	...	13.0	...	15.0	...	12.0	...
	W 7 A.M.	28.0	...	27.0	...	31.0	...	36.0	...	34.0	...	27.0	...
	W 2 P.M.	27.0	...	26.0	...	39.0	...	35.0	...	37.0	...	30.0	...

TABLE XVII—MEAN MONTHLY COOLING POWERS AT VARIOUS STATIONS AS DETERMINED BY THE KATATHERMOMETER—Continued.

PLACE	ELEMENT	JAN.	FEB.	MAR.	APR.	MAY	JUNE	JULY	AUG.	SEPT.	OCT.	NOV.	DEC.
Tabora[c], Tanganyika	D 7 A.M.	19.0	...	19.0	...	26.0	...	32.0	...	24.0	...	18.0	...
	D 2 P.M.	12.0	...	12.0	...	12.0	...	12.0	...	9.0	...	9.0	...
	W 7 A.M.	40.0	...	42.0	...	53.0	...	63.0	...	53.0	...	42.0	...
	W 2 P.M.	32.0	...	33.0	...	37.0	...	40.0	...	35.0	...	34.0	...
Brisbane, Queensland	D 9 A.M.[e]	11.0	11.2	11.7	13.5	15.5	16.6	17.0	16.6	14.9	13.7	12.5	11.5
	D (day)[d]	15.0	16.0	17.0	19.0	22.0	26.0	26.0	25.0	22.0	20.0	18.0	16.0
Townsville, Queensland	D 9 A.M.	8.8	8.8	9.7	11.0	13.0	14.2	14.4	13.9	12.7	11.0	9.9	9.1
Kew[a], England	D	38.3	39.6	40.2	34.6	27.3	24.3	21.4	21.4	24.9	26.2	36.1	38.1
	W	67.5	68.7	68.6	62.7	52.0	47.6	42.4	42.0	47.1	51.1	...	66.7
Quebec[a], Canada	D	48.7	62.8	41.5	47.3	19.4	22.6	18.4	19.8	37.4	28.4	44.9	44.4
	W	81.2	97.8	71.5	79.3	44.4	43.2	41.2	41.6	67.2	61.8	75.8	74.5

[a] Data from Leonard Hill: The Science of Ventilation and Open Air Treatment, Part I, National Health Insurance, Medical Research Committee, Special Report Series No. 32, London, 1919.

[b] Data from D. V. S. Reddy: Comfort Standards in the Tropics, Journ. Indian Medical Assn. Vol. 4. 1935. pp. 593-600.

[c] Data from G. Castens: Über Tropenklimatologie, Ann. der Hydrogr., Vol. 53, 1925, pp. 177-187.

[d] Data from W. A. Macky: Some Comparisons of the Invigorating Effect of the Climate in Different Parts of New Zealand, New Zealand Journ. of Science and Technology, Vol. 19, No. 3, 1937, p. 169.

[e] Data from H. Barkley: Zones of Physical Comfort in Australia, Commonweath Bureau of Meteorology, Bull. No. 20, 1934, p. 7.

and Karlsruhe, Germany, as determined by Dorno with aid of the so-called "Davos-frigorimeter," devised by him.

Figures 87 and 88 are nomograms for computing the dry and the wet cooling powers in the shade, given the wind velocity and the air temperature (wet-bulb in the case of the wet cooling power).

Figure 87 is plotted from a formula of Sir Leonard Hill published in 1923 for a calibration of the cooling of a katathermometer kept at 98° F. in a wind tunnel in which the atmospheric variables could be controlled. Although numerous calibrations

TABLE XVIII—Cooling Powers at Rio De Janeiro and Karlsruhe as Measured with the Davos Frigorimeter*

Monthly 24-hour means and monthly mean daily maximum and mean minimum values.

| | RIO DE JANEIRO | | | KARLSRUHE | | |
| | Mean | Mean Daily | | Mean | Mean Daily | |
		Max.	Min.		Max.	Min.
January..................	3.5	10.1	1.3	16.9	27.0	8.6
February.................	...	no data		11.3	32.3	6.6
March...................	3.1	8.7	1.2	17.0	30.8	8.2
April....................	3.1	7.5	2.0	11.1	18.0	4.6
May.....................	4.9	10.1	2.4	9.6	14.6	3.5
June....................	6.1	11.3	3.0	8.0	12.1	2.7
July....................	6.1	10.0	3.4	7.5	13.1	1.9
August..................	6.3	9.3	3.5	5.8	17.3	2.7
September...............	5.6	9.9	3.6	6.8	10.7	2.3
October.................	6.3	15.0	2.3	13.4	25.5	5.9
November................	4.2	7.6	1.5	12.5	22.9	8.3
December................	4.5	12.0	1.7	24.0	40.7	13.0
Year....................	4.9	10.1	2.4	12.0	22.1	5.7

*From C. Dorno: Die Abkuhlüngsgrösse in verschiedenen Klimaten nach Dauerregistrierungen mittels des "Davoser Frigorimeters," *Meteorol. Zeitschr.*, Vol. 45, 1928, pp. 407-409. Dorno gives the following comfort scale for these figures: C. P. 20, disagreeably cold; 15 cold; 12.5 agreeably cold; 10.0 cool; 7.5 pleasantly cool; 5.0 pleasantly warm; 2.5 hot. (All for clothing normal and suitable to the conditions.)

giving slightly different formulae have been published, the one most widely used by climatologists is due to Hill and is approximately of the form: H (the dry cooling power) $= (0.15 + 0.182\sqrt{v})$ $(98° - t)$, where v is the wind velocity in miles per hour and t is the ordinary dry-bulb temperature of the air in degrees F. (ventilated and in the shade) (E. Gold: The Effect of Wind, Temperature, Humidity and Sunshine on the Loss of Heat of a Body at Temperature 98° F., *Quart. Journ. Roy. Met. Soc.*, Vol. 61, 1935, pp. 316-331; reference on p. 318). As radiational heat loss and heat gain are assumed to cancel each other in this formula, it applies only in the shade and even there only approximately, since diffuse and reflected light by day or radiation to cold ground or clouds by night may have some effect. The cooling power measured by a katathermometer in the sun or in a room includes the effects of all radiational forces. As it is rather too difficult in practice to compute the radiational effects by a formula, we must content ourselves with the "shade" indication alone when using the formula or Figure 87 for evaluating the cooling power. Full sunshine greatly reduces the cooling power, it should be remembered. Clothing ordinarily cuts the cooling power by anywhere from 20 to 75 per cent.

Figure 88, for the wet cooling power, is plotted from the results of a calibration of a wet katathermometer under controlled atmospheric conditions. Radiational income and outgo of heat are assumed to balance; sunshine would lower the cooling power markedly, other factors being the same. The warming-power range, when the wet-bulb temperature is higher than the kata's (or, by analogy, the body's) temperature is also shown. The algebraic formula for such a diagram would be approximately of the form: H' (wet cooling power) $= (0.06 + 0.47 \sqrt[3]{v})\,(98° - t)$, where v is the wind velocity in miles per hour and t' is the ordinary wet-bulb temperature from a ventilated psychrometer in degrees F. (Gold, *loc. cit.*)

APPENDIX IV

ADDITIONAL REFERENCES ON PHYSIOLOGY AND ACCLIMATIZATION IN THE TROPICS

The following selected references are intended to supplement and round out those given in the Notes to Chapters XIV and XV on acclimatization and health and in the footnotes on pages 275, 284 and 293 above.

ABBATUCCI, S. Climat; acclimatisation. *Rév. d'Hyg.*, Vol. 55, 1933, pp. 505-526.

BENEDICT, F. G. Vital energetics: a study in comparative basal metabolism. *Carnegie Instn. of Washington Publ. 503*, 1938.

BORCHARDT, W. Beiträge zur Klimaphysiologie und Psychologie der Tropen, *Arch. Schiffs-u. Trop.-Hyg.*, Vol. 33, 1929, p. 505 ff.

BORCHARDT, W. Grundumsatz und spezifisch-dynamische Wirkung in künstlichem Tropenklima. *Arch. Schiffs-u. Trop.-Hyg.*, Vol. 34, 1930, p. 258 ff.

BORCHARDT, W. Die physiologische Chemie des Blutes in den Tropen. *Arch. Schiffs-u. Trop.-Hyg.*, Vol. 34, 1930, p. 608 ff.

BORCHARDT, W. Die Bedeutung der Gefassreaktionen des Peripheren und des Splanchnicusgebietes für den Tropenbewohner. *Arch. Schiffs-u. Trop.-Hyg.*, Vol. 35, 1931, p. 69 ff.

CAMIS, M. Metabolismo basali ed alimentazione in Somalia: Primo contributo alle fisiologia tropicale in Africa Orientale. Rome, 1936.

CHAKRAVARTI, D. N., and TYAGI, N. Biochemical and physical changes in 10 cases suffering from "effects of heat." *Indian Journ. Med. Res.*, Vol. 25, 1938, pp. 791-827.

CONTI, G. Comportamento della secrezione acida dello stomaco nell pasaggio dai climi temperati a quelle tropicali. *Ann. Med. Navale e Coloniale*, Vol. 1, 1937, pp. 151-154.

COTRUFO, P. Contributo allo studio dell'influenza dei climi tropicali sulla pressione arteriosa. *Giorn. Ital. di Clin. Trop.*, Vol. 1, 1937, pp. 301-302.

CRAMER, W. Fever, heat regulation, climate and the thyroid-adrenal apparatus. London, 1928.

DUERST, J. U. Sauerstoffschwankungen der Atemluft in ihrer formenbildenden Wirkung bei Mensch und Tier. Bern-Leipzig, 1937.

DUSATTI, C. Modificazioni funzionali in rapporto all'azione prolongata del caldo-umido: osservazione durante il viaggo Trieste-Belem e ritorno. *Minerva Med.*, Vol. 2, 1934, pp. 682-686.

GESSLER, H. Die Wärmeregulation des Menschen. *Erg. Physiol.*, Vol. 26, 1928, pp. 185 ff., bibliography (a thorough review).

GREGORY, R. A., and LEE, D. H. K. Effect of water intake upon human reactions to reduced cooling powers. *Journ. Physiol.*, Vol. 86, 1936, pp. 204-218.

GROBER, J. Die Akklimatisation. Jena, 1936 (a general, popular work; see review by Waibel, *Geogr. Zeit.*, Vol. 44, 1938, pp. 101-107).

GROS, H. L'acclimatement. *Paris Méd.*, Vol. 70, 1928, annexe, pp. 99, 132, 182.

HALDANE, J. S. Acclimatization to high altitudes. *Physiol. Rev.*, Vol. 7, 1927, pp. 362-384 (bibliography).

Handbuch der Allgemeinen Physiologie, Bd. 17, Wärme und Wärmeregulation, (edited by Von Bethe, Von Bergmann, Embden, and Ellinger), Berlin, 1926: Iodlbauer, A. Die Physikalische Wirkung des Lichtes, pp. 305-342. Schade, H. Wärme, pp. 392-443. Linke, F. Physikalische Faktoren des Klimas, pp. 463-493. Kestner, O. Physiologische Wirkung des Klimas, pp. 498-562. Knipping, H. W. Das Tropenklima, pp. 550-557. Isenschmid, R. Physiologie der Wärmeregulation, pp. 1-85. Freund, H. Pathologie und Pharmakologie der Wärmeregulation, pp. 86-104.

HAUER, A. Ärztlicher Berater für übersee und Tropen. 2nd ed. Berlin, 1936.

HOFFMAN, F. L. Problems of mortality and acclimatization in the Central American tropics. *Internatl. Cong. on Health Problems in Tropical America*, 1924, pp. 657-708 (experience of insurance official).

HUPPENBAUER, C. Buschdoktor: Ein Arzt erzählt Afrika. 6th ed. Tübingen, 1937.

KLIGLER, J. Influence of climate on susceptibility to enteric infection. *Trans. Royal Soc. Trop. Med. and Hyg.*, Vol. 29, 1936, pp. 531-546.

LEE, D. H. K. The effects of hot climate. *Lancet*, 1935, p. 1226.

LEE, D. H. K. Physiology and the tropics. *Malayan Med. Journ.*, Vol. 11, 1936, pp. 105-108.

LEE, D. H. K. The settlement of tropical Australia. *Med. Journ. of Australia*, Nov. 21, 1936.

LEGENDRE, J. L'acclimatisation des Européens. *Presse Médicale*, Vol. 36, 1928, pp. 1587-1588.

LOGHEM, J. J. VAN. Tropische Gezondheidsleer. Amsterdam, 1933.

McCANCE, R. A. Effect of salt deficiency in man on the volume of extracellular fluids and on composition of sweat, saliva, gastric juice, and cerebrospinal fluid. *Journ. Physiol.*, Vol. 92, 1938, pp. 208-218 (see also *ibid.*, Vol. 91, 1937, pp. 222-231, and *Biochem. Journ.*, Vol. 31, 1937, pp. 1276-1284.

McKINLEY, E. B. Climate and health. *Sci. Monthly*, Vol. 39, 1934, pp. 117-128.

MANOSA, M. Problems of ventilation in the tropics, with particular reference to climatic conditions of Manila. *Rev. Filip. de Med. y Farmacia*, Vol. 30, 1929, pp. 90-101.

NAUCK, E. G. Die Akklimatisation und ihre Bedeutung für die Siedlung in den Tropen. *Zeitsch. Gesell. Erdk. zu Berlin*, 1938, pp. 81-93.

NILIGAN, A. R., CASTELLANI, A., and others. Discussion on adaptation of European women and children to tropical climates. *Proc. Royal Soc. Med.,* London, Vol. 24, 1931, pp. 1315-1333.

NOCHT, B. Tropenhygiene. Berlin.

OUDENDAL, A. J. F., and others. Über Eisenhaushalt und Haemoglobin in den Tropen. *Krankheitsforschung,* Vol. 6, 1928, pp. 1-40.

PARDEY, H. H. Über die gesundheitlichen Schädigungen durch langjährigen Aufenthalt in den Tropen und Subtropen, 1937. (Diss.).

PETERS, J. P. Body water, the exchange of fluids in man. Baltimore and Springfield, Mass., 1935, (standard treatise).

RADSMA, W. CO_2-tension in the air of the lungs of 2 inhabitants of the tropics as compared with that of Europe. *Geneesk. Tijd. Ned. Indië,* Vol. 68, 1928, pp. 802-819 (see also pp. 781-801).

RADSMA, W. La téneur cholésterine du sang chez les inhabitants des tropiques. *Arch. Néerl. de Physiol.,* Vol. 14, 1929, pp. 371-385.

RADSMA, W. Metabolism during rest of the European in the tropics. *Arch. Néerl. de Physiol.,* Vol. 16, 1931, pp. 91-122.

RADSMA, W., and STREEF, G. M. Basal metabolism and albumin consumption by Europeans in the tropics. *Geneesk. Tijd. Ned. Indië,* Vol. 72, 1932, pp. 479-498.

RADSMA, W., STREEF, G. M., and KLERKS, J. V. On the acid-base equilibrium with inhabitants of the tropics. *Geneesk. Tijd. Ned. Indië,* Vol. 73, 1933, pp. 1357 ff., 1591 ff., 1651 ff. (also in *Arch. Nèerl. Physiol.* Vol. 18, 1933, pp. 536-577).

RADSMA, W., KLERKS, J., and EVERSE, J. Contributions to knowledge about mineral metabolism in inhabitants of the tropics. *Arch. Néerl. de Physiol.,* Vol. 21, 1937, pp. 574-586 (abstract in *Geneesk. Tijd. Ned. Indië,* Vol. 76, 1936, pp. 2590, 2840).

RHO, F. L'adattabilita degli Europei ai climi caldi. *Giron. Ital. Mal. Esot.,* Vol. 4, 1931, pp. 1-14. (This and the following reference give the views of the leading Italian investigator in the subject, who has been writing since 1894.)

RHO, F. Ancora sulla questione dell'acclimatamento degli europei nei paesi caldi. *Ann. Med. Navali* (Roma), Vol. 37, 1931, Part I, pp. 263-288.

RICART, E. E. Les prétendus méfaits du climat de Sainte Domingue. *Rév. de Med. et d'Hyg. Trop.,* Vol. 28, 1936, pp. 97-112.

RONNEFELT, F. Material zur Frage der Akklimatisation von Frauen und Kindern im tropischen Westafrika. *Arch. Schiffs-u. Trop.-Hyg.,* Vol. 34, 1930, p. 319.

SARDON, G. Acclimatement et adaptation climatique. *Prat. Méd. Franc.,* Vol. 8, 1929, pp. 235-242.

STIGLER, R. Tropentauglichkeit. *Wien. Med. Woch.,* Vol. 79, 1929, pp. 989-991.

STRAUSS, W., and others. Klima und Arbeit. *Arch. für Gewerbepathologie u. Gewerbehygiene,* Vol. 1, 1930, pp. 203-239; Vol. 1, 1931, pp. 624-655; Vol. 2, 1932, pp. 777-853; Vol. 3, 1933, pp. 362-383; Vol. 4, 1933, pp. 552-562.

STREEF, G. M. H-ion concentration of the blood in Europeans of the temperate zone as compared with inhabitants of the tropics. *Geneesk. Tijd. Ned. Indië,* Vol. 75, 1935, pp. 559-563.

SUNDSTROEM, E. S. Contributions to tropical biochemistry. *Univ. Calif. Publ. in Physiol.,* Vol. 7, No. 10, 1930.

SZÁVÁ-KOVÁTS, J. Verteilung der Luftfeuchtigkeit auf der Erde. *Ann. der Hydrogr.,* Vol. 66, 1938, pp. 373-378.

TOMS, M. W. European women and children in the tropics. *Brit. Med. Journ.* Vol. 1, 1931, pp. 1091-1092 (reply to Castellani).

TRABAUD, J. L'hygiène à la maison et la ville. *Rév. Prat. d. Mal. d. Pays Chauds,* Vol. 17, 1937, pp. 157-176.

ULLMAN, K. Über Tropentauglichkeit. *Wien. Med. Woch.,* Vol. 79, 1929, pp. 1145-1177.

Verhandlungen der Deutschen Tropenmedizinischen Gesellschaft, X. Tagung, vom 25-26 September, 1936 in Hamburg. *Arch. Schiffs-u. Trop.-Hyg.,* Vol. 41, 1937.

YAGLOU, C. P. Abnormal air conditions in industry, their effects on workers and methods of control. *Journ. Indust. Hyg.,* Vol. 19, 1937, pp. 12-43 (valuable summary of the whole subject, with bibliography).

INDEX

INDEX

Matter in the notes (pp. 241-271) that can readily be found from references in the text is omitted in the Index.
References to the Notes are to Chapter and note numbers, other references to pages.

Abbatucci, S., 300
Abbe, Cleveland, 196
Abbot, H. L., 148
Acclimatization, 194-205; equatorial tropics, 194; Panama, 151, 158, 163; physiological investigations, 213, 275-287
Adams, F. U., notes, IV, 2; IX, 36
Adams, Henry, notes, XVI, 9
Adams, R. C., notes, XII, 44
Administrative factors in early failures of w. s. in West Indies, 24-25
Administrative problems of w. s., 228-229
Africa, 136-145; area and population statistics, 138; British plateaus, 137-145; children, 140, 141, 204; climate, effects of, 137; climatic data, 138; climograms, 290; colored labor, 177; health conditions, 204; history of w. s. in, 136-137; housing, 140; isolation and comfort, 139-140; mortality and insurance company premiums, 201; negroes, 141-145; racial problems, 140-142
Agriculture, Florida, 45-47; Northern Territory, Australia, 113-115; Queensland, 55, 58, 59 (maps)
Aimes, A., notes, XIII, 15
Air conditioning, 224, 287
Air movement, notes, XV, 39
Albuquerque, 16
Alcoholism, 221-222; in early w. s. in West Indies, 25
Allen, Dexter, 195
Allison, R. V., 189
Altitudes, effect on white settlement, 133
Amazon Basin, 4, 220, 226; soils, 189
America, tropical, climograms, 291; population statistics, 19
American Geographical Society, Peruvian Expedition, 33
American Society of Heating and Ventilating Engineers, 284; comfort limit, notes, XV, 41
Americans, in Hawaii, 184
Andrews, J., 53, 55, 58-59
Angola, 145
Angström, Anders, notes, XIII, 21
Angus, T. C., 293
Arning, K., notes, X, 7
Ashford, Bailey K., 207
Ashton, Sir R. P., 150; notes, XI, 7
Asia, tropical, mortality and insurance company premiums, 201
Assheton, C. F., 284
Atherton Tableland, 58, 65, 75
Atwood, R. S., 45
Australia, aborigines, 118-120, 119 (map); cattle, 63 (map); climograms, 289; major soil divisions, 110 (map); population and social statistics, 64; rainfall, 54 (maps); sheep, 62 (map); transport facilities, 34
Australia, northern and central: communications, 109 (maps); rainfall, 109 (maps); vegetation, 109 (maps); white and aboriginal population, 119 (maps)
Australia, tropical, 36, 52-76, 103-121; arid regions, 103-104; climate 56, 66 (maps); climatic subdivisions, 53-57; diet, 221; his-tory 104-106; overoptimistic views regarding w. s. in, 52-53; rainfall, 66 (map); soils, 187; vegetation, 67 (map); wet-dry regions, 104-106

Babcock, M. E., notes, XII, 44
Bachmann, W., notes, XVI, 26
Badgett, W. H., notes, XVI, 29
Badham, C., 284
Bahamas, British settlers in, 101-102
Baitsell, G. A., notes, I, 15; XIV, 12
Baldwin, A. H., notes, XV, 19
Balfour, Andrew, 7, 191, 193, 208
Banana industry, Costa Rica, 128
Barbados, 20-30, 97; effects of climate, 29-30; emigration from, 25; population statistics, historical, 21; Red Legs, 98-100
Barger, G. J. P., 168, 195, 223
Barkley, Henry, 191, 297
Barns, T. A., 145; notes, X, 52
Barrett, James, notes, VI, 1
Barros Barreto, A. L. de, notes, XVI, 26
Bates, H. W., 131
Bauer, P. S., 215
Bay Islands, British settlers in, 100-101
Bazett, H. C., 275; notes, XVI, 3
Bedford, T., 293
Beeche, Luciano, notes, IX, 3
Benedict, F. G., 300
Bennett, H. H., 189
Bernard, J. S., 132; notes, IX, 25
Bernard, L. L., 132; notes, IX, 25
Bews, J. W., notes, XV, 3
Birth rates, Costa Rica, 128; Florida, 49-50; Panama, 163
Black, Kenneth, 194, 210
Black Irish, 28
Blackfan, K. D., notes, XIV, 18
Blackham, R. J., notes, XVI, 11
Blacklock, D. B., 204, 224; notes, IV, 10
Blakeslee, G. H., notes, I, 15
Blood, tropical effects on, 283
Bock, A. V., notes, XV, 43
Body-heat loss, 279-282
Body-heat production, 276, 281
Body temperature, 214, 215, 276-279
Body-tone, tropical effects on, 283
Bolivia, Murray's attempted colonisation, 134
Bonne, C., notes, XIII, 27
Borchardt, W., 275, 300; notes, XIII, 15; XVI, 41
Bowman, Isaiah, notes, IX, 11
Boyce, R. W., notes, IV, 6
Boyd, M. F., 209
Bradtke, F., 293
Brazil, 131; cooling power, 298; Germans, 133; highlands, 132; white population increases, 37; w. s. in, 134
Breinl, A., 12, 63; notes, I, 37; XV, 41
Brezina, E., notes, XVI, 26
Brigden, J. B., 64, 106; notes, VI, 2; VIII, 30
British Colonial Service, 204
British failures in the West Indies, 20-32
British settlers, Caribbean region, 96-102
British West Africa, 168

305

AMERICAN GEOGRAPHICAL SOCIETY
PARTIAL LIST OF PUBLICATIONS
SPECIAL PUBLICATIONS

[No. 1]—*Memorial Volume of the Transcontinental Excursion of 1912 of the American Geographical Society of New York.* Edited by W. L. G. Joerg. 418 pp., 116 maps, diagrams, and photographs. 1915.

[No. 2]—*The Andes of Southern Peru: Geographical Reconnaissance Along the Seventy-Third Meridian.* By Isaiah Bowman. 348 pp., 204 maps, diagrams, and photographs. 1916. (Out of print.)

[No. 3]—*The Frontiers of Language and Nationality in Europe.* By Leon Dominion. 393 pp., 67 maps and photographs, 9 map plates in color. 1917. (Out of print.)

No. 4 — *The Face of the Earth as Seen From the Air: A Study in the Application of Airplane Photography to Geography.* By Willis T. Lee. 122 pp., 82 maps and photographs. 1922.

No. 5 — *Desert Trails of Atacama.* By Isaiah Bowman. 367 pp., 117 maps, diagrams, and photographs. 1924. (Out of print.)

No. 6 — *China: Land of Famine.* By Walter H. Mallory. 215 pp., 103 maps and photographs. 1926.

No. 7 — *Problems of Polar Research.* Edited by W. L. G. Joerg. 484 pp., 96 maps, diagrams, and photographs. 1928.

No. 8 — *The Geography of the Polar Regions.* By Otto Nordenskjöld and Ludwig Mecking. 366 pp., 135 maps, diagrams, and photographs. 1928.

No. 9 — *The Coral Reef Problem.* By William Morris Davis. 596 pp., 227 maps, diagrams, and photographs. 1928.

No. 10 — *Richard Hakluyt and the English Voyages.* By George Bruner Parks. 306 pp., 32 halftone reproductions.

No. 11 — *Brief History of Polar Exploration Since the Introduction of Flying.* By W. L. G. Joerg. 95 pp., 9 text maps. Accompanying maps of the Arctic and Antarctic on the scale of 1:20,000,000. 1930.

No. 12 — *Peru from the Air.* By George R. Johnson. 171 pp., 141 aerial photographs. 1930.

No. 13 — *The Pioneer Fringe.* By Isaiah Bowman. 370 pp., 249 maps, diagrams, and photographs. 1931. (Out of print.)

No. 14 — *Pioneer Settlement.* Edited by W. L. G. Joerg. 479 pp., 98 maps and diagrams. 1932.

No. 15 — *The Grand Coulee.* By J. Harlen Bretz. 99 pp., 38 photographs, 15 line drawings, 1 insert map in color, and 8 stereoscopic views. 1932.

No. 16 — *New England's Prospect: 1933.* Edited by John K. Wright. 509 pp., 9 double-page maps, 26 smaller maps, and 13 diagrams. 1933.

No. 17 — *The Discovery of the Amazon According to the Account of Friar Gaspar de Carvajal and Other Documents.* 483 pp., 1 map and facsimiles of 2 documents. 1934.

No. 18 — *The Fiord Region of East Greenland.* By Louise A. Boyd and others. 381 pp., 2 maps, 361 photographs in text accompanied by slip case with 14 plates. 1935.

No. 19 — *The Colorado Delta.* By Godfrey Sykes. 200 pp., 74 maps and photographs. 1937.

No. 20 — *Polish Countrysides.* By Louise A. Boyd. 247 pp., 9 maps, 486 halftones. 1937.

No. 21 — *Rainfall and Tree Growth in the Great Basin.* By Ernst Antevs. 104 pp., 6 maps and 1 diagram in text, 2 plates. 1938.

No. 22 — *Northernmost Labrador Mapped from the Air.* By Alexander Forbes and others. 275 pp., 12 maps and diagrams, 166 halftones in text accompanied by slip case containing 6 plates and "Navigational Notes on the Labrador Coast," by Alexander Forbes. 1938.

No. 23 — *White Settlers in the Tropics.* By A. Grenfell Price. 325 pp., 30 maps and diagrams, 58 halftones. 1939.

RESEARCH SERIES

Nos. 1 and 2 — *Bering's Voyages: An Account of the Efforts of the Russians to Determine the Relation of Asia and America.* By F. A. Golder. Vol. 1: *The Log Books and Official Reports of the First and Second Expeditions, 1725–1730 and 1733–1742.* With a chart of the second voyage, by Ellsworth P. Bertholf. 371 pp., 15 maps, facsimiles, etc., 1 plate, 1922. Vol. 2: *Steller's Journal of the Sea Voyage from Kamchatka to America and Return on the Second Expedition, 1741–1742.* Translated and in part annotated by Leonhard Stejneger. 291 pp., 30 maps, facsimiles, etc., 2 plates. 1925. Reprinted in 1935.

No. 3 — *Battlefields of the World War, Western and Southern Fronts: A Study in Military Geography.* By Douglas Wilson Johnson. 648 pp., more than 100 photographs, 60 maps, block diagrams, and diagrams, and a separate case of plates comprising 5 maps, 3 block diagrams, and 6 panoramas. 1921.

No. 4 — *The Position of Geography in British Universities.* By Sir John Scott Keltie. 33 pp. 1921.

No. 4a — *Geography in France.* By Emmanuel de Martonne. 70 pp. 1924.

No. 5 — *The Agrarian Indian Communities of Highland Bolivia.* By George McCutchen McBride. 27 pp., 5 maps and photographs. 1921.

No. 6 — *Recent Colonization in Chile.* By Mark Jefferson. 52 pp., 15 maps, diagrams, and photographs. 1921.

No. 7 — *The Rainfall of Chile.* By Mark Jefferson. 32 pp., 10 maps and diagrams. 1922.

No. 8 — *Legendary Islands of the Atlantic: A Study in Medieval Geography.* By William H. Babcock. 196 pp., 25 maps. 1922.

No. 9 — *A Catalogue of Geological Maps of South America.* By Henry B. Sullivan. 191 pp., 1 map. 1922.

No. 10 — *Aids to Geographical Research: Bibliographies and Periodicals.* By John Kirtland Wright. 243 pp. 1923. (Out of print.)

No. 11 — *The Recession of the Last Ice Sheet in New England.* By Ernst Antevs. 120 pp., 19 maps, diagrams, and photographs, 6 plates. 1922.

No. 12 — *The Land Systems of Mexico.* By George McCutchen McBride. 204 pp., 33 maps and photographs.

No. 13 — *The Vegetation and Soils of Africa.* By H. L. Shantz and C. F. Marbut. 263 pp., 50 photographs, 2 maps in color in separate case. 1923. (Out of print.)

No. 14 — *The Geographical Conceptions of Columbus: A Critical Consideration of Four Problems.* By George E. Nunn. 148 pp., 16 maps, 2 plates. 1924.

No. 15 — *The Geographical Lore of the Time of the Crusades: A Study in the History of Medieval Science and Tradition in Western Europe.* By John Kirtland Wright. 563 pp., 12 maps and diagrams. 1925.

No. 16 — *Peopling the Argentine Pampa.* By Mark Jefferson. 211 pp., 67 maps, diagrams, and photographs, 1 plate. 1926.

No. 17 — *The Last Glaciation: With Special Reference to the Ice Retreat in Northwestern North America.* By Ernst Antevs. 292 pp., 30 maps and diagrams, 9 plates. 1928.

No. 18 — *The Vinland Voyages.* By Matthias Thórdarson. Translated by Thorstina Jackson Walters. 76 pp., 24 maps and photographs. 1930.

No. 19 — *Chile: Land and Society.* By George McCutchen McBride. 408 pp., 58 maps, facsimiles, and photographs. 1936.

No. 20 — *The Frame of the Ancient Greek Maps: With a Discussion of the Discovery of the Sphericity of the Earth.* By William Arthur Heidel. 141 pp., 1 map, 1 diagram. 1937.